Volume 2

Molecular Genetic Medicine

Molecular Genetic Medicine

Editor

Theodore Friedmann
University of California, San Diego
La Jolla, California

Editorial Board

Raju Kucherlapati
Albert Einstein College of Medicine
Bronx, New York

Victor McKusick
The Johns Hopkins University School of Medicine
Baltimore, Maryland

Frank Ruddle
Yale University
New Haven, Connecticut

Volume 2

Molecular Genetic Medicine

Edited by
Theodore Friedmann
Department of Pediatrics
Center for Molecular Genetics
School of Medicine
University of California, San Diego
La Jolla, California

Academic Press, Inc.
Harcourt Brace Jovanovich, Publishers
San Diego   New York   Boston
London   Sydney   Tokyo   Toronto

This book is printed on acid-free paper. ∞

Copyright © 1992 by ACADEMIC PRESS, INC.
All Rights Reserved.
No part of this publication may be reproduced or transmitted in any form or by any
means, electronic or mechanical, including photocopy, recording, or any information
storage and retrieval system, without permission in writing from the publisher.

Academic Press, Inc.
1250 Sixth Avenue, San Diego, California 92101

United Kingdom Edition published by
Academic Press Limited
24–28 Oval Road, London NW1 7DX

International Standard Serial Number: 1057-2805

International Standard Book Number: 0-12-462002-7

PRINTED IN THE UNITED STATES OF AMERICA
92 93 94 95 96 97   BB   9 8 7 6 5 4 3 2 1

Contents

7 Regulatory Genes of Human Immunodeficiency Viruses   189
Flossie Wong-Staal and William A. Haseltine

Contributors

B. Andersson, Department of Clinical Genetics, Karolinska Institute, 104 01 Stockholm, Sweden

Patricia E. Berg, Department of Pediatrics, Division of Pediatric Hematology/Oncology, University of Maryland School of Medicine, Baltimore, Maryland 21201

W. Ted Brown, Department of Human Genetics, New York State Institute for Basic Research in Developmental Disabilities, Staten Island, New York 10314

Francis V. Chisari, Department of Molecular and Experimental Medicine, Division of Experimental Pathology, The Scripps Research Institute, La Jolla, California 92037

Karen A. Dyer, Vivigen, Inc., Sante Fe, New Mexico 87505

Charles J. Epstein, Departments of Pediatrics and Biochemistry and Biophysics, University of California, San Francisco, San Francisco, California 94143

Stanley M. Gartler, Departments of Medicine and Genetics, University of Washington, Seattle, Washington 98195

Michael A. Goldman, Department of Biology, San Francisco State University, San Francisco, California 94132

William A. Haseltine, Division of Human Retrovirology, Dana-Farber Cancer Institute, Harvard University, Cambridge, Massachusetts 02138

S.-M. He, Department of Clinical Genetics, Karolinska Institute, 104 01 Stockholm, Sweden

David M. Holtzman, Department of Neurology, University of California, San Francisco, San Francisco, California 94143

Edmund C. Jenkins, Department of Cytogenetics, New York State Institute for Basic Research in Developmental Disabilities, Staten Island, New York 10314

B. Lambert, Department of Clinical Genetics, Karolinska Institute, 104 01 Stockholm, Sweden

S. Marcus, Department of Clinical Genetics, Karolinska Institute, 104 01 Stockholm, Sweden

Alan N. Schechter, Laboratory of Chemical Biology, National Institute of Diabetes and Digestive and Kidney Diseases, National Institutes of Health, Bethesda, Maryland 20892

A.-M. Steen, Department of Clinical Genetics, Karolinska Institute, 104 01 Stockholm, Sweden

Flossie Wong-Staal, Department of Medicine and Biology, University of California, San Diego, La Jolla, California 92093

Preface

This second volume of *Molecular Genetic Medicine* contains chapters that summarize progress in several of the most important areas of modern molecular genetics and medicine. These chapters deal with ancient and common genetic diseases, a new infectious disease that threatens to become a world-wide scourge for all of humanity, and two of the most important and still poorly understood causes of mental retardation. The common thread winding through these separate stories is the astounding illumination of all these disorders by modern molecular genetic studies.

Genetic diseases of the hematopoietic system have represented some of the most important model systems for understanding the mechanisms of pathogenesis, detection, and therapy of human genetic disease. In 1949, the work of Pauling and his associates demonstrated that sickle cell anemia was caused by an alteration in the physiochemical properties of the hemoglobin molecule, making this disorder the first characterized "molecular disease." In 1956, Vernon Ingram became the first to identify the precise defect in the structure of a disease-related gene product, when he described the amino acid substitution responsible for the abnormal properties of sickle cell hemoglobin. Thereafter, the human beta globin gene became the first known disease-related gene to be isolated and characterized at the nucleotide sequence level. The chapter by Berg and Schechter in this volume brings this story up to date by describing the history of the molecular approach to the thalassemias, among the most common and severe of all human genetic diseases.

The fragile X syndrome has been recognized for several decades to be associated with a severe and exceedingly common form of mental retardation. However, until the past several years, there has been very little understanding of the peculiar genetic properties of this disorder and virtually no understanding whatsoever of the chemical or genetic defects. Although it is not the first disease to fall to the attack of what used to be called reverse genetics and is now called "positional cloning," the recent identification of the genetic lesion underlying this disorder is easily one of the most stunning and important successes of the new molecular approach to human genetics. Very important screening programs will become feasible and will no doubt lead to major reductions in the incidence of this extremely important disorder. The history and current state of the fragile X syndrome is reviewed here by Brown and Jenkins.

Hepatitis B infection is a worldwide scourge that carries an enormous burden of illness and death. Infection with this virus is probably responsible for a very high proportion of one of mankind's most common cancers, hepatocellular carcinoma. Through current molecular and cell biological approaches, as reviewed by Chisari, the mechanisms of hepatitis B viral gene expression, its relation to liver cancer, and the development of effective preventive measures are beginning to be understood and characterized.

Holtzman and Epstein examine progress in the second of the most common causes of mental retardation, Down syndrome. This disorder rivals fragile X in its importance as a cause of retardation and developmental anomalies, and is the defect in which a cytogenetic abnormality was first described in humans. While the mechanism of retardation is far from understood, the relevant regions of chromosome 21 are identified and candidate genes and possible molecular mechanisms for the developmental defects seen in this disorder are now beginning to emerge. Production of mouse models promises to add greatly to an understanding of the physiological consequences of the genetic defect.

The disease-rich human X chromosome has long been a favorite among medical geneticists, because of the fact that mutations on this chromosome are immediately obvious in hemizygous males. Gene dosage compensation in females has been known for several decades to result from the random inactivation of one of the two X chromosomes in females, and the role of genetic and epigenetic mechanisms underlying this form of gene regulation will provide important generalizable information on the ways in which very large portions of the human genome are expressed and regulated. Such events are reviewed here by Gartler, Dyer, and Goldman.

One of the most thoroughly studied human genes, one that resides on the X chromosome, is the gene hypoxanthine phosphoribosyltransferase, HPRT. The central role of HPRT in purine biosynthesis and metabolism has been long recognized, and its role in the peculiar phenotype of Lesch–Nyhan syndrome was described in 1967. The gene for HPRT was the first human enzyme deficiency gene to be cloned and sequenced, and it now serves as a model for the study of mechanisms, frequency, and environmental influence on mutational events in humans. The history and recent developments in this field are described by Lambert, Andersson, He, Marcus, and Steen.

Very little needs to be said in this preface on the importance of work during the past decade on HIV virus and its role in AIDS. Never before has the understanding of a human disease progressed as rapidly as it has in the case of AIDS. Starting from a situation in which the disease was not even recognized and the etiological agent not identified more than 20 years ago, a stunning quantity of work has been done on its pathogenesis and the role of HIV in this disorder. It is probably safe to say that AIDS is now the best understood of all infectious diseases. That, of course, is not to say that we know all that needs to be known about its pathogenesis, and the current controversy surrounding the precise role of HIV in this disease reflects a persistent and troublesome insecurity about the depth of our understanding. Nevertheless, the pace of accumulating knowledge is staggering, and despite the current level of our sophisticated understanding of the HIV virus, there is a great deal still to learn about its role in this devastating disease. Few investigators could have reviewed this field as well as Wong-Staal and Haseltine.

Theodore Friedmann

1 The Impact of Molecular Biology on the Diagnosis and Treatment of Hemoglobin Disorders

Patricia E. Berg* and Alan N. Schechter
Laboratory of Chemical Biology
National Institute of Diabetes and Digestive and Kidney Diseases
National Institutes of Health
Bethesda, Maryland

I. DISEASES OF HEMOGLOBIN

Disorders of hemoglobin can be of two general types, expression abnormalities (thalassemias) and structural abnormalities (hemoglobinopathies; although the term hemoglobinopathy is sometimes used for both types). Thalassemias are due to changes in the expression of the genes for hemoglobin due to mutations in the DNA within, surrounding, or even many kilobases removed from the gene. Such mutations affect the regulation of the gene, and if they could be corrected, the gene would function normally because it is structurally normal. It is only in recent years, through the use of molecular techniques, that the detailed basis for the effect of these mutations on globin gene expression has begun to be understood.

Structural abnormalities, on the other hand, are mutations in the polypeptide encoding-gene itself. Early studies of hemoglobinopathies of necessity focused on protein abnormalities, because DNA methodologies had not yet been developed. Pauling and his colleagues discovered the abnormal electrophoretic behavior of hemoglobin S (Pauling et al., 1949). Amino acid sequencing techniques led to identification of specific amino acid substitutions in abnormal hemoglobins (Ingram, 1956) as well as the total amino acid sequences of many hundreds of normal and abnormal hemoglobins (Dayhoff, 1972; Fermi and Perntz, 1981). More recently DNA sequencing has elucidated the genetic de-

*Current Address: Department of Pediatrics, Division of Pediatric Hematology/Oncology, University of Maryland School of Medicine, Baltimore, Maryland 21201.

fects associated with many of these abnormal hemoglobins. The nature of our approaches to these diseases has been greatly altered with the advent of this and other techniques used in molecular biology.

This review will focus on the impact of molecular biology, especially molecular genetics, on the diagnosis and treatment of hemoglobin disorders. We will begin with a review of the organization of globin genes and the control of their expression, then discuss diagnosis and treatment of the genetic diseases of hemoglobin and, finally, prospects for their genetic therapy. It is the authors' hope that this will be of a sufficiently general nature that as new concepts and techniques are developed they will fall within the framework presented here, because molecular biology is such a rapidly evolving area of research that specific aspects of the paradigm change rapidly.

II. GLOBIN GENE ORGANIZATION

A. Chromosomal location and ontogeny

The human globin genes are arranged in two clusters, the α-like genes on chromosome 16 and the β-like genes on chromosome 11 (Figure 1.1) (Collins and Weissman, 1984). Characteristics of the two gene clusters differ markedly: the α-like cluster DNA is 60% G + C, is early replicating in all cell types, is associated with unmethylated CpG-rich islands, and does not contain nuclear

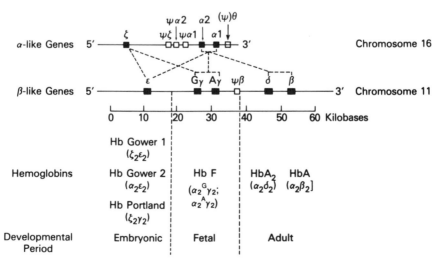

Figure 1.1. Organization of the human hemoglobin genes and the developmental stages of their expression. Black boxes denote genes and open boxes denote pseudogenes. Dashed lines connect genes that are coexpressed; the various hemoglobin species formed at different developmental stages are shown.

matrix attachment sites, whereas the β-like cluster DNA is 40% G + C (similar to the genomic G + C content), replicates early only in β-globin-expressing cells, does not contain CpG-rich islands, but does contain nuclear attachment sites (reviewed in Higgs *et al.*, 1990). The characteristics of the α-globin cluster DNA are typical of so-called housekeeping genes, and are unusual for a gene that is expressed in a tissue-specific manner.

The hemoglobin tetramer is composed of two α-like chains and two β-like polypeptide chains. The genes are arranged in their order of expression, i.e., the α-like genes, ζ, α2, and α1, are sequentially and coordinately expressed with the β-like genes, ε, $^{G}\gamma$, $^{A}\gamma$, δ, and β. The α1 and α2 proteins are the same, but the genes differ in their second intervening sequences and in their 3′ untranslated regions; α2 mRNA is expressed at about a 2.6-fold higher level than α1 (for reviews, see Liebhaber, 1989; Higgs *et al.*, 1990). The $^{A}\gamma$ protein has an alanine at amino acid 136, where $^{G}\gamma$ has a glycine at that position.

During embryonic development primarily ζ and ε are expressed, with lesser amounts of α and γ, to give $\zeta_2\epsilon_2$, $\alpha_2\epsilon_2$, and $\zeta_2\gamma_2$. Fetal hemoglobin (HbF) consists of α and γ chains ($\alpha_2\gamma_2$), about 70% of the γ chains being $^{G}\gamma$ and 30% $^{A}\gamma$ (Alter, 1979). Adult red cells contain hemoglobin that is a mixture of three primary types, HbA, HbA$_2$, and HbF, with at least 95% HbA ($\alpha_2\beta_2$), a few percent HbA$_2$ ($\alpha_2\delta_2$), and less than 1% HbF. The small amount of HbF in the adult contains 40% $^{G}\gamma$ and 60% $^{A}\gamma$ (Jensen *et al.*, 1982).

The open boxes in Figure 1.1 denote pseudogenes, which are DNA sequences that are closely related to the globin genes but are nonfunctional due to mutations such as deletions, insertions, frameshifts, or substitutions. Pseudogenes are thought to have been generated in the globin cluster by gene duplication and subsequent mutation. The α-globin cluster contains three pseudogenes, and the β-globin cluster contains one. There is also a recently described α-like globin gene, θ1, with an undetermined function (Hsu *et al.*, 1988). RNA from this gene has been detected, but no protein. Deletions of θ1 have no recognizable phenotype (Higgs *et al.*, 1990).

B. Gene organization

The general structure of a globin gene is shown in Figure 1.2. Globin genes have three exons, which consist of the polypeptide encoding information, and two introns, IVS1 and IVS2. RNA polymerase II transcribes the DNA into a long RNA transcript called pre-mRNA. The pre-mRNA is processed to remove the introns, then the mRNA is translated into protein.

The promoter is the DNA immediately upstream or 5′ to the gene and is usually considered to include about the first 100 to 200 base pairs (bp) prior to the transcriptional start site, called the cap. A detailed description of promoter elements is given in Section III.B.1.

Downstream, or 3′ to the gene, is the poly(A) site, which corresponds

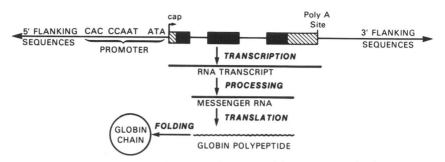

Figure 1.2. Structure of a typical globin gene and overview of the transcriptional and posttranscriptional mechanisms of its expression as a globin polypeptide chain. The single line represents the double strand of DNA; the black boxes indicate exon boundaries separating the two intervening sequences (IVS1 and IVS2). The hatched boxes indicate transcribed but untranslated mRNA sequences. Important transcriptional regulatory sites, the ATA, CCAAT, and CAC motifs, or "boxes," are shown as part of the promoter. Other regulatory motifs have been identified further 5', as well as 3', to the gene.

to the place on the mRNA where poly(adenylic) acid is added to the mRNA. This is important for correct transport of the message from nucleus to ribosome. This poly(A) addition site is not coded on the DNA but the poly(A) is added after transcription, a reaction catalyzed by poly(A) polymerase. Figure 1.2 illustrates such a poly(A) site for the globin gene. We will consider the other features of this gene as depicted in Figure 1.2 when we discuss in detail the control of globin gene expression.

C. Haplotypes

One way of looking at the genetics of the globin genes is by examining their haplotype. This analysis depends on the observation that restriction enzymes (enzymes that recognize specific combinations of bases and cleave at those sites, regardless of the origin of the DNA) cleave the DNA located in the two globin gene clusters at reproducible sites. However, there is some variability in the length of restriction fragments among different individuals, due to an altered DNA sequence that could eliminate or add a restriction site, or due to addition or deletion of DNA between two restriction sites. These changes are not random and appear to have little effect on gene expression. Individuals tend to fall into genetically determined groups with the same restriction fragment length combinations. The groups are called haplotypes, and the differently sized DNA fragments are restriction fragment length polymorphisms (RFLPs) (Orkin *et al.*, 1982). A more detailed discussion of this method of analysis will be given later in this review.

III. CONTROL OF GLOBIN GENE EXPRESSION

A. Chromatin

1. Nucleosomes

In general DNA does not exist naked in the cell, but is associated with protein; this protein–DNA complex is called chromatin (for a detailed review, see Lewin, 1990, and references therein). Each repeating unit, or nucleosome, consists of about 200 bp of DNA. The DNA is wound around an octamer of basic proteins into structures resembling beads on a string. The length of DNA actually wound around protein is 146 bp, with the rest of the DNA representing the "string." The proteins include five classes of basic proteins, called histone proteins, as well as nonhistone proteins. Most of the DNA in a cell exists in the form of nucleosomes.

The chromatin of genes that are active, i.e., being transcribed, is altered. It is likely that nucleosomes are temporarily displaced as RNA polymerase II transcribes DNA, but then are reassembled after transcription. Nonhistone proteins specific for certain DNA sequences may modify the DNA to exclude histones, allowing RNA polymerase II to bind and transcribe DNA. This suggests that histone proteins act as general repressors of gene transcription (Lewin, 1990).

2. Hypersensitivity

Active genes can be identified experimentally by their sensitivity to the enzyme DNase I, a nuclease that cleaves individual strands of DNA with very little sequence specificity. It has been found that active genes are more sensitive to DNase I than are inactive genes (Elgin, 1981) and that there are specific regions of DNA that are especially sensitive to DNase I; these regions are called hypersensitive sites (HSS). The HSS are located primarily 5' to active genes and seem to be necessary but not sufficient for transcriptional activity. More recently, HSS have been found in other known functional sites such as enhancers or silencers of transcription, origins of replication, and sites of recombination, any of which may be located 5' or 3' to a gene or intragenically (Elgin, 1888). HSS are regions from which nucleosomes have been excluded, probably due to changes in the patterns of DNA structure and DNA interaction with histone and nonhistone proteins.

Although earlier work studying the DNase I sensitivity of active globin genes was done with chicken globin genes (reviewed in Evans *et al.*, 1990), more recently the HSS flanking human globin genes have begun to be delineated.

Groudine *et al.* (1983) studied the appearance of HSS 5' to $^G\gamma$-, $^A\gamma$-, δ-, and β-globin genes in globin-expressing and -nonexpressing cells. They found one HSS between 150 and 200 bp 5' to each gene in fetal liver, where fetal genes are expressed, but 5' only to δ and β in bone marrow, where adult genes are expressed. None of these HSS are found in leukocytes, which do not express globin genes. These data suggest that fetal gene expression ($^G\gamma$ and $^A\gamma$) is directly related to the appearance of 5' HSS, whereas in adult gene expression (δ and β), although the 5' HSS must be present, other factors are also necessary. Two HSS were also found 3' to the cap site of the β-globin gene, one in IVS2 and the other downstream from the gene. All three of these sites marking the β-globin gene are near positive control regions or enhancers (Behringer *et al.*, 1987; Antoniou *et al.*, 1988).

The presence of HSS was also determined for the human cell line K562 (Moon and Ley, 1991). These cells are able to synthesize embryonic and fetal globins but they do not make adult globin because their β-globin gene is not transcribed, for reasons not yet determined (Rutherford *et al.*, 1979; Benz *et al.*, 1980; Dean *et al.*, 1983). The ε-globin gene exhibits two major sites of DNase I hypersensitivity in K562 cells, one at −200 bp and the other at the cap. Both HSS are also transcriptional start sites (Bushel *et al.*, 1990). HSS were also found about 100 bp 5' to both the $^G\gamma$ and $^A\gamma$ genes (Lachman and Mears, 1983; Gimble *et al.*, 1988). Interestingly, although the two HSS 3' to the β-globin gene are present, the site at about −150 bp is absent in K562 cells. However, there is a new site at −800 bp (Cao and Schechter, 1988). Thus, the site at −150 bp seems to be critical for expression of the β-globin gene.

3. Locus control region

An important discovery was the identification of HSS that are extremely sensitive to DNase I ("super" hypersensitive sites) and that are located both upstream and downstream of the entire β-globin cluster (Tuan *et al.*, 1985; Forrester *et al.*, 1986). There are six sites: five sites are located between 6 and 22 kb upstream of the ε-globin gene and one site 22 kb downstream of the β-globin gene (Figure 1.3) (Orkin, 1990). At least three of the upstream sites, at −6, −11, and −17.5 kb, and the downstream site are erythroid specific and must be in a DNase I-sensitive state for any of the β-like globin genes to be expressed. Collectively these HSS were originally called the locus-activating region (LAR) (Forrester *et al.*, 1987) or dominant control region (DCR) (Grosveld *et al.*, 1987), but are now known as the locus control region (LCR) (Orkin, 1990). Their significance was first tested experimentally in transgenic mice, which are mice into which foreign genes have been stably introduced. Grosveld and co-workers (1987) added LCR DNA to DNA containing the human β-globin gene and found that it conferred high levels of expression of the human gene in mice,

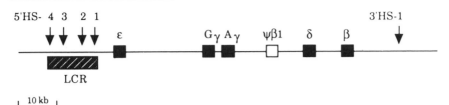

Figure 1.3. The locus control region (LCR) of the β-globin gene cluster. The globin genes and a
pseudogene are shown as open boxes, and the arrows indicate the hypersensitive (HSS)
sites. (From Orkin, 1990, with permission of the author.)

independent of the integration site of the newly introduced DNA but dependent
on the number of integrated gene copies. This was significant because previous
studies that introduced the human β-globin gene into mice showed low and
erratic expression, making it very difficult to study globin gene expression or to
develop mouse models for human hemoglobinopathies. Now that regulated expression is possible in mice of not only the β-globin gene, but also the ε-, γ-,
and α-globin genes, it has been possible to perform many interesting studies. For
example, several laboratories have made mouse models of sickle cell anemia
(Ryan *et al.*, 1990; Greaves *et al.*, 1990).

There is strong evidence that the LCR is functionally important: a
deletion that removes the upstream LCR sites causes Dutch γβ-thalassemia,
although the β-globin gene is intact (Kioussis *et al.*, 1983). When this deletion
was first observed, it was intriguing but inexplicable. As our understanding of
the control of β-globin expression has expanded to include LCR sequences, the
basis for this thalassemia seems quite logical.

Recently a comparable activating region upstream of the α-globin gene
cluster was identified by its effect in cultured mouse cells and transgenic mice. It
spans the region between 28 and 65 kb 5′ to the ζ gene (Higgs *et al.*, 1990). A
naturally occurring deletion of 62 kb that removes this DNA causes α-thalassemia, although both α genes are normal (Hatton *et al.*, 1990).

The molecular basis for the effect of the LCR is under active investigation by a number of laboratories (Moi and Kan, 1990; Ney *et al.*, 1990; Moon
and Ley, 1991; Ley, 1991), and the eventual understanding of this effect will
greatly enhance our understanding of how the globin genes are regulated.
Eventually, one or more of these HSS LCR sequences will probably be part of
any DNA construction introduced into humans for the purpose of correcting
genetic defects, i.e., human gene therapy.

4. Methylation

The DNA of higher eukaryotes exhibits methylation of some 70% of cytosine
residues when found in the combination of 5′-CpG-3′. This methylation is at

position 5 of the pyrimidine ring of cytidine. A number of experiments have established a correlation between hypomethylation of CpG in the 5′ flanking region of a gene and gene activity, and, conversely, methylation has been associated with inactive genes (reviewed in Cedar, 1988; Dynan, 1989). In the case of the globin genes, a strong correlation was found between activity of a gene and hypomethylation near that gene (Mavilio et al., 1983). An interesting experiment was performed using the γ-globin gene (Busslinger et al., 1983), which is normally inactive in fibroblasts. When unmethylated γ-globin DNA was introduced into fibroblasts, the introduced γ gene was active, yet γ-globin DNA methylated in vitro and then introduced into fibroblasts was transcriptionally inactive, suggesting a direct cause and effect. However, there are examples involving other genes for which this association is not observed.

There may be a correlation between the methylation status of a gene, its DNase I sensitivity, and activity. When methylated genes were introduced into mouse fibroblast cells, not only were the genes inactive, but they were in a DNase I-resistant conformation (Keshet et al., 1986). Unmethylated genes introduced into the same cells were active and DNase I sensitive.

One mechanism by which methylation could influence gene expression is to inhibit protein binding at sites critical for transcription, and this has been shown for several genes (Cedar, 1988; Dynan, 1989). Another example of this is the inhibition of cleavage by certain restriction enzymes when the target sequence is methylated. An assay for methylation status is based on this fact. Two restriction enzymes with the same recognition site (CCGG) but different activities on methylated DNA are used to cleave the DNA in question: HpaII will cleave only the unmethylated sequence whereas MspI will cleave the DNA whether it is methylated or unmethylated. Differential cleavage by the two enzymes indicates the presence of methylated DNA.

It should be noted that in many cases wherein methylation is correlated with gene expression, it is not clear in vivo whether hypomethylation is the cause or effect of gene activation. The increase in fetal hemoglobin in patients induced by treatment with 5-azacytidine, a demethylating agent, is such an example (Ley, 1991).

B. Cis-acting DNA sequences

1. Promoters

The DNA immediately upstream from the start site of transcription is called the promoter. It is generally considered to comprise about the first 100 to 200 bp and contains several well-recognized short DNA sequences, or motifs, which are believed to be involved in the control of transcription including correct initiation of transcription. This is the site of RNA polymerase II binding for genes transcribed by this enzyme. The promoter, as distinguished from enhancers and silencers (described below), acts as a positive control element only in its native position. If it is moved or its orientation is changed, it is no longer active.

The human globin promoters have three major motifs. As an example, consider the β-globin promoter (Figure 1.4A). The region from the cap to about −100 bp is called the proximal promoter. The cap, or transcriptional start site, is located at +1; it is the center of the binding site for RNA polymerase II. At −30 bp is the TATA element, or "box," so called because of its nucleotide sequence. This is a common element found in many eukaryotic promoters. In the case of the β-globin gene, the actual sequence is ATA at this site. In a series of elegant deletion studies of the mouse β-globin promoter, Charnay et al. (1985) found that mutations in ATA significantly decreased transcription of the β-globin gene, in agreement with previous studies of other genes (cited in Charnay et al., 1985). It was also found that transcripts were initiated at incorrect start sites when the ATA box was mutated, again indicating the importance of this sequence for transcription. Mutations at this site in humans cause β^+-thalassemia, reducing the transcription of the affected gene by 70 to 80% (Charnay et al., 1985; Kazazian and Boehm, 1988).

A sequence called the CCAAT motif is located at −70 bp. Although not required for transcription of all genes, the CCAAT sequence is apparently important for activity of the β-globin gene, because mutation of the mouse gene causes a significant decrease in transcription (Charnay et a., 1985). Thus far no natural mutations have been found in the CCAAT box of the human β-globin gene.

The third important sequence is the CACCC element. The β-globin gene has two CACCC elements, one at −90, the other at −105, but other globin genes have only one. Although highly conserved among mammalian β-like globin genes, it is also found in several other sites such as the simian virus 40 (SV40) enhancer (Xiao et al., 1987). Mutation of the proximal CACCC sequence causes β-thalassemia (Charnay et al., 1985; Kazazian and Boehm, 1988), suggesting that the upstream CACCC motif is not sufficient to compensate for its loss. It is interesting that the proximal CACCC sequence is the site of binding of an erythroid-specific protein; this binding is disrupted by the mutation seen in a form of thalassemia. No protein binding is observed to the distal CACCC sequence (Mantovani et al., 1988a).

The next 100-bp region, from about −100 to −200, is called the distal promoter in the β-globin gene, because a number of ubiquitous regulatory sequences have also been found in this region. They will be discussed later.

2. Enhancers

Enhancers are DNA sequences that increase gene transcription independent of their position (5′ or 3′) and orientation relative to that gene. In experimental constructs, enhancers often can increase expression from a heterologous promoter.

A. BETA

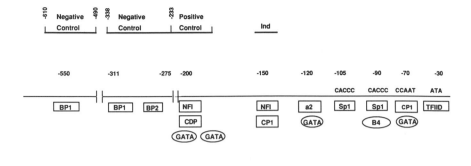

B. GAMMA

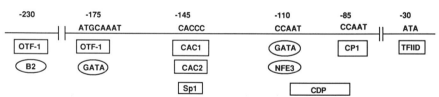

Figure 1.4. Protein-binding sites 5' to several globin genes. General factors are shown in rectangles and erythroid-specific factors are shown in ellipses. Protein-binding sites are shown for the β (A), γ (B), ε (C), and ζ (D) genes. Abbreviations: BP1 and BP2, β proteins 1 and 2; NF-1, nuclear factor 1; CDP, CCAAT displacement protein; GATA represents four of the nucleotides required for binding of the GATA protein; CP1, CCAAT-binding protein 1; TFIID, transcription factor IID; OTF-1, octamer-binding transcription factor 1; CAC1 and CAC2, CACCC box-binding proteins; NFE3, nuclear factor erythroid 3; CBF, CCAAT box-binding factor (may be the same as CP1); ZF1 and ZF2, ζ globin factors 1 and 2. Further information regarding the possible mechanisms of action of these proteins is given in Table 1.1. References to the literature upon which these diagrams are based are in the text.

C. EPSILON

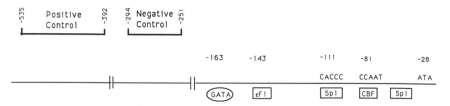

D. ZETA

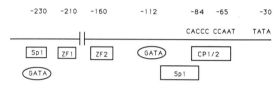

Figure 1.4. (*cont.*)

The first discovery of an enhancer was in SV40 (Gruss *et al.*, 1981), and subsequently many genes have been discovered to have enhancers. Enhancers consist of smaller subregions, or motifs, which are the target for binding proteins, and may act in a tissue-specific fashion. Although there are models for the mechanism of action of enhancers, it is not yet known how they interact with promoter sequences to activate genes, although it is suspected that the effect is via the binding of proteins (trans-acting factors). *In vivo,* enhancers are cis to the gene they affect. However, it was found experimentally that as long as an enhancer can physically interact with a promoter, it does not have to be on the same DNA fragment (Mueller-Storm *et al.*, 1989).

Several of the human globin genes have been shown to have associated enhancers, and the others probably have as yet undiscovered enhancers. The β-globin gene has two known enhancers, one intragenic and the other at about +2400 (Antoniou *et al.*, 1988; Behringer *et al.*, 1987). The γ gene also has a 3' enhancer (Bodine and Ley, 1987). Both the β and ε genes have upstream positive control regions that are necessary for expression but have not yet been shown to fit the definition of enhancers (P. E. Berg and A. N. Schechter, unpublished; S.-X. Cao and A. N. Schechter, unpublished).

The LCR at about −11 kb acts as an erythroid-specific enhancer when tested in cultured cells (Tuan *et al.*, 1989). The core or critical element of this enhancer activity has been narrowed to a small DNA sequence of 18 bp (Ney *et al.*, 1990) that contains binding sites for several known proteins (see below).

3. Silencers

Another class of regulatory DNA elements consists of silencers, which are the functional opposites of enhancers. Silencers cause decreased transcription of a linked gene, independent of position and orientation. Proteins that bind to silencers may act as repressors in the classical sense of excluding binding of transcription factors or, in the case of action at a distance, through protein–protein interaction between proteins binding to the silencer and proteins binding to the promoter (Renkawitz, 1990).

Two silencers have been identified 5' to the human β-globin gene (Berg *et al.*, 1989), one 5' to the ε-globin gene (Cao *et al.*, 1989; Lamb *et al.*, 1989) and one 5' to the α-globin gene (Atweh *et al.*, 1988). In the case of β and ε, the silencers are near positive control elements, suggesting there could be interaction between these regulatory elements via their binding proteins. There is also a negative regulatory region 5' to the ζ-globin gene; this region has not yet been shown to be a silencer (Lamb *et al.*, 1989).

There is probably interaction among proteins binding to silencers, enhancers, and promoters to determine the transcriptional status of a gene. A schematic illustration of a complex of this type is shown in Figure 1.5. With respect to the globin genes, unlocking these interactions will lead to understanding normal regulation and thus some hemoglobin disorders.

C. Trans-acting factors

The DNA regulatory regions described above exert their effects at least partly through the action of proteins that bind to specific DNA sequences. There are ubiquitous transcription factors that bind to the same promoter sequences 5' to many genes, as well as tissue-specific binding proteins that activate particular genes via promoters or enhancers, or suppress genes via silencers. There also may be repressor proteins bound to specific sequences (Evans *et al.*, 1990; Mitchell and Tjian, 1989). Transcriptional control is thus a complex sum of activator and repressor proteins binding to many different cis-acting DNA elements.

General transcription factors include, among others, TFIID, the TATA-binding factor; CP1, one of several CCAAT-binding factors; Sp1, which binds to specific sequences in many promoters; CDP, which is able to displace CCAAT box-binding proteins; NFI, or nuclear factor I, important in transcription and replication; and a2, a ubiquitous protein that binds competitively with GATA (see below). These proteins are described in Table 1.1.

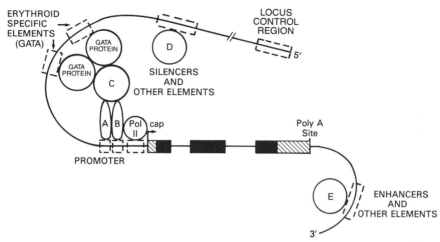

Figure 1.5. Schematic model of a typical transcriptionally active globin gene. The single line represents double-stranded DNA, the black boxes represent exons (separating two introns), and the hatched boxes represent transcribed but untranslated regions. Dashed boxes are the cis-acting elements or DNA-binding sites for trans-acting factors, shown as circles or ellipses, whose interaction with DNA mediates the function of these elements. Some proteins, as indicated by C, may not interact directly with DNA but bind to other proteins that do interact with DNA. It is believed that the mechanism of action of enhancers or silencers is through the binding of specific proteins; this is less certain with regard to the locus control region.

Several erythroid-specific binding proteins have been discovered. The first and best characterized is the transcription factor previously called GF-1, NFE-1, or Eryf1, now known as GATA-1. This protein has been purified and its gene cloned from the human genome and the chicken genome (Zon *et al.*, 1990; Trainor *et al.*, 1990). There are binding sites for GATA-1 5' to every chicken and human globin gene examined and within enhancers for the globin genes, as well as flanking other genes expressed during erythroid development (Evans *et al.*, 1990). Thus this protein, which is a potent transcriptional factor, seems to be required for activation of erythroid genes (Martin and Orkin, 1990). It may also regulate the transcription of genes specifically expressed in megakaryoctes and mast cells (Martin *et al.*, 1989b; Romeo *et al.*, 1989). Its functional importance was further demonstrated when it was shown that increased activity of the $^A\gamma$ promoter, due to a mutation at -175, is mediated by GATA-1 (Martin *et al.*, 1989a).

Another erythroid factor is GATA-2 (GF-2), which binds 5' to the erythroid gene porphobilinogen deaminase (Mignotte *et al.*, 1989), but no other binding sites have yet been found near other erythroid genes. B4 is an uncharacterized erythroid-specific binding protein that is different from GATA-1 and

Table 1.1. Trans-Acting Factors

Protein	Binding site	Activities	References
General			
TFIID	TATA box	Transcription	Sawadago and Roeder (1985)
CP1/CP2	CCAAT box	Transcription	Chodosh et al. (1988)
Sp1	GGGCGG	Transcription	Dynan and Tjian (1983)
CDP	CCAAT box	Repressor?	Barberis et al. (1987)
NF-1	CCAAT box; origin of replication	Transcription and replication	Jones et al. (1987)
a2	GATA site	Repressor?	Wall et al. (1989)
OTF-1	ATTTGCAT	Transcription and replication	Murphy et al. (1989)
BP1	A/T T A/C A/T ATAT A/G	Repressor?	Berg et al. (1989)
ZF1	GTGGTCA	Unknown	Yu et al. (1990)
ZF2	Unknown	Unknown	Yu et al. (1990)
εF1	TCCATCCATCACTGC	Unknown	Yu et al. (1991)
Erythroid			
GATA-1	A/T GAT A/T A/G	Transcription	Evans et al. (1990)
GF-2	TGACTCA	Transcription?	Mignotte et al. (1989)
NFE3	GCCTTG	Repressor?	Mantovani et al. (1989)
B4	CACCC box	Unknown	Wall et al. (1989)

binds 5' to the β-globin gene (Mantovani et al., 1988b). NFE3 is an erythroid-specific binding protein that binds 5' to the ^Aγ-globin gene (Mantovani et al., 1989).

Identification of proteins binding to silencers (repressors) has lagged behind identification of activator proteins. To date, no erythroid gene repressors have been purified, although there are candidate proteins binding 5' to the ε-, γ-, and β-globin genes (Cao et al., 1989; P. Gutman and A. N. Schechter, unpublished; Mantovani et al., 1989; Berg et al., 1989).

A number of protein binding sites have been identified flanking the globin genes. Proteins binding upstream from the β-globin promoter are shown in Figure 1.4A. Many of these data are summarized in Wall et al. (1989). The proximal promoter has binding sites for general factors such as TFIID, CP1, and Sp1, in combination with the erythroid-specific proteins B4 and GATA-1. The distal promoter includes a sequence at about −150 bp, which is necessary for induction of the β-globin gene in cultured cells (Wall et al., 1989), indicated by Ind, and which is the location of a HSS. Either the −120- or −200-bp region is also required for maximal induction (deBoer et al., 1988). This DNA has binding sites for CP1 and NF-1, neither of which are erythroid specific, and so they may interact with an adjacent GATA-1 protein to confer erythroid inducibility on this region. A positive control region upstream of this site (P. E. Berg and

A. N. Schechter, unpublished) binds ubiquitous proteins (NF-1 and CDP), as well as GATA. Two silencers even further upstream are binding sites for the ubiquitous protein BP1, which may be a repressor, and BP2, of unknown function (Berg et al., 1989).

The upstream region of the $^A\gamma$ gene has also been studied in some detail, especially at the known mutational sites causing hereditary persistence of fetal hemoglobin (HPFH). Figure 1.4B illustrates some of the proteins binding in this region. Ubiquitous factors binding to the ATA and CCAAT sequences include TFIID, CP1, and CDP. The erythroid factor GATA also binds here (Superti-Ferga et al., 1988). Two factors have been found that bind to the γ CACCC box, CAC1 and CAC2, but they have not been identified as known binding proteins (Gumucio et al., 1988). The transcription factor Sp1 binds to this site as well (Catala et al., 1989).

An HPFH mutation at -117 bp causes increased binding of CP1 and CDP, with decreased binding of GATA-1 and NFE3 (Superti-Ferga et al., 1988); a deletion of the CCAAT box at -110 bp, causing HPFH, abolishes binding of CP1, CDP, and NFE3, but not that of GATA-1 (Mantovani et al., 1989). The commonality in these two HPFH effects seems to be loss of NFE3 binding, suggesting that NFE3 may be a negatively acting factor. Further upstream, at -175 bp, there is another site of HPFH mutations. Binding to this site are OTF-1, a ubiquitous protein, and GATA-1 (Mantovani et al., 1988b). Mutations causing HPFH cause increased binding of GATA and decreased binding of OTF-1 (Mantovani et al., 1988b). Detailed analysis of this site has shown that the increased γ gene expression caused by mutation is mediated by increased GATA-1 binding (Martin et al., 1989a). These point mutations account for only part of the HPFH mutations, many of which are caused by long DNA deletions in the β cluster (see below).

Proteins binding to the ϵ-globin gene are now beginning to be defined. As shown in Figure 1.4C, two regulatory regions have been determined, a silencer between -251 and -294 bp (Cao et al., 1989) and a positive control region between -535 and -392 bp (S.-X. Cao and A. N. Schechter, unpublished). Two proteins bind to the silencer, one ubiquitous and one erythroid specific (P. Gutman and A. N. Schechter, unpublished). There is a GATA-1 site at -163 bp and a site for a ubiquitous protein, ϵF1, at -143 bp (Yu et al., 1991).

The ζ-globin 5' region has sites for the ubiquitous proteins Sp1 and CP1 or CP2, for two unidentified ubiquitous proteins, ZF1 and ZF2, and for GATA-1 (Watt et al., 1990; Yu et al., 1990). The Sp1-binding site near the CACCC box overlaps both GATA-1 and a protein which may be CP1 or CP2, and Sp1 binding is displaced by GATA-1 or CP1/CP2. GATA-1 binding also displaces Sp1 at -230 bp, suggesting Sp1 may be acting as a repressor (Yu et al., 1990). Mutations in the GATA-1 site drastically decrease promoter activity (Watt et al., 1990).

The factors mention here are described in more detail in Table 1.1. A complete listing of factors and a more complete set of references can be found in Wingender (1988).

IV. THALASSEMIAS

A. Diagnosis

1. Restriction mapping and haplotype analysis

Thalassemia syndromes may be among the most common single gene diseases in the world. β-Thalassemia is present in approximately 3% of the world's population and α-thalassemia is very common in the Asiatic population (Weatherall, 1991a). The number of different mutations causing β-thalassemia is over 100, yet 90% of abnormalities are due to about 20 specific mutant alleles (Kazazian and Boehm, 1988). The thalassemia syndromes may be due to point mutations or deletions.

Thalassemias were originally diagnosed from hematological indices based in reduced red cell volume and hemoglobin, but the introduction of chain biosynthetic methods allowed more precise delineation of this complex group of diseases (Weatherall and Clegg, 1981). DNA diagnosis of β-thalassemia, which further clarified these syndromes, was initially performed using restriction enzyme analysis. Examples of loss of restriction enzyme sites for thalassemias are given in Nienhuis et al. (1984).

The pattern of restriction enzyme cleavage sites in the β-globin gene cluster that define haplotypes was coupled to specific β-thalassemias in 1982 (Orkin et al., 1982). Nine haplotypes were described, thus allowing prenatal diagnosis of some thalassemias by testing for cleavage with a battery of five restriction enzymes that cleaved at seven DNA sites. It was found, for example, that a nucleotide substitution at codon 39, which creates a stop signal, is associated with haplotype I. None of the restriction enzymes cleaves at that particular codon, so restriction enzyme site changes are associated with but not caused by the mutation. There are also cases wherein point mutations are associated with multiple haplotypes.

Technically haplotype analysis is done by Southern blotting, the genomic DNA being tested is cleaved with appropriate restriction enzymes, denatured to produce single-stranded DNA, then transferred to a membrane filter. The specific region of interest is distinguished from the DNA of the entire genome by adding to the filter a radiolabeled DNA probe containing that region. The probe recognizes homologous DNA and binds to that area of the filter, producing a radioactive band. The length of the band is measured to compare with bands associated with defined haplotypes. Haplotype analyses are still useful in certain circumstances but are being supplanted by other techniques.

2. Oligonucleotide probes

It is possible to test for the presence of single base pair mutations using oligonucleotide probes about 20 base pairs in length. Under the appropriate hybridization conditions, the probes will only recognize a 100% match. The first example of the use of this method was the detection of the β^S allele (Conner *et al.*, 1983). Two oligonucleotides were used as probes, one complementary to β^A, the other to β^S. DNA from individuals homozygous for β^A hybridized only to the β^A probe, DNA from people homozygous for β^S hybridized only to the β^S probe, and DNA from heterozygous people ($\beta^A\beta^S$) hybridized to both. This is a very sensitive method for the detection of single base changes and thus has important applications in prenatal diagnosis. Using a number of different probes, one can determine the precise base sequence of any known single base change mutation.

Diagnosis of β-thalassemias has also been performed using this approach. For example, Pirastu *et al.* (1983) used two oligonucleotide probes, one complementary to the normal DNA sequence, the other complementary to the β 39 nonsense mutation, for prenatal diagnosis of β^0 thalassemia due to this mutation. The technique involved first hybridizing with one probe, washing the filter, then hybridizing with the other probe.

There are two problems concerning the general application of this method. Success depends on having a probe of high specific activity and, because there are other sequences in the genome that could cross-hybridize with a small oligonucleotide probe, it is necessary to cleave the total DNA with a restriction enzyme that will give a band of known length containing the DNA sequence of interest. Despite these problems this method has been used in many applications.

3. Polymerase chain reaction

The polymerase chain reaction (PCR) has in many ways revolutionized molecular biology by making detection of DNA or RNA exquisitely sensitive (reviewed in Erlich *et al.*, 1991). The method, developed in 1985, is conceptually simple (Saiki *et al.*, 1985). In the case of double-stranded DNA, two oligonucleotide primers are used which flank the gene or region of interest, one homologous to the 5' end of each DNA strand (sense and anti-sense strands). DNA polymerase is used to amplify enzymatically each strand from its primer after heat denaturation of the target DNA. Once a new strand is synthesized, it becomes a template for future amplification. A modification was introduced by Saiki *et al.* (1988), who used a heat-stable DNA polymerase (Taq) that allowed amplification at elevated temperatures, thus decreasing the background due to cross-hybridization of the probes with other DNA sequences and increasing the sensitivity and the yield. Because amplification is exponential, repeated rounds of amplification can yield a 10^7-fold or greater increase in DNA. This makes it possible to use unpurified DNA for amplification; Saiki *et al.* (1988) were able to detect a DNA molecule present only once in 10^5 cells. In addition, this polymerase is highly processive, allowing amplification of DNA greater than 1 kb in length. The error frequency is about 1 per 20,000 nucleotides. Because PCR is so sensitive, the major problem is amplification of contaminating DNA molecules (one molecule is enough to be detected!).

Due to PCR, it is now possible to use labeled oligonucleotide probes with amplified DNA that has not been cleaved with restriction enzymes but has been applied to a filter as a spot prior to hybridization; this is called a dot blot. Dot blot hybridization allows the analysis of many samples simultaneously.

One example of the use of PCR is in the detection of hemoglobin Constant Spring (Kropp *et al.*, 1989), which is a mutation of the α2-globin gene resulting in an elongated protein and causing a thalassemic phenotype. It is difficult to diagnose this condition due to the small amount of protein present. Because there is extensive homology between α1 and α2 in this region, it is not possible to detect this mutation by oligonucleotide probes. However, it is possible to diagnose this condition by PCR amplification of α2 with primers from IVS2 and a 3′ region where α1 and α2 are not homologous. The amplified DNA can be analyzed by dot blot hybridization.

A clever adaptation of PCR was developed by Huang *et al.* (1990) to screen β-thalassemia mutations among the Chinese. They collected samples as dried blood specimens, which could be mailed to screening centers, and used PCR amplification of the β-globin gene in cell lysates without prior DNA purification. The amplified DNA was analyzed using dot blot hybridization with 10 different probes. This has allowed screening of many hundreds of thousands of individuals.

4. DNA sequencing

New mutations are characterized by sequencing the DNA. Initially this was accomplished by cloning the gene in question. Because the globin genes' sequences are known, this is not difficult, but it is time consuming, involving the use of a suitable probe to identify clones of interest that have been generated from a DNA library. If the individual is heterozygous, it may be necessary to sequence several cloned DNAs before obtaining the new mutant DNA. With the advent of PCR it is now possible to directly sequence from amplified genomic DNA. Using this approach, heterozygous and homozygous mutations in the human γ- and β-globin genes have been sequenced in 3 days with less than 1 μg of genomic DNA (Engelke *et al.*, 1988).

5. RNA analysis

Thalassemias, which cause decreased amounts of globin chain synthesis, can be due to transcriptional or translational defects. Transcriptional defects can be of several types. They may cause decreased transcription, such as mutations 5′ to the gene (discussed above), or they may allow synthesis of mRNA that is aberrantly spliced or unstable. A summary of splicing mutations is given by Orkin (1987).

Transcription can be quantitated directly by hybridizing a labeled DNA probe to the cellular RNA and analyzing the product by polyacrylamide gel electrophoresis. Alternatively, if the gene is cloned, the RNA it produces can be analyzed after introducing the cloned gene into tissue culture cells. In some cases it is now possible to eliminate the use of a labeled probe and obviate the need for cloning by using PCR. The mRNA is amplified by first synthesizing a cDNA copy, then amplifying that DNA. The product, if present, is in such large quantities that it can be analyzed directly by gel electrophoresis and, if compared with a reference that has been coamplified, can be quantitated. This was used to detect a 23-kb deletion in the α-globin gene cluster in two fetuses with hydrops fetalis (Chehab et al., 1987). Although it is much easier to detect an all-or-nothing effect, it is also possible to quantitate a thalassemic heterozygote (Huang et al., 1991).

Aberrant splicing causes a difference in size of the mRNA, thus it can be detected by hybridization of a labeled DNA probe to total cellular mRNA, as described above. PCR amplification of the mRNA allows sequencing of the altered RNA product. Specific types of splicing mutations will be discussed below.

B. Types of mutations

1. Deletions

α-Thalassemia is usually caused by deletion of one or more of the four α genes on chromosome 16. The high frequency of the deletion mechanism in the α-thalassemias is probably due to the high sequence homology between $\alpha 1$ and $\alpha 2$, allowing for recombination and deletion events. Deletion of one α-globin gene is most common, with two predominant types, a 3.7-kb deletion called $-\alpha^{3.7}$, and 4.2-kb deletion called $-\alpha^{4.2}$; both delete $\alpha 2$ (Liebhaber, 1989; Higgs et al., 1990). The $-\alpha^{3.7}$ deletion is present as a heterozygote in up to 90% of the population of parts of India and Papua New Guinea. Clinical symptoms vary greatly, depending on the number of genes remaining. Deletion of one gene causes no clinical symptoms (silent carrier), deletion of two genes gives α-thalassemia trait, deletion of three genes is called HbH disease (production of β_4), and deletion of all four genes is lethal during fetal development (hydrops fetalis with production of γ_4). Quantitative differences in the number of α genes can be detected by Southern blot analysis and dot blot hybridization.

Deletion of all or part of the β-globin gene, but not upstream genes, is rare (Orkin, 1987). Much more common is the deletion of part of the entire β-globin gene cluster. $\gamma\delta\beta$-Thalassemias are due to large deletions of DNA that include far upstream sequences in the β cluster and may or may not include the β gene itself (Driscoll *et al.*, 1989, and references therein). A recent paper described a γδβ-thalassemia in which the DNA deleted included three of the four LCR sites upstream of ε, leaving the site at −6.1 kb and all of the globin genes intact but inactive, strongly suggesting the molecular basis for the phenotype was deletion of the LCR sites (Driscoll *et al.*, 1989). In Spanish $^{G}\gamma^{A}\gamma$ δβ-thalassemia, δ and β are deleted, as well as sequences over 60 kb downstream of β, but the γ genes are intact (Feingold and Forget, 1989, and references therein).

Four cases are known of deletions of δβ that cause HPFH, i.e., HPFH-1, -2, -3, and -4. HPFH-1 and -2 contain deletions of about 105 kb, whereas HPFH-3 and -4 contain deletions of about 55 kb (see references in Feingold and Forget, 1989). The 5′ ends of all four deletions are similar. The DNA region immediately downstream of the deletion in HPFH-1 was cloned and shown to have enhancer activity, suggesting that the HPFH phenotype is due to bringing an enhancer close to the γ genes; this enhancer DNA is deleted in Spanish δβ-thalassemia (Feingold and Forget, 1989). Because the 5′ end of the Spanish deletion is almost the same as that of HPFH-1, this further strengthens the idea that the enhancer is necessary for activation of the γ genes.

2. Nondeletion mutations

Nondeletion mutations causing α-thalassemia are relatively rare and include point mutations and very small deletions or insertions (Orkin, 1987; Liebhaber, 1989; Higgs *et al.*, 1990). Types of mutations not located intragenically include a splice junction mutation, initiation mutations (the initiator ATG is mutated to ACG or GTG), polyadenylation mutations leading to unstable mRNA, and chain termination mutations leading to elongated mRNA. The latter mutation can lead to the most common form of nondeletion α-thalassemia, (α2 Constant Spring) characterized by the addition of 31 amino acids to the protein and instability of the mRNA (Liebhaber, 1989). There are also intragenic thalassemic mutations, giving a total of 12 nondeletion mutations identified thus far. Of these, 11 are in or near α2.

Many point mutations in the DNA coding for the β chain have been identified as causing thalassemia. The mutations include nonsense mutations and frameshift and missense mutations in the coding region (Orkin, 1987). Several types of nonexon mutations occur in and near the β gene. As with the α-thalassemias, RNA-processing mutations are found; these cause altered splice junctions and altered polyadenylation (Kazazian and Boehm, 1988; Adams and Steinberg, 1988). Promoter mutations are observed in the TATA box and CAC-CC box, discussed above, as well as in the cap site. Evidence for the importance of DNA sequences at about 530 bp 5′ to the cap site in determining the level of β protein has also been presented (Berg *et al.*, 1991).

Structural mutations are rarely found in the γ genes (Adams and Steinberg, 1988), but a very interesting class of promoter mutants, HPFH, is known; HPHF mutants allow continued synthesis of fetal hemoglobin. There is an HPFH mutation at −117, −196, or −198 bp 5′ to $^A\gamma$, and at −158, −161, −175, or −202 bp 5′ to $^G\gamma$ (Schwartz *et al.*, 1988). These mutations can increase HbF levels of up to 20% (Karlsson and Nienhuis, 1985). The −175 bp HPFH has been studied in detail. Two proteins bind to this region of DNA, GATA-1 and OTF-1 (Table 1). The HPFH mutation causes decreased OTF-1 binding, but the HPFH effect is mediated through binding of GATA-1 (Martin *et al.*, 1989a; Nicolis *et al.*, 1989; Gumucio *et al.*, 1990).

V. HEMOGLOBINOPATHIES

The hemoglobinopathies, i.e., the diseases of hemoglobin due to mutations in the genes coding for the structure of the globin polypeptides, comprise a large array of syndromes ranging from those causing severe disease to those almost undetectable except with sophisticated laboratory tests (Bunn and Forget, 1986). Indeed, of the more than 300 known mutations in the α- and β-globin chains, most are functionally silent and have been detected incidentally during protein characterization or DNA sequencing studies.

With respect to prevalence, the sickle hemoglobin mutation ($\beta^{6glu \rightarrow val}$), which gives rise to sickle hemoglobin or hemoglobin S ($\alpha_2\beta_2{}^S$) rather than the normal adult hemoglobin A ($\alpha_2\beta_2$), is both the most common hemoglobinopathy and causes the most severe disease state (Schechter *et al.*, 1987). Other prevalent hemoglobin mutants are hemoglobin C ($\beta^{6glu \rightarrow lys}$) and hemoglobin E ($\beta^{26glu \rightarrow lys}$), which primarily manifest disease states when they exist in the double heterozygous state with the hemoglobin S mutation (for hemoglobin C) or a thalassemic mutation (for hemoglobin E). Other mutations are, in general, much less common but cause, especially when in the homozygous state, symptoms due to the unusual functional properties that they impart to the hemoglobin molecules. These include mutations which cause instability of the hemoglobin molecule, which give rise to hemolytic anemias associated with Heinz body formation as the unstable hemoglobin molecules precipitate on the erythrocyte membrane. Other functional abnormalities include those due to altered oxygen affinity: increased affinity generally causes a polycythemic phenotype, while decreased affinity may cause anemia.

The sickle syndromes include a variety of genotypes with at least one chromosome containing the β^S gene (Schechter *et al.*, 1987). These syndromes include simple β^S homozygotes and those with coexisting α-thalassemia or genes for HPFH. The syndromes also include individuals who are double heterozygotes for the β^S gene and β-thalassemia or $\delta\beta$-thalassemia genes, or hemoglobins C or A (the usual carrier state). All of these syndromes, except the AS genotype, cause the sickle cell disease state to varying extents.

Sickle cell disease is manifested by a severe but well-tolerated anemia, variable acute painful crises, and chronic tissue damage involving most of the major organ systems of the individual. These manifestations are due to the relative insolubility of deoxyhemoglobin S inside the red cell, which causes the formation of aggregated or polymerized hemoglobin S as the sickle hemoglobin-containing erythrocyte traverses the tissues of the body and gives up oxygen. These hemoglobin S polymer molecules cause the red cell to be less flexible than normal and result in chronic hemolysis as well as occlusion of the microcirculatory vessels (probably both arterioles and capillaries), leading to extensive tissue damage. These processes cause the severe morbidity and early mortality that are hallmarks of these syndromes. Recent advances in molecular genetics, however, have raised the possibility of effective therapy at the genetic level. These advances, discussed below, include the use of pharmacological agents that specifically increase the synthesis of the γ chain of fetal hemoglobin (hemoglobin F) and reciprocally decrease the synthesis of the β^S chain; hemoglobin F has a strong "sparing" effect on the polymerization of hemoglobin S. In addition, gene replacement strategies, including the goal of homologous recombination, are targeting the β^S gene for replacement with normal β-globin genes.

Molecular genetic studies have recently made two other major contributions to the medical genetic aspects of the hemoglobinopathies, especially the sickle syndromes. First, restriction enzyme digestion and Southern blotting have allowed an extensive characterization of the RFLPs associated with the mutant genes. These analyses, as discussed previously, have allowed inferences to be made about the origins and dispersal of these abnormal genes in populations during recent history and have allowed the identification of some genetic markers associated with various aspects of these syndromes. Of equal importance, these methods have allowed the development of methods for precise and sensitive prenatal diagnosis (Weatherall et al., 1985). Initially RFLP analyses of restriction site polymorphisms closely linked to the β^S mutation were used (Kan and Dozy, 1978), but these were soon replaced by restriction enzymes that cut or did not cut at the site of the mutation itself (Geever et al., 1981; reviewed in Nienhuis et al., 1984). Subsequently, allele-specific oligonucleotide probes (Conner et al., 1983) and then PCR methods (Saiki et al., 1985) were introduced to increase further the utility of these approaches. These methods, all developed initially for the diagnosis of the β^S mutation, have since been successfully applied to the diagnosis of many other genetic diseases, continuing a pattern that has characterized sickle cell research for more than 40 years.

VI. ANALYSIS OF GLOBIN GENE FUNCTION

A. Expression in cultured cells

1. Chromosome transfer

It is possible to transfer chromosomes into cells by fusing two cell types, with selection or screening for the transferred chromosome. This technique has been used to study expression of the β-like globin genes. Early studies involved the transfer of human chromosome 11, containing the β-like genes, into mouse erythroleukemia (MEL) cells (Willing et al., 1979; Pyati et al., 1980). Willing et al. (1979) screened human fibroblast × MEL cell hybrids for the presence of human chromosome 11 by looking for lactose dehydrogenase A (LDH-A), also on chromosome 11. They detected activation of the human adult β-globin gene in mouse cells containing chromosome 11, but the γ gene was never activated. Pyati et al. (1980), fusing lymphocytes and MEL cells, obtained similar results. Thus, the globin genes are not irreversibly repressed, but can be activated in the presence of appropriate regulatory factors. These early studies paved the way for the discovery by Papayannopoulou et al. (1988) that when MEL cells are fused with lymphocytes from patients with HPFH, the human fetal γ genes are activated. This suggests that there are positive factors in the MEL cells that can act on HPFH but not normal γ genes, perhaps due to the chromatin structure of the normal gene as compared with the HPFH gene.

2. DNA transfer (transfection)

Naked DNA, i.e., DNA without protein, can be directly introduced into cells; this type of transfer is called transfection. A variety of physical techniques can be used, depending on the recipient cell type. Once the DNA has been transfected, there are two types of in vitro expression system currently in use. One is a stable system, so called because the DNA being tested is stably integrated into the genome, albeit in apparently random sites in the chromosome. Cell clones that have integrated the test gene and are expressing it are selected by growth in a medium that is preferential for the survival of these cells due to the coexpression of a selectabe "marker" gene. The test DNA may consist of a gene under investigation or of a promoter being studied fused to a reporter gene, such as the gene for chloramphenicol acetyl transferase (CAT), for luciferase, or for human growth hormone (hGH), as well as the selectable marker. This method has the advantage that chromatin is present after the integration of the transferred DNA, perhaps giving a more accurate reflection of the in vivo situation. Also, the expression level is high because every cell contains the transferred DNA; these cells can then be treated with different agents to gauge the response of the gene construct being tested. The disadvantage is that the marker gene, which can be positively or negatively selected, must be transfected either on the same plasmid or on another plasmid (cotransfection). The cotransfection rate can be optimized to be about 80%, so this is not normally a hindrance. However, in the case of some globin genes, there has been a more serious problem: a strong dependence of gene expression level on the site of integration, making it necessary to assay pools of clones in order to obtain an average level of expression. Now that it is known that the LCR relieves this integration site dependence, if at least part of the LCR (part of hypersensitive site 2) is included on the plasmid construct, it is possible to use the data from individual clones.

Transient assays, the other type of *in vitro* assay, are useful because they are much quicker than creating stable transformants. The DNA of interest is introduced into cells without selection. The cells are harvested about 3 days later, before the plasmid DNA has integrated into the genome. This method, for example, has been recently used to assess the relative importance of the binding of the GATA-1 protein in the −175 HPFH mutation. It was found that the −175 mutation leads to increased promoter activity when introduced into erythroid cells but not when introduced into nonerythroid cells. However, if a mutation is introduced into the OTF-1-binding site there is no effect, showing that the GATA-1 binding is the critical factor (Martin *et al.*, 1989a; Nicolis *et al.*, 1989; Gumucio *et al.*, 1990).

A more general use of the transient assay approach is to search for regulatory sequences surrounding a gene. Several types of experiment have been successfully used that take advantage of this technique. The 5' region of one globin gene can be substituted for the 5' region of another; in this case the native gene, not a reporter gene, is used (Karlsson and Nienhuis, 1985). With this method, it was found that either the β-globin 5' flanking region or the coding sequence can confer inducibility by chemical agents (Wright *et al.*, 1984) and that the control of β-globin gene expression in certain human erythroid cells is due to changes in the trans factors operating on the 5' flanking regions (Fordis *et al.*, 1984, 1986). In another approach, deletions of various sizes are created in the flanking DNA that has been fused to a reporter gene. For example, the β-globin region 5' to −639 bp was fused to the *CAT* gene, deletions were generated, and the resulting plasmids were analyzed by transfection into erythroid and nonerythroid cells (Berg *et al.*, 1989). In this way, two silencer regions were detected 5' to the β gene. The transient assay method has also been used to detect enhancer sequences 3' to several globin genes.

B. Transgenic mice

Although many experiments aimed at studying the regulation of human globin genes have used the MEL cell line, there are obvious limitations to such *in vitro* approaches. In order to attempt to study regulation in an *in vivo* model, transgenic mice are being used. The most commonly used method to transfer foreign DNA into mice is microinjection of the DNA into pronuclei of fertilized eggs, with transfer of the eggs to pseudopregnant females (Gordon *et al.*, 1980). An early experiment using this method showed that the cloned rabbit β-globin gene could be successfully transferred into mice and transmitted to progeny (Constantini and Lacy, 1981). It was later shown that the human β-globin gene, when introduced into mice, shows both tissue-specific and developmental-specific regulation (Townes *et al.*, 1985), thus making the mouse a viable model for studies of human globin gene expression. Transgenic mice have been used extensively to characterize the importance of various DNA sequences with respect to tissue and developmental specificity (see below). The functionality of the human β-globin gene in mice was demonstrated by an interesting experiment in which the β-globin gene was introduced into a mouse that has a deletion of its $β^{maj}$-globin gene, causing β-thalassemia; the human gene was able to correct the thalassemia by forming a heterodimer with mouse α protein (Constantini *et al.*, 1986). By introducing both the human α- and β-globin genes into mice on separate constructs, each containing an LCR, Behringer *et al.* (1989) obtained functional human hemoglobin. This allowed attempts to develop mouse models of human hemoglobin disorders, most notably sickle cell anemia. A mouse producing HbS has been developed by microinjecting the human α- and $β^S$-globin genes (Ryan *et al.*, 1990). The transgenic mice were crossed with β-thalassemic mice to reduce the level of mouse hemoglobin, and the resulting mice exhibited some characteristics of sickle cell trait, including sickling of their erythrocytes upon deoxygenation.

VII. SWITCHING

A. Mechanism

During human development there are three switches in hemoglobin synthesis: the initial activation of globin genes in primitive erythroid tissues, the subsequent switch from embryonic to fetal hemoglobin, and then the switch at birth from fetal to adult hemoglobin (Figure 1.1) (Collins and Weissman, 1984). Despite the fact that a great effort has been made to understand these switches, especially the fetal-to-adult switch, the molecular bases of these phenomena are still not known. The fetal-to-adult switch is important in that it is known that fetal hemoglobin can substitute functionally for adult hemoglobin and ameliorate the clinical severity of several hemoglobin disorders. One example is sickle cell anemia, wherein the production of the γ-globin (fetal) chain can decrease the tendency toward polymerization of hemoglobin, which occurs with the sickle β (adult) chain (Schechter *et al.*, 1987). In cases of β-thalassemia, wherein the amount of adult hemoglobin is reduced, the production of fetal globin can compensate for this reduction and reduce the imbalance of α- and β-globin chain synthesis (Shinar et al., 1987). In normal adults, however, the level of fetal hemoglobin is less than 1% of the total hemoglobin. Being able to reactivate fetal hemoglobin synthesis would thus have enormous clinical benefits.

It has been possible to observe the fetal-to-adult switch in cultured cells. Cell hybrids made between human fetal erythroblasts and MEL cells initially expressed human fetal globin, then switched to adult hemoglobin synthesis (Papayannopoulou et al., 1986). Hybrids formed using second trimester erythroblasts switched faster than those formed using first trimester erythroblasts, which implicates a developmental clocklike mechanism of control. Activities present in the serum used in culture can influence this switch: there is an activity in fetal sheep serum that induces the switch from fetal to adult globin (Stamatoyannopoulos et al., 1983). On the other hand, cultured adult erythroid progenitors produce physiologic levels of HbF when grown without fetal calf serum, but significantly higher levels of HbF when grown in the presence of fetal calf serum, as if the switch were delayed (Fujimori et al., 1990). The factors responsible for these opposing effects have not been identified.

Experiments with transgenic mice have markedly changed the field and are beginning to suggest a general model for switching (Orkin, 1990). The ϵ, γ, and β genes are all appropriately regulated when individually microinjected into mice, although expression is very low. When the LCR is added to the DNA construct being microinjected, γ and β are both expressed at all stages of development, showing the LCR can override stage-specific development (Enver et al., 1990; Behringer et al., 1990). However, DNA with γ, δ, β, and the LCR linked once again shows appropriate developmental expression. On the other hand, ϵ with the LCR is still expressed correctly, i.e., only in the yolk sac. An interpretation of these data is that γ and β compete for activation by the LCR, whereas ϵ is regulated independently. A model derived from this type of experiment is shown in Figure 1.6. The LCR is believed to interact with ϵ, γ, or β to determine which gene is activated; inactive genes are kept silent by factors such as repressors. The specifics of how the LCR might do this is not known. A wave of supercoiling might move ahead of the LCR, causing DNA melting, or there may be a DNA loop formed, held together by protein–protein interactions between the LCR and the gene being activated. There may also be reciprocal interaction between the γ genes and the β/δ genes such that activation of β and δ decreases expression of the γ genes, while inactivation of β and δ increases γ gene expression, but this model has recently been challenged (Dillon and Grosveld, 1991).

B. Manipulation of HbF synthesis

Several agents have been used in an attempt to increase the level of fetal hemoglobin in patients with sickle cell anemia and β-thalassemia. The first drug

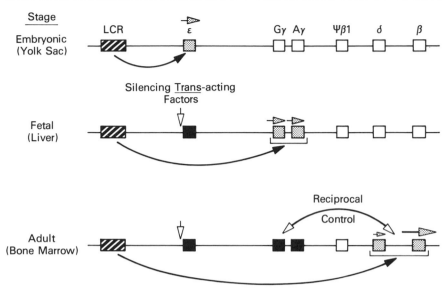

Figure 1.6. Model for hemoglobin switching at various developmental stages. The locus control region (LCR) is shown. The globin genes and one pseudogene are shown as open boxes; a globin gene being transcribed is denoted as a dotted box with an arrow showing the direction of transcription. Vertical arrows show binding sites for silencing proteins or other factors that mediate the developmental specificity of globin gene expression. (Modified from Orkin, 1990.)

used was 5-azacytidine, a cytotoxic drug that demethylates DNA and thus has the potential to activate inactive genes (Ley *et al.*, 1983; Charache *et al.*, 1983; Humphries *et al.*, 1985). Although this drug does increase HbF, its use was discontinued because of its carcinogenic potential. A drug now being used to treat sickle cell anemia and β-thalassemia patients is hydroxyurea, another cytotoxic drug that increases the production of F cells and the amount of HbF per F cell by unknown means, not involving demethylation (Rodgers *et al.*, 1990; Goldberg *et al.*, 1990, and references therein). Hydroxyurea is a DNA synthesis inhibitor that can cause chromosome damage (Timson, 1975), so its use also presents potential problems, although to date no serious side effects have been observed at the doses administered (G. Rogers, personal communication).

VIII. GENE THERAPY

Gene therapy is a term used for introducing a normal gene into the cells of patients with a defective gene. Due to ethical considerations, at present gene therapy is only being considered for somatic cells, not germ-line cells, to avoid introducing permanent changes into the gene pool. The transferred gene can theoretically be introduced either in addition to the existing defective gene or can replace it, which, by inserting the gene into the correct DNA site, has the advantages of retaining its context and eliminating the defective gene, whose product may be deleterious. On the other hand, gene addition therapy has the advantage of allowing expression of a particular gene in cells that do not normally express that gene, broadening the range of possible target cells (Kohn *et al.*, 1989; Miller, 1990).

A. Techniques

The target cells being primarily used for human gene therapy are hematopoietic cells because they are capable of self-renewal, can be removed for DNA insertion, and can then be replaced by autologous bone marrow transplantation. Of course this limits the genetic diseases amenable to treatment, but hematopoietic cells are ideal targets for gene therapy of hemoglobin disorders. However, recently the retroviral transfer of genes into other cell types, such as endothelial cells, fibroblasts, hepatocytes, and keratinocytes, has been accomplished (Weatherall, 1991a,b). This paves the way for potentially introducing genes into fibroblasts, for example, and treating the patient with a skin graft.

      Several methods have been used to introduce DNA into cells *in vitro*, such as calcium phosphate-mediated transfection, electroporation (the delivery of electrical current to cells, which creates pores in the cell membrane through which DNA can penetrate into the cell), fusion of the cell membrane with liposomes or with bacterial protoplasts carrying DNA, microinjection, or infection with viral vectors, most commonly retroviruses. Some of these methods are unsuitable for gene therapy, for example, transfection, which is inefficient, and microinjection, which is very labor intensive. Fusion and electroporation have not yet been well enough studied to make a judgment about their usefulness.

      A different approach that is now being explored is the introduction of purified genes, independent of a vector, into cells (Felgner and Rhodes, 1991). The DNA can be expressed over a period of time, but does not permanently integrate into the genome. This makes it comparable to a drug that must be readministered periodically. For this reason, this approach is called gene therapeutics. It has the advantages of not causing permanent changes and of being able to be withdrawn or changed if needed. It is at present too new to evaluate. We will therefore confine our discussion to the carrier-mediated methods currently in use.

      Currently the method of choice is retroviral vectors, because their efficiency of transfer can approach 100%. A single, unrearranged DNA copy of the virus is stably inserted into the genome and transmitted to progeny cells. The life cycle and utility as vehicles for gene transfer of these RNA viruses have been described elsewhere (Varmus, 1988; Williams, 1990). Up to 80% of viral genes can be deleted to create vectors for inserting the gene of interest. A maximum of about 10 kb of DNA can be inserted into the viral vector.

It is now possible to obtain high-level expression of the human β-globin gene cloned in a retroviral vector and introduced into murine erythroleukemia cells in culture (Novak et al., 1990). This result was achieved only after several important facts were discovered: the entire β-globin gene must be used because the cDNA is not expressed, and part of the LCR must be included in the construct. This type of construct can now be tested in mice, where it is already known that a retrovirally transferred β-globin gene without LCR sequences is expressed in a tissue-specific manner, but at a low level (Dzierzak et al., 1988).

For gene therapy of hemoglobin diseases to be effective, one needs very high levels of globin gene expression, as well as close coordination of expression of the α-like and β-like globin genes. Otherwise a thalassemic phenotype could be caused by the attempt at therapy. It is also critical in the globin system that an introduced gene be expressed at the proper time during development. In one approach, the normal β-globin gene would recombine with the mutated gene by homologous recombination, replacing it. The first report of homologous recombination between a transfected gene and its genomic counterpart was with the human β-globin gene; the frequency of recombination was about 1 in 1000 cells (Smithies et al., 1985). Homologous recombination has now been used in cultured cells to replace a β^S-globin gene with its normal counterpart (Shesely et al., 1991). These experiments are very promising for gene therapy, once the frequency of homologous recombination is increased, and would allow proper timing of β-globin protein synthesis and normal levels of synthesis, and thus coordinate regulation with α protein synthesis.

B. Animal models

The most common animal model for gene therapy is the mouse. In mice, homologous recombination has been used to disrupt genes in order to understand their function. The basic strategy involves mutating the gene of interest in vitro, introducing the mutant gene into pluripotent, embryonic stem (ES) cells using homologous recombination, microinjecting these cells into mouse blastocysts to create chimeric mice, then breeding these heterozygotes to make homozygotes (Capecchi, 1989). Clearly this strategy is not applicable to humans, but it is yielding important information about gene regulation.

Another widely used method to introduce genes into mice is the microinjection of DNA into the male pronucleus of a fertilized egg, which is then implanted into a pseudopregnant female (Gordon et al., 1980), as discussed previously. As mentioned, this method is too labor intensive to be applicable to humans and in addition would alter the germ line, so it is generally considered not acceptable.

As a prelude to human gene therapy, the adenosine deaminase (ADA) gene has been successfully introduced into mice and monkeys via a retroviral vector introduced into bone marrow cells (Osborne *et al.*, 1990; Kantoff *et al.*, 1987). In mice, human ADA was found in the blood for six months after transplantation of infected marrow at high levels (Osborne *et al.*, 1990). In contrast, only small amounts of human ADA were detected in the peripheral blood cells of monkeys, with levels peaking at 2 to 3 months and disappearing after 160 days (Kantoff *et al.*, 1987).

C. Prospects for human gene therapy

The first fully approved introduction of foreign DNA into humans for the purpose of integrating this DNA into the genome was the marking of tumor-infiltrating lymphocytes (TILs) with the *Escherichia coli* neomycin gene, introduced on a retroviral vector (Rosenberg *et al.*, 1990). The purpose of the experiment was to track the TILs in melanoma patients in an attempt to study the progress of this new type of cancer therapy (treatment of patients with their own TILs), and so this does not constitute gene therapy. This experiment is still in progress as this is written and the results are not known.

Subsequently, permission was obtained to introduce a copy of a normal ADA gene in a retroviral vector into peripheral blood lymphocytes of ADA-deficient children and then reintroduce these modified cells into the patients; these experiments have recently begun (Anderson *et al.*, 1990). This has paved the way for attempts at gene therapy of other diseases. It is too early to say when successful gene therapy will be demonstrated, or whether it will become part of routine clinical treatment.

Acknowledgments

We gratefully acknowledge helpful comments on the manuscript by Drs. W. French Anderson, Pablo Gutman, Constance T. Noguchi and Griffin Rodgers.

References

Adams, J. G., and Steinberg, M. H. (1988). Hemoglobinopathies and thalassemias. *Curr. Hematol. Oncol.* **6**:89–130.
Alter, B. P. (1979). The $^G\gamma$:$^A\gamma$ composition of fetal hemoglobin in fetuses and newborns. *Blood* **54**:1158–1163.
Anderson, W. F., Blaese, R. M., and Culver, K. (1990). The ADA human gene therapy clinical protocol. *Hum. Gene Ther.* **1**:331–362.
Antoniou, M., deBoer, E., Habets, G., and Grosveld, F. (1988). The human β-globin gene

contains multiple regulatory regions: Identification of one promoter and two downstream enhancers. *EMBO J.* **7**:377–384.

Atweh, G. F., Liu, J. M., Brickner, H. E., and Zhu, X. X. (1988). A silencer element from the α-globin gene inhibits expression of β-like genes. *Mol. Cell. Biol.* **8**:5047–5051.

Barberis, A., Superti-Furga, G., and Busslinger, M. (1987). Mutually exclusive interaction of the CCAAT-binding factor and of a displacement protein with overlapping sequences of a histone gene promoter. *Cell (Cambridge, Mass.)* **50**:347–359.

Behringer, R. R., Hammer, R. E. Brinster, R. L., Palmiter, R. D., and Townes, T. (1987). Two 3′ sequences direct adult erythroid-specific expression of human β-globin genes in transgenic mice. *Proc. Natl. Acad. Sci. U.S.A.* **84**:7056–7060.

Behringer, R. R., Ryan, T. M., Reilly, M. P., Asakura, T., Palmiter, R. E., Brinster, R. L., and Townes, T. M. (1989). Synthesis of functional human hemoglobin in transgenic mice. *Science* **245**:971–973.

Behringer, R. R., Ryan, T. M., Palmiter, R. C., Brinster, R. L., and Townes, T. M. (1990). Human γ- to β-globin gene switching in transgenic mice. *Genes Dev.* **4**:380–389.

Benz, E. J., Murnane, J. J., Tankanow, B. L., Beoman, B. W., Mazur, E. M., Cavallesco, C., Jenko, T., Snyder, E. L., Forget, B. G., and Hoffman, R. (1980). Embryonic-fetal erythroid characteristics of a human leukemic cell line. *Proc. Natl. Acad. Sci. U.S.A.* **77**:3509–3513.

Berg, P. E., Williams, D. M., Qian, R.-L., Cohen, R. B., Cao, S. X., Mittelman, M., and Schechter, A. N. (1989). A common protein binds to two silencers 5′ to the human β-globin gene. *Nucleic Acids Res.* **17**:8833–8852.

Berg, P. E., Mittelman, M., Elion, J., Labie, D., and Schechter, A. N. (1991). Increased protein binding to a −530 mutation of the human β-globin gene associated with decreased β-globin synthesis. *Am. J. Hematol.* **36**:42–47.

Bodine, D. M., and Ley, T. (1987). An enhancer element lies 3′ to the human ^Aγ globin gene. *EMBO J.* **6**:2997–3004.

Bunn, H. F., and Forget, B. G. (1986). "Hemoglobin: Molecular, Genetic and Clinical Aspects." Saunders, Philadelphia, Pennsylvania.

Bushel, P., Rego, K., Mendelsohn, L., and Allan, M. (1990). Correlation between patterns of DNase I-hypersensitive sites and upstream promoter activity of the human ε-globin gene at different stages of erythroid development. *Mol. Cell. Biol.* **10**:1199–1208.

Busslinger, M., Hurst, H., and Flavell, R. A. (1983). DNA methylation and the regulation of globin gene expression. *Cell (Cambridge, Mass.)* **34**:197–206.

Cao, S.-X., and Schechter, A. N. (1988). Nuclease hypersensitivity in the β-globin gene region of K562 cells. *Eur. J. Biochem.* **173**:517–522.

Cao, S.-X., Gutman, P. D., Dave, H. P. G., and Schechter, A. N. (1989). Identification of a transcriptional silencer in the 5′-flanking region of the human ε-globin gene. *Proc. Natl. Acad. Sci. U.S.A.* **86**:5306–5309.

Capecchi, M. R. (1989). The new mouse genetics: Altering the genome by gene targeting. *Trends Genet.* **5**:70–76.

Catala, F., deBoer, E., Habets, G., and Grosveld, F. (1989). Nuclear protein factors and erythroid transcription of the human ^Aγ-globin gene. *Nucleic Acids Res.* **17**:3811–3827.

Cedar, H. (1988). DNA methylation and gene activity. *Cell (Cambridge, Mass.)* **53**:3–4.

Charache, S., Dover, G., Smith, K., Talbot, C. C., Jr., Moyer, M., and Boyer, S. (1983). Treatment of sickle cell anemia with 5-azacytidine results in increased fetal hemoglobin production and is associated with nonrandom hypomethylation of DNA around the γ–δ–β-globin gene complex. *Proc. Natl. Acad. Sci. U.S.A.* **80**:4842–4846.

Charnay, P., Mellon, P., and Maniatis, T. (1985). Linker scanning mutagenesis of the 5′ flanking region of the mouse beta-major globin gene: Sequence requirements for transcription in erythroid and nonerythroid cells. *Mol. Cell. Biol.* **5**:1498–1511.

Chehab, F. F., Doherty, M., Cai, S., Kan, Y. W., Cooper, S., and Rubin, E. M. (1987). Detection of sickle cell anaemia and thalassaemias. *Nature (London)* **329**:293–294.

Chodosh, L. A., Baldwin, A. S., Carthew, R. W., and Sharp, P. A. (1988). Human CCAAT-binding proteins have heterologous subunits. *Cell (Cambridge, Mass.)* **53**:11–24.

Collins, F. S., and Weissman, S. M. (1984). The molecular genetics of human hemoglobin. *Prog. Nucleic Acid Res. Mol. Biol.* **31**:315–438.

Conner, B. J., Reyes, A. A., Morin, C., Itakura, K., Teplitz, R. L., and Wallace, R. B. (1983). Detection of sickle cell β^S-globin allele by hybridization with synthetic oligonucleotides. *Proc. Natl. Acad. Sci. U.S.A.* **80**:278–282.

Constantini, F., and Lacy, E. (1981). Introduction of a rabbit β-globin gene into the mouse germ line. *Nature (London)* **294**:92–94.

Constantini, F., Chada, K., and Magram, J. (1986). Correction of murine β-thalassemia by gene transfer into the germ line. *Science* **233**:1192–1194.

Dayhoff, M. O. (1972). "Atlas of Protein Sequence and Structure." Natl. Biomed. Res. Found., Washington, D.C.

Dean, A., Ley, T. T., Humphries, R. K., Fordis, C. M., and Schechter, A. N. (1983). Inducible transcription of five globin genes in K562 human leukemia cells. *Proc. Natl. Acad. Sci. U.S.A.* **80**:5515–5519.

deBoer, E., Antoniou, M., Mignotte, V., Wall, L., and Grosveld, F. (1988). The human β-globin promoter; nuclear protein factors and erythroid specific induction of transcription. *EMBO J.* **7**:4203–4212.

Dillon, N., and Grosveld, F. (1991). Human α-globin genes silenced independently of other genes. *Nature (London)* **350**:252–254.

Driscoll, M. C., Dobkin, C. S., and Alter, B. P. (1989). $\gamma\delta\beta$-Thalassemia due to a *de novo* mutation deleting the 5′ β-globin gene active region hypersensitive sites. *Proc. Natl. Acad. Sci. U.S.A.* **86**:7470–7474.

Dynan, W. S. (1989). Understanding the molecular mechanism by which methylation influences gene expression. *Trends Genet.* **5**:35–36.

Dynan, W. S., and Tjian, R. (1983). Isolation of transcription factors that discriminate between different promoters recognized by RNA polymerase II. *Cell (Cambridge, Mass.)* **32**:669–680.

Dzierzak, E. A., Papayannopoulou, T., and Mulligan, R. C. (1988). Lineage-specific expression of a human β-globin gene in murine bone marrow transplant recipients reconstituted with retrovirus-transduced stem cells. *Nature (London)* **331**:35–41.

Elgin, S. C. R. (1981). DNAse I-hypersensitive sites of chromatin. *Cell (Cambridge, Mass.)* **27**:413–415.

Elgin, S. C. R. (1988). The formation and function of DNase I hypersensitive sites in the process of gene activation. *J. Biol. Chem.* **263**:19259–19262.

Engelke, D. R., Hoener, P. A., and Collins, F. S. (1988). Direct sequencing of enzymatically amplified human genomic DNA. *Proc. Natl. Acad. Sci. U.S.A.* **85**:544–548.

Enver, T., Raich, N., Ebens, A. J.,. Papayannopoulou, T., Costantini, F., and Stamatoyannopoulos, G. (1990). Developmental regulation of human fetal-to-adult globin gene switching in transgenic mice. *Nature (London)* **344**:309–313.

Erlich, H. A., Gelfand, D., and Sninsky, J. J. (1991). Recent advances in the polymerase chain reaction. *Science* **252**:1643–1651.

Evans, T., Felsenfeld, G., and Reitman, M. (1990). Control of globin gene transcription. *Annu. Rev. Cell Biol.* **6**:95–124.

Feingold, E. A., and Forget, B. G. (1989). The breakpoint of a large deletion causing Hereditary Persistence of Fetal Hemoglobin occurs within an erythroid DNA domain remote from the β-globin cluster. *Blood* **74**:2178–2186.

Felgner, P. L., and Rhodes, G. (1991). Gene therapeutics. *Nature (London)* **49**:351–352.

Fordis, C. M., Anagnou, N. P., Dean, A., Nienhuis, A. W., and Schechter, A. N. (1984). A β-globin gene, inactive in the K562 leukemic cell, functions normally in an heterologous expression system. *Proc. Natl. Acad. Sci. U.S.A.* **81:**4485–4491.

Fordis, C. M., Nelson, N., McCormick, M., Padmanabhan, R., Howard, B., and Schechter, A. N. (1986). The 5′-flanking sequences of human globin genes contribute to tissue specific expression. *Biochem. Biophys. Res. Commun.* **134:**128–133.

Fermi, G. and Perntz (1981). "Atlas of Molecular Structures in Biology, v. 2: Haemoglobin and Myoglobin." Clarenden Press, Oxford.

Forrester, W. C., Thompson, C., Elder, J. T., and Groudine, M. (1986). A developmentally stable chromatin structure in the human β-globin gene cluster. *Proc. Natl. Acad. Sci. U.S.A.* **83:**1359–1363.

Forrester, W. C., Takegawa, S., Papayannopoulou, T., Stamatoyannopoulos, G., and Groudine, M. (1987). Evidence for a locus activation region: The formation of developmentally stable hypersensitive sites in globin-expressing hybrids. *Nucleic Acids Res.* **15:**10159–10177.

Fujimori, Y., Ogawa, M., Clark, S. C., and Dover, G. J. (1990). Serum-free culture of enriched hematopoietic progenitors reflects physiologic levels of fetal hemoglobin biosynthesis. *Blood* **75:**1718–1722.

Geever, R. F., Wilson, L. B., Nallaseth, F. S., Milner, P. F., Bittner, M., and Wilson, J. T. (1981). Direct identification of sickle cell anemia by blot hybridization. *Proc. Natl. Acad. Sci. U.S.A.* **78:**5081–5085.

Gimble, J. M., Max, E. E., and Ley, T. J. (1988). High-resolution analysis of the human γ-globin gene promoter in K562 erythroleukemia cell chromatin. *Blood* **72:**606–612.

Goldberg, M. A., Brugnara, C., Dover, G. J., Schapira, L., Charache, S., and Bunn, H. F. (1990). Treatment of sickle cell anemia with hydroxyurea and erythropoietin. *N. Engl. J. Med.* **323:**366–372.

Gordon, J. W., Scangos, G. A., Plotkin, D. J., Barbosa, J. A., and Ruddle, F. H. (1980). Genetic transformation of mouse embryos by microinjection of purified DNA. *Proc. Natl. Acad. Sci. U.S.A.* **77:**7380–7384.

Greaves, D. R., Fraser, P., Vidal, M. Q., Hedges, M. J., Ropers, D., Luzzatto, L., and Grosveld, F. (1990). A transgenic mouse model of sickle cell disorder. *Nature (London)* **343:**183–185.

Grosveld, F., van Assendelft, G. B., Greaves, D. R., and Kollias, G. (1987). Position-independent, high-level expression of the human β-globin gene in transgenic mice. *Cell (Cambridge, Mass.)* **51:**975–985.

Groudine, M., Kohwi-Shigematsu, T., Gelinas, R., Stamatoyannopoulos, G., and Papayannopoulou, T. (1983). Human fetal to adult hemoglobin switching: Changes in chromatin structure of the β-globin gene locus. *Proc. Natl. Acad. Sci. U.S.A.* **80:**7551–7555.

Gruss, P., Dhar, R., and Khoury, G. (1981). Simian virus 40 tandem repeated sequences as an element of the early promoter. *Proc. Natl. Acad. Sci. U.S.A.* **78:**943–947.

Gumucio, D. L., Rood, L. L., Gray, T. A., Riordan, M. F., Sartor, C. I., and Collins, F. S. (1988). Nuclear proteins that bind the human γ-globin gene promoter: Alterations in binding produced by point mutations associated with hereditary persistence of fetal hemoglobin. *Mol. Cell. Biol.* **8:**5310–5322.

Gumucio, D. L., Lockwood, W. K., Weber, J. L., Saulino, A. M., Delgrosso, K., Surrey, S., Schwartz, E., Goodman, M., and Collins, F. S. (1990). The −175 T → C mutation increases promoter strength in erythroid cells: Correlation with evolutionary conservation of binding sites for two trans-acting factors. *Blood* **75:**756–761.

Hatton, C. S. R., Wilkie, A. O. M., Drysdale, H. C., Wood, W. G., Vickers, M. A., Sharpe, J., Ayyub, H., Pretorius, I.-M., Buckle, V. J., and Higgs, D. (1990). α-Thalassemia caused by a large (62 kb) deletion upstream of the human α globin gene cluster. *Blood* **76:**221–227.

Higgs, D. T., Wood, W. G., Jarman, A. P., Sharpe, J., Lida, J., Pretorius, I.-M., and Ayyub, H.

(1990). A major positive regulatory region located far upstream of the human α-globin gene locus. *Genes Dev.* **4:**1588–1601.

Hsu, S.-L., Marks, J., Shaw, J.-P., Tam, M., Higgs, D. R., Shen, C. C., and Shen, E.-D. J. (1988). Structure and expression of the human θ1 globin gene. *Nature (London)* **331:**94–96.

Huang, S.-Z., Zhou, X.-D., Zhu, H., Ren, Z.-R., and Zeng, Y.-T. (1990). Detection of β-thalassemia mutation in the Chinese using amplified DNA from dried blood specimens. *Hum. Genet.* **84:**129–131.

Huang, S.-Z., Rogers, G. P., Zeng, F.-Y., Zeng, Y.-T., and Schechter, A. N. (1991). Diagnosis of thalassemia using cDNA amplification of reticulocyte mRNA with the polymerase chain reaction. *Blood* **78:** 2433–2437.

Humphries, R. K., Dover, G., Young, N. S., Moore, J. G., Charache, S., Ley, T., and Nienhuis, A. W. (1985). 5-Azacytidine acts directly on both erythroid precursors and progenitors to increase production of fetal hemoglobin. *J. Clin. Invest.* **75:**547–557.

Ingram, V. M. (1956). A specific chemical difference between the globins of normal human and sickle-cell anaemia haemoglobin. *Nature (London)* **178:**792–794.

Jensen, M., Attenberger, H., Schneider, C. H., and Walther, J.-U. (1982). The developmental change in the $^G\gamma$ and $^A\gamma$ globin proportions in hemoglobin F. *Eur. F. Pediatr.* **138:**311–314.

Jones, K. A., Kadonaga, J. T., Rosenfeld, P. J., Kelly, T. J., and Tjian, R. (1987). A cellular DNA-binding protein that activates eukaryotic transcription and DNA replication. *Cell (Cambridge, Mass.)* **48:**79–89.

Kan, Y. W., and Dozy, A. M. (1978). Polymorphism of DNA sequence adjacent to human β-globin structural gene: Relationship to sickle mutation. *Proc. Natl. Acad. Sci. U.S.A.* **75:**5631–5635.

Kantoff, P. W., Gillio, A. P., McLachlin, J. R., Bordignon, C., Eglitis, M. A., Kernan, N. A., Moen, R. C., Kohn, D. B., Yu, S.-F., Karson, E., Karlsson, S., Zwiebel, J. A., Gilboa, E., Blaese, R. M., Nienhuis, A., O'Reilly, R. J., and Anderson, W. F. (1987). Expression of human adenosine deaminase in nonhuman primates after retrovirus-mediated gene transfer. *J. Exp. Med.* **166:**219–234.

Karlsson, S., and Nienhuis, A. W. (1985). Developmental regulation of human globin genes. *Annu. Rev. Biochem.* **54:**1071–1108.

Kazazian, H. H., Jr., and Boehm, C. D. (1988). Molecular basis and prenatal diagnosis of β-thalassemia. *Blood* **72:**1107–1116.

Keshet, I., Lieman-Hurwitz, J., and Cedar, H. (1986). DNA methylation affects the formation of active chromatin. *Cell (Cambridge, Mass.)* **44:**535–543.

Kioussis, D., Vanin, E., deLange, T., Flavell, R. A., and Grosveld, F. G. (1983). β-globin gene inactivation by DNA translocation in γβ-thalassaemia. *Nature (London)* **306:**662–666.

Kohn, D. B., Anderson, W. F., and Blaese, R. M. (1989). Gene therapy for genetic diseases. *Cancer Invest.* **7:**179–192.

Kropp, G. L., Fucharoen, S., and Embury, S. H. (1989). Selective enzymatic amplification of α2-globin DNA for detection of the Hemoglobin Constant Spring mutation. *Blood* **73:**1987–1992.

Lachman, H. M., and Mears, J. G. (1983). DNase I hypersensitivity in the γ globin gene locus of K562 cells. *Nucleic Acids Res.* **11:**6065–6077.

Lamb, P., Watt, P., and Proudfoot, N. J. (1989). Negative regulation of the human embryonic globin genes ζ and ε. *Prog. Clin. Biol. Res.* **316A:**269–277.

Lewin, B. (1990). "Genes IV." Oxford Univ. Press, New York.

Ley, T. J. (1991). The pharmacology of hemoglobin switching: Of mice and men. *Blood* **77:**1146–1152.

Ley, T. J., DeSimone, J., Noguchi, C. T., Turner, P. H., Schechter, A. N., Heller, P., and Nienhuis, A. W. (1983). 5-Azacytidine increases γ-globin synthesis and reduces the proportion of dense cells in patients with sickle cell anemia. *Blood* **62:**370–380.

Liebhaber, S. A. (1989). α-Thalassemia. *Hemoglobin* **13:**685–731.

Mantovani, R., Malgaretti, N., Nicolis, S., Giglioni, B., Comi, P., Cappellini, N., Bertero, M. T., Caligaris-Cappio, F., and Ottolenghi, S. (1988a). An erythroid specific nuclear factor binding to the proximal CACCC box of the β-globin gene promoter. *Nucleic Acids Res.* **16**:4299–4313.

Mantovani, R., Malgaretti, N., Nicolis, S., Ronchi, A., Giglioni, B., and Ottolenghi, S. (1988b). The effects of HPFH mutations in the human γ-globin promoter on binding of ubiquitous and erythroid specific nuclear factors. *Nucleic Acids Res.* **16**:7783–7797.

Mantovani, R., Superti-Ferga, G., Gilman, J., and Ottolenghi, S. (1989). The deletion of the distal CCAAT box region of the ^Aγ-globin gene in black HPFH abolishes the binding of the erythroid specific protein NFE3 and of the CCAAT displacement protein. *Nucleic Acids Res.* **17**:6681–6691.

Martin, D. I. K., and Orkin, S. H. (1990). Transcriptional activation and DNA binding by the erythroid factor GF-1/NF-E1/eryf1. *Genes Dev.* **4**:1886–1898.

Martin, D. I. K., Tsai, S.-F., and Orkin, S. H. (1989a). Increased γ-globin expression in a nondeletion HPFH mediated by an erythroid-specific DNA-binding factor. *Nature (London)* **338**:435–438.

Martin, D. I. K., Zon, L. I., Mutter, G., and Orkin, S. H. (1989b). Expression of an erythroid transcription factor in megakaryocytic and mast cell lineages. *Nature (London)* **344**:444–447.

Mavilio, F., Giampaolo, A., Care, A., Migliaccio, G., Calandrini, M., Russo, G., Pagliardi, G. L., Mastroberardino, G., Marinucci, M., and Peschle, C. (1983). Molecular mechanisms of human hemoglobin switching: Selective undermethylation and expression of globin genes in embryonic, fetal, and adult erythroblasts. *Proc. Natl. Acad. Sci. U.S.A.* **80**:6907–6911.

Mignotte, V., Wall, L., deBoer, E., Grosveld, F., and Romeo, P.-H. (1989). Two tissue-specific factors bind the erythroid promoter of the human porphobilinogen deaminase gene. *Nucleic Acids Res.* **17**:37–54.

Miller, A. D. (1990). Progress toward human gene therapy. *Blood* **76**:271–277.

Mitchell, P. J., and Tjian, R. (1989). Transcriptional regulation in mammalian cells by sequence-specific DNA binding proteins. *Science* **245**:371–378.

Moi, P., and Kan, Y. W. (1990). Synergistic enhancement of globin gene expression by activator protein-1-like proteins. *Proc. Natl. Acad. Sci. U.S.A.* **87**:9000–9004.

Moon, A. M., and Ley, T. F. (1991). Functional properties of the β-globin locus control region in K562 erythroleukemia cells. *Blood* **77**:2272–2284.

Mueller-Storm, H. P., Sogo, J. M., and Schaffner, W. (1989). An enhancer stimulates transcription in trans when attached to the promoter via a protein bridge. *Cell (Cambridge, Mass.)* **58**:767–777.

Murphy, S., Pierani, A., Scheidereit, C., Melli, M., and Roeder, R. G. (1989). Purified octamer binding transcription factors stimulate RNA polymerase III-mediated transcription of the 7SK RNA gene. *Cell (Cambridge, Mass.)* **59**:1071–1080.

Ney, P. A., Sorrentino, B. P., McDonagh, K. T., and Nienhuis, A. W. (1990). Tandem AP-1 binding sites within the human β-globin dominant control region function as an inducible enhancer in erythroid cells. *Genes Dev.* **4**:993–1006.

Nicolis, S., Ronchi, A., Malgaretti, N., Mantovani, R., Giglioni, B., and Ottolenghi, S. (1989). Increased erythroid-specific expression of a mutated HPFH γ-globin promoter requires the erythroid factor NFE-1. *Nucleic Acids Res.* **17**:5509–5516.

Nienhuis, A. W., Anagnou, N. P., and Ley, T. J. (1984). Advances in thalassemia research. *Blood* **63**:738–758.

Novak, U., Harris, E. A. S., Forrester, W., Groudine, M., and Gelinas, R. (1990). High-level β-globin expression after retroviral transfer of locus activation region-containing human β-globin gene derivatives into murine erythroleukemia cells. *Proc. Natl. Acad. Sci. U.S.A.* **87**:3386–3390.

Orkin, S. H. (1987). Disorders of hemoglobin synthesis: The thalassemias. In "The Molecular Basis of Blood Diseases" (G. Stamatoyannopoulos, A. W. Nienhuis, P. Leder, and P. W. Majerus, eds.), pp. 106–126. Saunders, Philadelphia, Pennsylvania.

Orkin, S. H. (1990). Globin gene regulation and switching: Circa 1990. Cell (Cambridge, Mass.) 63:665–672.

Orkin, S. H., Kazazian, H. H., Jr., Antonarakis, S. E., Goff, S. C., Boehm, C. D., Sexton, J. P., Waber, P. B., and Giardina, P. J. V. (1982). Linkage of β-thalassemia mutations and β globin gene polymorphisms with DNA polymorphisms in the human β globin gene cluster. Nature (London) 296:627–631.

Osborne, W. R. A., Hock, R. A., Kaleko, M., and Miller, A. D. (1990). Long-term expression of human adenosine deaminase in mice after transplantation of bone marrow infected with amphotropic retroviral vectors. Hum. Gene Ther. 1:31–41.

Papayannopoulou, T., Brice, M., and Stamatoyannopoulos, G. (1986). Analysis of human hemoglobin switching in MEL X human fetal erythroid cell hybrids. Cell (Cambridge, Mass.) 46:469–476.

Papayannopoulou, T., Enver, T., Takegawa, S., Anagnou, N. P., and Stamatoyannopoulos, G. (1988). Activation of developmentally mutated human globin genes by cell fusion. Science 242:1056–1058.

Pauling, I., Itano, H. A., Singer, S. J., and Wells, I. C. (1949). Sickle cell anemia: A molecular disease. Science 110:543–549.

Pirastu, M., Kan, Y. S., Cao, A., Conner, B. J., Teplitz, R. L., and Wallace, R. B. (1983). Prenatal diagnosis of beta-thalassemia. Detection of a single nucleotide mutation in DNA. N. Engl. J. Med. 309:284–287.

Pyati, J., Kucherlapati, R. S., and Skoultchi, A. I. (1980). Activation of human β-globin genes from nonerythroid cells by fusion with murine erythroleukemia cells. Proc. Natl. Acad. Sci. U.S.A. 77:3435–3439.

Renkawitz, R. (1990). Transcriptional repression in eukaryotes. Trends Genet. 6:192–197.

Rodgers, G. P., Dover, G. J., Noguchi, C. T., Schechter, A. N., and Nienhuis, A. W. (1990). Hematologic responses of patients with sickle cell disease to treatment with hydroxyurea. N. Engl. J. Med. 322:1037–1045.

Romeo, P.-H., Prandini, M.-H., Joulin, V., Mignotte, V., Prenant, M., Vainchenker, W., Marguerie, G., and Uzan, G. (1989). Megakaryocytic and erythrocytic lineages share specific transcription factors. Nature (London) 344:447–449.

Rosenberg, S. A., Aebersold, P., Cornetta, K., Kasid, A., Morgan, R. A., Moen, R., Karson, E. M., Lotze, M. T., Yang, J. C., Topalian, S. L., Merino, M. J., Culver, K., Miller, A. D., Blaese, R. M., and Anderson, W. F. (1990). Gene transfer into humans—Immunotherapy of patients with advanced melanoma, using tumor-infiltrating lymphocytes modified by retroviral gene transduction. N. Engl. J. Med. 323:570–578.

Rutherford, T. R., Clegg, F. B., and Weatherall, D. J. (1979). K562 human leukaemic cells synthesize embryonic hemoglobin in response to haemin. Nature (London) 280:164–165.

Ryan, T. M., Townes, T. M., Reilly, M. P., Asakura, T., Palmiter, R. D., Brinster, R. L., and Behringer, R. R. (1990). Human sickle hemoglobin in transgenic mice. Science 247:566–568.

Saiki, R., Scharf, S., Faloona, F., Mullis, K. B., Horn, G. T., Erlich, H. A., and Arnheim, N. (1985). Enzymatic amplification of β-globin genomic sequences and restriction site analysis for diagnosis of sickle cell anemia. Science 230:1350–1354.

Saiki, R. K., Gelfand, D. H., Stoffel, S., Scharf, S. J., Higuchi, R., Horn, G. T., Mullis, K. B., and Erlich, H. A. (1988). Primer-directed enzymatic amplification of DNA with a thermostable DNA polymerase. Science 239:487–494.

Sawadogo, M., and Roeder, R. G. (1985). Interaction of a gene-specific transcription factor with the adenovirus major late promoter upstream of the TATA box region. Cell (Cambridge, Mass.) 43:165–175.

Schechter, A. N., Noguchi, C. T., and Rogers, G. P. (1987). Sickle cell disease. In "The Molecular Basis of Blood Diseases" (G. Stamatoyannopoulos, A. W. Nienhuis, P. Leder, and P. W. Majerus, eds.), pp. 179–218. Saunders, Philadelphia, Pennsylvania.

Schwartz, E., Cohen, A., and Surrey, S. (1988). Overview of the β thalassemias: Genetic and clinical aspects. Hemoglobin 12:551–564.

Shesely, E. G., Kim, H.-S., Shehee, W. R., Papayannopoulou, T., Smithies, O., and Popovich, B. W. (1991). Correction of a human βS-globin gene by gene targeting. Proc. Natl. Acad. Sci. U.S.A. 88:4294–4298.

Shinar, E., Shalev, O., Rachmilewetz, E. A., and Schrier, S. L. (1987). Erythrocyte membrane skeleton abnormalities in severe β-thalassemia. Blood 70:158–164.

Smithies, O., Gregg, R. G., Boggs, S. S., Koralewski, M. A., and Kucherlapati, R. S. (1985). Insertion of DNA sequences into the human chromosomal β-globin locus by homologous recombination. Nature (London) 317:230–234.

Stamatoyannopoulos, G., Nakamoto, B., Kurachi, S., and Papayannopoulou, T. (1983). Direct evidence for interaction between human erythroid progenitor cells and a hemoglobin switching activity present in fetal sheep serum. Proc. Natl. Acad. Sci. U.S.A. 80:5650–5654.

Superti-Ferga, G., Barberis, A., Schaffner, G., and Busslinger, M. (1988). The −117 mutation in Greek HPFH affects the binding of three nuclear factors to the CCAAT region of the γ-globin gene. EMBO J. 7:3099–3107.

Timson, J. (1975). Hydroxyurea. Mutat. Res. 32:115–132.

Townes, T. M., Lingrel, J. B., Chen, H. Y., Brinster, R. L., and Palmiter, R. D. (1985). Erythroid-specific expression of human β-globin genes in transgenic mice. EMBO J. 4:1715–1723.

Trainor, C. D., Evans, T., Felsenfeld, G., and Boguski, M. S. (1990). Structure and evolution of a human erythroid transcription factor. Nature (London) 343:92–96.

Tuan, D. Y. H., Solomon, W. B., Li, Q., and London, I. M. (1985). The "β-like-globin" gene domain in human erythroid cells. Proc. Natl. Acad. Sci. U.S.A. 82:6384–6388.

Tuan, D. Y. H., Solomon, W. B., London, I. M., and Lee, D. P. (1989). An erythroid-specific, developmental-stage-independent enhancer far upstream of the human "β-like globin" genes. Proc. Natl. Acad. Sci. U.S.A. 86:2554–2558.

Varmus, H. (1988). Retroviruses. Science 240:1427–1435.

Wall, L., Catala, F., Antoniou, M., deBoer, E., and Grosveld, F. (1989). The regulation of the human γ- and β-globin domain. Prog. Clin. Biol. Res. 316A:1–13.

Watt, P., Lamb, P., Squire, L., and Proudfoot, N. (1990). A factor binding GATAAG confers tissue specificity on the promoter of the human ζ-globin gene. Nucleic Acids Res. 18:1339–1350.

Weatherall, D. J. (1991a). "The New Genetics and Clinical Practice," 2nd ed. Oxford Univ. Press, Oxford.

Weatherall, D. J. (1991b). Gene therapy in perspective. Nature (London) 349:275–276.

Weatherall, D. J., and Clegg, J. B. (1981). "The Thalassemia Syndromes," 3rd ed. Blackwell, Oxford.

Weatherall, D. J., Old, J. M., Thein, S. L., Wainscoat, J. S., and Clegg, J. B. (1985). Prenatal diagnosis of the common haemoglobin disorders. J. Med. Genet. 22:422–430.

Williams, D. A. (1990). Expression of introduced genetic sequences in hematopoietic cells following retroviral-mediated gene transfer. Hum. Gene Ther. 1:229–239.

Willing, M. C., Nienhuis, A. W., and Anderson, W. F. (1979). Selective activation of human β- but not γ-globin gene in human fibroblast x mouse erythroleukemia cell hybrids. Nature (London) 227:534–538.

Wingender, E. (1988). Compilation of transcription regulating proteins. Nucleic Acids Res. 16:1879–1902.

Wright, S., Rosenthal, A., Flavell, R., and Grosveld, F. (1984). DNA sequences required for regulated expression of β-globin genes in murine erythroleukemia cells. Cell (Cambridge, Mass.) 38:265–273.

Xiao, J., Davidson, I., Macchi, M., Rosales, R., Vigneron, M., Staub, A., and Chambon, P. (1987). *In vitro* binding of several cell-specific and ubiquitous nuclear proteins to the GT-1 motif of the SV40 enhancer. *Genes Dev.* **1**:794–807.

Yu, C.-Y., Chen, J., Lin, L.-L., Tam, M., and Shen, J. C.-K. (1990). Cell type-specific protein–DNA interactions in the human ζ-globin upstream promoter region: Displacement of Sp1 by the erythroid cell-specific factor NF-E1. *Mol. Cell Biol.* **10**:282–294.

Yu, C.-Y., Motamed, K., Chen, J., Bailey, A. D., and Shen, C.-K. (1991). The CACC box upstream of the human embryonic ε globin gene binds Sp1 and is a functional promoter element *in vitro* and *in vivo*. *J. Biol. Chem.*, **266**: 8907–8915.

Zon, L. I., Tsai, S.-F., Burgess, S., Matsudaira, P., Bruns, G. A. P., and Orkin, S. H. (1990). The major human erythroid DNA-binding protein (GF-1): Primary sequence and localization of the gene to the X chromosome. *Proc. Natl. Acad. Sci. U.S.A.* **87**:668–672.

2

The fragile X Syndrome

W. Ted Brown
Department of Human Genetics
New York State Institute for Basic Research in Developmental Disabilities
Staten Island, New York

Edmund C. Jenkins
Department of Cytogenetics
New York State Institute for Basic Research in Developmental Disabilities
Staten Island, New York

I. INTRODUCTION

Males with a distinct form of mental retardation known as the fragile X [fra(X)] syndrome inherit an X chromosome with a distinctive fragile site at band Xq27.3, known as the fragile X chromosome. Males who possess the fra(X) chromosome are usually moderately to severely retarded. About 1 in 5 males who have inherited the fragile X chromosome are normal carrier males who are nonpenetrant for the mutation and do not express the fragile site. They transmit the mutation to all their daughters, who are also generally nonexpressing for the mutation but who then can have affected sons. This X-linked syndrome is considered to be the most common Mendelian inherited form of mental retardation. Overall, in the general population the prevalence of affected and transmitting males is estimated as approximately 1 in 1000. The prevalence of female carriers is estimated to be about 1 in 700. Although the majority of female carriers are mentally normal and two-thirds of these are negative on cytogenetic testing, approximately 1 in 3 female carriers have some evidence of mental impairment and about 1 in 10 are considered mentally retarded. The high prevalence of individuals of this X-linked syndrome, in which the affected males do not reproduce, indicates the syndrome is likely to have the highest known new mutation rate of any known human genetic disease. Estimates are that approximately 1 sperm or egg in 3000 carries a new mutation.

In addition to the high prevalence of the fra(X) syndrome, there are a number of unusual aspects regarding inheritance that make this syndrome one of great interest to geneticists. These include nonpenetrance in some transmitting males, an apparent deficit of affected males born to some carrier women, and differing rates of genetic recombination around the fra(X) locus in various families. The development of methods for detecting fra(X) in blood and amniotic fluid cells has allowed for routine screening as well as prenatal diagnosis of the syndrome. However, the majority of unaffected carrier women are negative on cytogenetic testing and prenatal diagnosis by cytogenetic methods alone is not fully reliable. Methods using DNA restriction fragment length polymorphisms (RFLPs) are used to provide carrier testing, to complement prenatal cytogenetic diagnosis, and to study the inheritance of the fra(X) mutation. Molecular studies to analyze the underlying mutation are underway. The following article will review clinical and molecular aspects of the fra(X) syndrome.

II. HISTORY OF THE FRAGILE X SYNDROME

Because of the relatively normal features of affected males, the delineation of fra(X) as a distinct syndrome was quite recent. In 1943 Martin and Bell described a large British family with apparent X-linked mental retardation. There were 11 mentally retarded males who were descendants of two brothers and a sister, all apparently normal. They concluded that the X-linked gene in these two brothers was suppressed by the presence of some controlling factor. In retrospect, this family showed nonpenetrance in these two males, a finding that now has been recognized as being very common in large pedigrees. In 1981 this family was subsequently tested and found to have the fra(X) chromosome present (Richards *et al.*, 1981).

The first family in which a marker X chromosome was observed in association with X-linked mental retardation was reported by Lubs in 1969. The marker was described as a small satellite separated from the main long arm of the chromosome by a constriction. There were four mentally retarded male members of this family with the marker chromosome. Four normal female carriers, including the mother of the two proband brothers, were also found to have the marker present. Although Escalante also described a family with a marker chromosome in 1971, the importance of the initial observation by Lubs or that of Escalante was not realized until the late 1970s. At that time two studies identified the marker chromosome in a total of 25 affected males and 1 affected female among 10 families (Giraud *et al.*, 1976; Harvey *et al.*, 1977).

In 1977, Sutherland discovered that a cell culture medium deficient in folic acid was necessary in order to induce the visibility of fragile chromosome sites in general, and the fra(X) site in particular (Sutherland, 1977a,b). He had studied a family with a fragile chromosome marker in one laboratory and upon moving to another laboratory was unable to identify the fragile site (Sutherland, 1983). After analysis of the differences in the medium, he discovered a medium deficient in folic acid was necessary to induce the marker chromosomes. This type of folate-deficient medium had been in use in the late 1960s but was no longer in general use. Following the discovery of the need to use folate-deficient medium, additional families with apparent X-linked mental retardation were tested and the fra(X) chromosome was identified in many (Turner et al., 1978; Turner et al., 1980b). Overall, it now appears that about one-third of families with apparent X-linked mental retardation of unknown cause will have the fragile X chromosome present on testing.

III. EPIDEMIOLOGY OF FRAGILE X SYNDROME

There are about 25% more mentally retarded males than females in the general population of which perhaps half is due to the fra(X). This 25% excess was first noted by Penrose in 1938. Luehrke (1972) suggested that the explanation for this excess could be due to the presence of undiagnosed forms of X-linked mental retardation. More than 50 X-linked disorders associated with mental retardation are now recognized, but, except for the fra(X) syndrome, their individual frequencies are relatively low.

There have been several large epidemiological surveys on the prevalence of the fra(X) chromosome in unselected samples of mentally retarded clients. Blomquist et al. (1982, 1983) conducted a prevalence study of all mild and severely retarded males in a rural Swedish county. Records on a total population base of some 40,871 individuals born between the years 1959 and 1970 and alive at 1 year of age were studied. Of those, 332 (8.1 per 1000) were considered mentally retarded, among which 205 were boys. The sample of 205 was analyzed for possible causes for their mental retardation. Among these, 140 had no diagnosis and were selected for fra(X) studies. Permission was granted by parents for testing of 64% of this sample. Of 89, 12 (15.5%) were found to have the fra(X) chromosome on testing. If the same proportion was present in the 51 cases in which permission for study was not obtained, then 19 out of the total of 205 (9.3%) would be expected. Thus they found that about 1 per 1076 males in the general population would be expected to have the presence of the fra(X) chromosome. A second large epidemiological survey was conducted by Webb et al. (1986) in England. They found a fra(X) prevalence of 16 per 219 (7.3%) among mentally retarded boys. Similar to Blomquist et al., they calculated a prevalence of 21 per 305 mentally retarded males or about 1 per 1362 males in the general population. Combining the data from these two studies leads to a calculated prevalence of 40 affected males per 49,946 or 1 per 1226. Genetic analysis by Sherman *et al.* (1984, 1985) (discussed below) indicates that approximately 20% of males who inherit the fra(X) chromosome do not express it. Therefore the true prevalence in males who carry the fra(X) chromosome can be estimated to be 50 per 49,046 or about 1 per 1000.

The prevalence of affected females in the population is approximately 1 per 2000 (Webb *et al.*, 1986). About one-third of female carriers are mentally impaired and about 10% are mentally retarded (Turner *et al.*, 1980a; Sherman *et al.*, 1984, 1985). Thus the overall prevalence of female carriers can be estimated to be about 1 in 700. This high degree of expression of an X-linked gene among carrier females is unusual and suggests that the syndrome might best be considered to be X-linked, semidominant with decreased penetrance, rather than truly X-linked recessive.

IV. FEATURES OF AFFECTED AND TRANSMITTING MALES

Compared to many genetic or chromosomal syndromes, affected fra(X) males usually are fairly normal in appearance, as are the individuals shown in Figure 2.1. This helps to explain the fact that they are frequently undiagnosed and that the syndrome was only recently recognized as a distinct entity. The fra(X) males often show subtle facial and physical differences, as indicated in Table 2.1. As adults, they usually have enlarged testicular volume, known as macroorchidism. This is often in the range of 50–100 ml, as compared to the normal adult male mean volume of 17 ml (±4 ml). Thus, mentally retarded males with testicular volumes above 30 ml should be tested for fra(X). Macroorchidism can be evaluated by measuring the length and the width of the testes with a ruler or with calipers. The formula for the volume of an ellipsoid ($v = l \times w^2 \times \pi/6$) is used. Because $\pi/6 = .052$, the length times the width squared divided by 2 gives a close approximation of testicular volume.

Before the discovery of the fra(X) chromosome, there were several

Table 2.1. Common Features of fragile X Males

Prominent large ears	Prominent forehead
High arched palate	Facial asymmetry
Narrow midfacial diameter	Prominent thumbs
Narrow intereye distance	Hyperextensible joints
Long facial distance	Mitral valve prolapse
Large head circumference	Macroorchidism

families that had been identified with X-linked mental retardation, specifically associated with macroorchidism (Turner and Turner, 1974). When these families were later tested, most were found to have the fra(X) chromosome present. In a survey of institutionalized males who showed macroorchidism, we found approximately 80% were positive for fra(X) (Brown et al., 1981). Macroorchidism and a family history of mental retardation are probably the most useful indicators of which adult mentally retarded males are likely to have the fra(X) chromosome on testing. There are occasional instances of mentally impaired males, identified within fragile X families, who are phenotypically positive and positive by DNA linkage criteria, but who are cytogenetically negative (Voelckel et al., 1989; Sklower-Brooks et al., 1991).

The fra(X) syndrome shows an unusual X-linked inheritance pattern in a number of respects. In addition to the original Martin–Bell family, there have been many families identified in which normal grandfathers have affected relatives and affected grandchildren as well. On chromosome analysis such males are negative. They are considered to be nonpenetrant transmitting males for the fra(X) mutation. All the daughters of a transmitting male inherit their X chromosome and thus are carriers. The daughters of such transmitting males also are usually negative on cytogenetic testing and are mentally unimpaired. Among the sons born to carrier women, overall, about 40% are fra(X) positive and mentally retarded, whereas 10% are nonpenetrant males (Sherman et al., 1984, 1985). Thus there is about a 20% excess of normal male sons born to carrier women, which appears to be due the occurrence of nonpenetrance in these sons.

The majority of fra(X)-positive males have an IQ in the moderate to severe range, between 20 and 50. Approximately 7% have an IQ below 20 and approximately 23% have an IQ above 50 (Sutherland and Hecht, 1985). It has been recognized that there appears to be a decline in IQ among young males as they grow from prepubertal to pubertal ages (Borghgraeg et al., 1987; Lachiewicz et al., 1987). This result appears to be consistent with the findings that a number of young fra(X) syndrome boys often have been considered to be only mildly impaired or learning disabled (Hagerman et al., 1985), whereas adults with the syndrome are usually moderately to severely impaired (Sutherland and Hecht, 1985). The reason for this decline in measured IQ appears to be due to a relative inability of young affected males to continue to acquire more complex cognitive abilities with maturity. No specific regression is seen but rather a static central nervous system encephalopathy is present without focal lateralizing signs (Wisniewski et al., 1985).

Approximately 20% of fra(X) males have a history of seizures. These may be transient, but about 10% have persistent seizures that are well controlled with anticonvulsion medication. Limited neuropathological information is available on the fra(X) syndrome. We studied one fra(X) male who died at age 62 (Rudelli et al., 1983). Immaturity of dendritic spines and decreased areas of

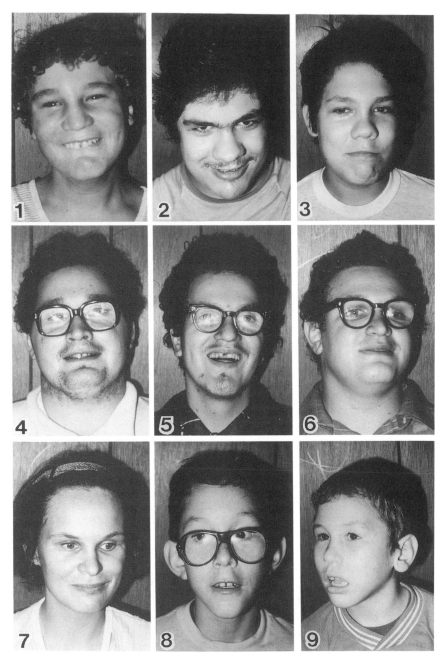

Figure 2.1. Individuals possessing the fragile X chromosome. Photographs 1–9 are members of family F20 illustrated in Figure 1.6 (photographs 1–3 are IV 1, 3, and 5; photographs 4–7 are IV 7, 9, 10, and 6; photographs 8 and 9 are IV 32 and 33). Photographs 10 and 11 are two brothers in a second family; photographs 13–16 are four brothers in another

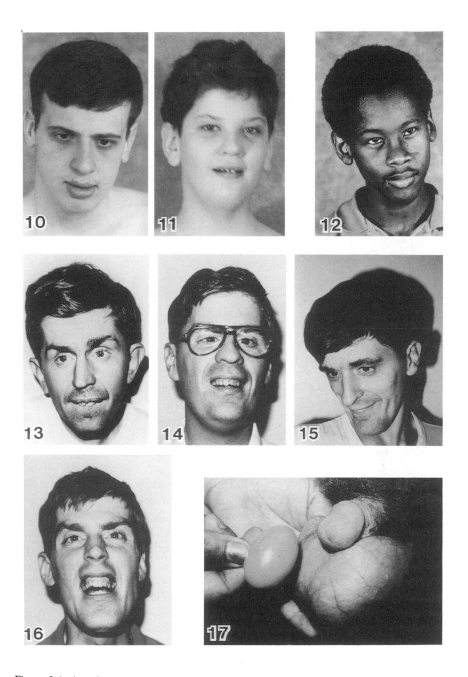

Figure 2.1. (*cont.*)

family. Photograph 17 illustrates macroorchidism with a testicular volume of 80 ml compared to the 25-ml upper limit of normal as indicated by the orchidometer.

synaptic contact were seen as the main differences in underlying brain pathology. There is a need for further neuropathological analysis and a brain repository has been suggested (Brown et al., 1988c). A study by Reiss et al. (1991) of 14 fra(X)-positive males utilizing magnetic resonance imaging (MRI) found a significantly decreased size of the posterior vermis of the cerebellum and increased size of the fourth ventricle compared to controls. Similar findings have been reported for a subgroup of autistic males by Courchesne et al. (1988). The posterior vermis of the cerebellum is a major site of integration of motor, sensory, and emotional stimuli. This defect may help to explain the observation that fra(X) males are frequently overwhelmed by excessive sensory stimulation.

Hyperactivity with a short attention span is often quite pronounced in young fra(X)-positive males. They frequently have unusual hand mannerisms such as hand flapping and hand biting, which often leads to callus formation at the site of biting. They also frequently show speech delay and a relative lack of expressive language ability. The speech abnormalities of highly functioning fra(X) males have been described as "cluttering" (Hanson et al., 1986). Repetitive speech patterns are quite common and often include stereotypical vocalizations, jargon, dysrhythmia, perseveration, echolalia, conditioned statements, inappropriate tangential comments, and talking to self (Wolf-Schein et al., 1987). Many fra(X) males are quite social and have an outgoing personality. But they generally have poor eye contact and tactily defensive, which may interfere with social interactions and development.

V. THE ASSOCIATION OF FRAGILE X AND AUTISM

There is a significant association of fra(X) with infantile autism. Autistic individuals are usually male and a 4:1 male:female ratio is commonly observed. In 1982, we identified 5 autistic males with fra(X) and emphasized that there appeared to be a significant association of fra(X) and autism (Brown et al., 1982). Our finding of an association of fra(X) and autism was confirmed by other studies (Blomquist et al., 1984; Hagerman et al., 1986b). We subsequently conducted a multicenter survey and screened 183 autistic males. We found 24, or 13.1%, to be positive for fra(X) (Brown et al., 1986a). We have currently screened 363 males with a prior diagnosis of autism and have found 29 fra(X)-positive cases, representing 8% of the total screened. We have also screened 33 female with a prior diagnosis of autism, finding 4 (12%) positive (Cohen et al., 1989). Combining all studies, it appears that approximately 10% of autistic males will be found to have the fra(X) chromosome present on testing (Brown et al., 1986a). Approximately 20% of fra(X) males are considered autistic. We have found that the majority of fra(X) males have features that are most autistic-like than a group of Down syndrome subjects (Cohen et al., 1988). Thus, fra(X) is likely to be the single most common biomedical condition specifically associated with autism. We maintain that fra(X) testing is warranted in any autistic male of undiagnosed etiology.

VI. CARRIER FEMALES

About 53% of carriers show fra(X) expression, but if a female carrier is mentally impaired the chances are approximately 90% that she will be positive on cytogenetic testing. Overall, approximately 56% of carriers are cytogenetically positive and/or mentally impaired (Sherman et al., 1984, 1985). Thus the female penetrance is 56%. The fact that some female carriers are more affected than others appears to be consistent with random inactivation of one of the two X chromosomes. There is a general correspondence between late replication of the normal X chromosome, reflecting X inactivation, and the presence of mental impairment (Uchida and Joyce, 1982; Uchida et al., 1983; Fryns and Van den Bergh, 1988; Tuckerman and Webb, 1989). In fact, a set of identical fra(X) twin sisters was described by Tuckerman et al. (1985) in which one sister had high normal intelligence while the other sister was mentally retarded.

A characteristic profile of cognitive defects in affected carriers may be present. We and others have observed increased verbal and decreased performance scores on the Wechsler IQ test and relatively lower subtest scores on arithmetic digit, block design, and object assembly (Kemper et al., 1986; Miezejeski et al., 1984) tests. Wolff et al. (1988) reported lowered academic abilities, particularly in the area of arithmetic, in a group of 15 nonretarded carriers. Reiss et al. (1988) studied a group of 35 carriers and found that about one-third had schizotypal features that included inappropriate affect, odd communication, and social isolation, whereas about 40% had chronic recurrent depression.

VII. CYTOGENETICS OF THE FRAGILE X SYNDROME

Generally, 20 to 40% of the blood cells of a male with fra(X) syndrome will show a fragile site near the end of the long arm of the X chromosome at band Xq27, as illustrated in Figure 2.2. The site appears to easily stretch or break when the cells are grown under conditions of induction. The fragile site was sublocalized by high-resolution microscopy to band Xq27.3 (Krawczun et al., 1985; Brookwell and Turner, 1983). When viewed with the scanning electron microscope, the fragile site resembles an isochromatid gap (Harrison et al., 1983). In addition to the fragile site at Xq27.3, approximately 87 common (i.e., found in most of the population) and 26 rare (i.e., less than 1% of the population) fragile sites

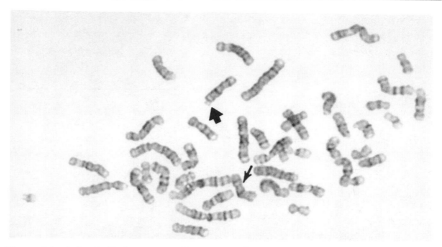

Figure 2.2. A fragile X chromosome (large arrow) detected in the sample from a female fetus (normal X indicated by smaller arrow). The figure is a laser print generated from a PSI-Genetiscan digitized image of an amniotic fluid cell culture G-banded metaphase spread (provided by Dr. M. Krawczun, New York State Institute for Basic Research, Staten Island, New York.)

have been identified (Sutherland and Ledbetter, 1989). Almost all of these other fragile sites are not associated with mental deficiency.

The exact mechanism underlying fragile site expression is unknown, but it appears to involve the availability of DNA synthetic precursors, as illustrated in Figure 2.3. Adequate concentrations of thymidine and/or cytidine are necessary and reducing their concentration can lead to fragile site expression. The expression can be induced by a medium that is deficient in folic acid, which reduces the availability of thymidine. The fragile site can also be induced by inhibitors of dihydrofolate reductase, such as trimethoprim and methotrexate. The drug 5-fluorodeoxyuridine (FUdR) inhibits the enzyme thymidylate synthetase and can effectively induce fragile site expression. Sutherland *et al.* (1985) have also shown that excess thymidine can induce folate-sensitive fragile sites, presumably by reducing the availability of cytidine. They have suggested the fra(X) region may represent a pyrimidine-rich region that may be relatively late replicating. It has been observed that there is an increase in sister chromatid exchange frequencies at fragile sites (Glover and Stein, 1987).

Ledbetter *et al.* (1986) observed that the X chromosomes of transmitting males could be induced to express a fragile site at Xq27 at a level of about 12% when analyzed in a somatic cell hybrid system. Further, X chromosomes from normal males and chimpanzees were also induced to express a fragile site in this special system, although at lower frequencies of 5 and 1%. We have ob-

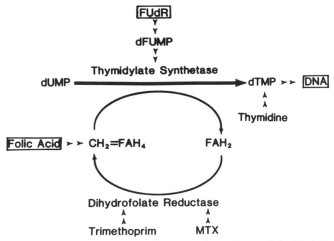

Figure 2.3. Metabolic pathway involved in the induction of the fragile X
site expression; FUdR, 5-fluorodeoxyuridine; MTX, methotrexate.

served a low frequency of approximately 0.5% of apparent fragile sites in normal
males (Jenkins *et al.*, 1986). Marlhens *et al.* (1986) observed at least one cell
with an apparent fra(X) site in six normal individuals studied using conditions of
thymidylate stress. Glover *et al.* (1984) used aphidicolin (APC) to induce a
fragile site at Xq27 in about 1% of cells from several fra(X) males. Sutherland
and Baker (1990) demonstrated both a common fragile site and Xq27.2 and the
rare fra(X) site at Xq27.3 in the same cell using a simultaneous induction by
APC and excess thymidine. In retrospect, the common fragile site observed in
the previous studies on the X chromosome and inducible by APC probably
reflects the common site at Xq 27.2. The ability to resolve both the common
and rare sites is important and may help to resolve questionable fra(X) syndrome
diagnoses.

VIII. TREATMENT

Folic acid therapy was advocated by LeJeune (1982). However, controlled studies in general have not shown significant improvements in IQ (Hagerman *et al.*,
1986a; Fisch *et al.*, 1988). It appears that some young males may respond
positively, particularly with reduction of hyperactivity. This may represent a
mild stimulatory affect of the folic acid to reduce hyperactivity. Stimulant-type
drugs have been tried with some success and may be considered on an individual
basis (Gustavson *et al.*, 1985). Hagerman *et al.* (1988) conducted a controlled

trial of methylphenidate, dextroamphetamine, and placebo in 15 young fra(X) individuals. They found that significant improvement was seen in attention span and socialization skills of the children treated with methylphenidate. Clonidine has been found to decrease hyperactivity in three fra(X) subjects. (J. Leckman, personal communication). The major tranquilizers, such as Thioridazine, have frequently been employed to help control aggressive outbursts and agitation in adult fra(X) males. The fact that some affected males carry the fra(X) mutation and do not express it may suggest that it is to some degree under environmental control and may ultimately be a treatable condition.

IX. PRENATAL DIAGNOSIS

Following the development by Sutherland (1977a,b) of methods using low levels of folic acid for induction of fragile site expression in lymphocytes, Glover (1981) and Tommerup et al. (1985) reported that FUdR was effective in inducing fragile site expression in both lymphocytes and fibroblasts. Obtained from the amniotic fluid, fetal amniocytes are similar to fibroblasts in growth properties. The feasibility of prenatal identification of fra(X) in amniotic fluid cells was demonstrated in 1981, using the FUdR induction method (Jenkins et al., 1981). These findings were confirmed in a prospective prenatal diagnosis (Shapiro et al., 1982). It is also possible to perform fra(X) analysis with chorionic villus (CV) samples (Tommerup et al., 1985). Because fra(X) studies of amniotic cells and CV samples are technically difficult, involve using several different induction systems, and often involve the analysis of several hundred cells, only a few specialized laboratories have had significant experience in doing fra(X) testing. Approximately 400 trials on an international basis have been undertaken (Jenkins et al., 1988, 1991). Our most recent report tabulates the detection of 76 positive cases as well as several false-negative cases that were obtained from chorionic villus sample cultures, amniotic fluid (AF) cell cultures, and peripheral umbilical blood sample (PUBS) cultures (Webb et al., 1989). An overall reliability of about 90% can be estimated from the results of CV, AF, and PUBS cultures. We have suggested ways to prevent these false negatives, thereby increasing the reliability of the system (Jenkins et al., 1991). If cytogenetic analysis with multiple systems is combined with DNA marker analysis (Brown et al., 1988a) or newer molecular testing (Verkerk et al., 1991), the reliability of prenatal diagnosis of fra(X) can be increased to over 99%.

X. DNA MOLECULAR MARKERS

DNA marker testing in fra(X) has several potential clinical uses (Brown et al., 1988a). It can be used to test both males and females for carrier status. It also allows a determination of which grandparent transmitted the fra(X) chromosome to affected grandchildren. It serves as a complementary test to prenatal diagnosis and increases the accuracy of prediction of a negative result (Brown *et al.*, 1988a).

Cytogenetic testing of normal females to determine if they are fra(X) carriers is often unreliable. Although among the mentally impaired carriers about 90% are positive on testing, among the mentally unimpaired carriers about 63% are cytogenetically negative (Sherman *et al.*, 1984, 1985). It is a common question for the sister of an affected male to wish to know her risks of being a carrier. Her risks can be reduced from the *a priori* risk of 50% to 41% if she is mentally unimpaired and to 30% if she is negative on cytogenetic testing. If she can be shown to have inherited a different set of flanking DNA markers than those seen in her fra(X)-positive brother, her risks can be reduced to less than 1%. The general approach is illustrated in Figure 2.4. Thus DNA testing allows for considerably improved reliability of carrier detection (Brown *et al.*, 1988a).

Similar testing also can be used to determine if brothers of affected males are nonpenetrant for fra(X). We have studied 51 normal brothers who were fully informative for flanking markers on both sides of fra(X). We found that 10 of the 51 brothers (19.6%) had inherited the same set of flanking markers as found in their affected brothers and thus were most likely nonpenetrant transmitting males (Brown *et al.*, 1991). This molecular method of testing thus confirmed the predictions of Sherman *et al.* (1984, 1985) based on population genetic analysis that about 1 of 6 normal brothers is nonpenetrant.

In order to conduct this type of DNA testing, flanking DNA probes are necessary. Probes have been isolated and RFLPs identified for several expressed genes adjacent to the *fra(X)* locus. Included on the distal side are the genes for clotting factor F8 (Gitscher *et al.*, 1985) and iduronate sulfatase (IDS) (Suthers *et al.*, 1989), which underlies Hunter syndrome. Included on the proximal side are genes for hypoxanthine/guanosine phosphoribosyltransferase (HGPRT) and clotting factor F9 (Camerino *et al.*, 1983). The F9 locus maps on average at about 20% recombination with *fra(X)* (Brown *et al.*, 1988b). A number of random DNA segment probes also have been identified adjacent to *fra(X)* (Dryana *et al.*, 1984). On the distal side of the *fra(X)* locus near F8, probe ST14 detects a highly polymorphic locus, *DXS52* (Oberlé *et al.*, 1985). This locus maps about 12% distal to *fra(X)*. On the proximal side, probes 52A (Davies *et al.*, 1985), 55E (Heilig *et al.*, 1988; Carpenter *et al.*, 1988), and 4D8 (Brown *et al.*, 1987b) detect loci *DXS51*, *DXS105*, and *DXS98*, which map at about 22, 10, and 7%, respectively from *fra(X)*.

For purposes of clinical carrier testing, it is most useful to have probes that are within about 5% of *fra(X)* to reduce the risk of recombination and improve the predictive certainty of DNA-based diagnostic testing. However, although much effort had been expended, up until 1989 none of the identified probes was closer on average than about 7%. This led to the impression that

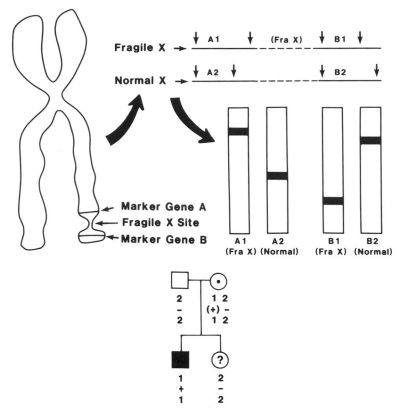

Figure 2.4. DNA marker analysis of fragile X. (A) When polymorphic probes that flank the fra(X) site are available, they can be used to track the inheritance of the fragile X within families. (B) The most common situation in clinical testing is the need to determine if a sister of an affected male is a carrier. If she has inherited a different set of markers than her brother, her risks can be said to be reduced to less than 1%.

regions flanking *fra(X)* were either difficult to clone or were subject to unusually high rates of recombination. The idea that there may exist unusual recombination in this region was supported by findings of genetic linkage heterogeneity in the proximal region. We observed that in some families, such as the pedigree illustrated in Figure 2.5, there was very little recombination between *F9* and *fra(X)*, whereas in other families, such as the pedigree illustrated in Figure 2.6, there was a high degree of recombination (Brown *et al.*, 1985, 1986b). Heterogeneity tests showed there was significant linkage heterogeneity on the proximal side of *fra(X)* but not on the distal side (Brown *et al.*, 1987d, 1988b). The

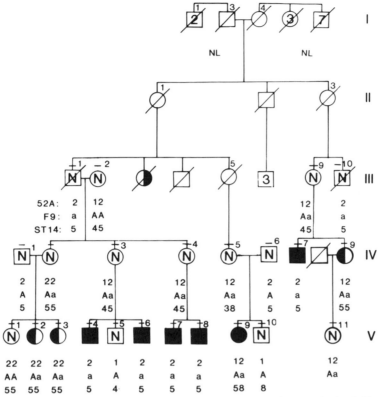

Figure 2.5. A fragile X pedigree (No. 22) that showed no recombination between the fragile X site and the factor 9 (*F9*) locus. In this family, individual III-1 was a normal transmitting male.

underlying basis for this difference is unknown. It may reflect structural differences in the mutation within different families, such as inversions or an amplifications.

In 1989, the loci detected by three probes—U6.2, VK21, and RN1—and the *IDS* locus were identified, all of which map to within about 5% of *fra(X)*. The probe U6.2 (locus *DXS304*) was isolated by Dahl *et al.* (1989a,b). This interesting locus maps to the distal side at about 3–4% recombination (Dahl *et al.*, 1989a,b; Goonewardena *et al.*, 1991). It detects RFLPs with a large number of different enzymes. However, all the RFLPs are in linkage disequilibrium, suggesting that an underlying insertion/deletion is present. We sequenced the 1103-bp U6.2 probe and found it contained a large 121-bp direct repeated element and several smaller inverted repeated elements (Pergolizzi *et al.*, 1991).

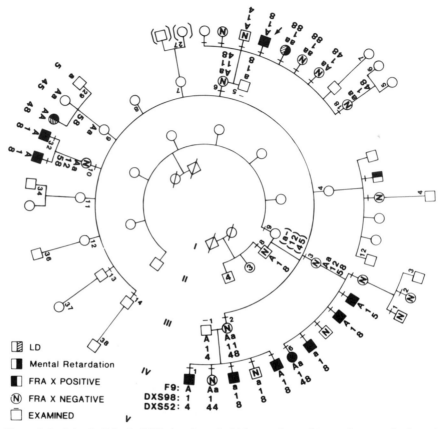

Figure 2.6. A fragile X family (F20) that showed a high rate of recombination between the factor 9 (F9) locus and the *fra*(X) locus. The grandfather (II-8) was a transmitting male who passed the mutation to all his daughters. Linkage studies of this and other families indicated genetic linkage heterogeneity (Brown *et al.*, 1986b).

Probe VK21 (locus *DXS296*), characterized by Suthers *et al.* (1989), was one of a series of VK probes derived from a somatic hybrid cell panel with defined X chromosome breakpoints near *fra*(X) (Hyland *et al.*, 1989). The use of this panel allowed localization of isolated X chromosome probes to the region adjacent to *fra*(X) prior to searching for RFLPs. VK21 was found to be polymorphic and mapped at about 1 cM distal to *fra*(X), adjacent to the *IDS* locus (Suthers *et al.*, 1989). Probe RN1 (locus *DXS369*) was isolated by Van Oostra *et al.* (1990) and maps at about 5% recombination proximal to *fra*(X). Using a somatic cell hybrid panel, Rousseau *et al.* (1991) recently were able to isolate four new probes that map between RN1 (*DXS369*) and *IDS*. Three of these probes were found to be polymorphic: St677 (*DXS463*), 2–35 (*DXS477*), and Do33 (*DXS465*). The localizations of these three probes were quite close to the *fra(X)* locus. The approximate genetic locations of these various loci are illustrated in Figure 2.7.

Highly informative probes such as ST14, located very close to *fra(X)*, help to reduce the ambiguity that can occur with uninformative dimorphic probes. A new class of highly polymorphic sequences known as CA repeats have been defined; these sequences appear to be widely dispersed and can be detected by polymerase chain reaction testing (Weber and May, 1989). Probes with CA repeats close to *fra(X)* will probably be most useful for clinical testing purposes. Efforts are underway to search for and identify such probes.

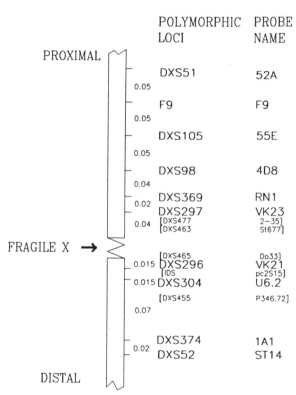

Figure 2.7. Location of various useful polymorphic loci adjacent
to the *fra(X)* locus. The estimated positions of the
probes are based upon average results of various mul-
tipoint investigations (Brown *et al.*, 1988b; Suthers
et al., 1990; Rousseau *et al.*, 1991).

XI. THEORIES REGARDING THE NATURE OF THE *fra(X)* MUTATION

Because of the very unusual nature of the inheritance pattern, it was difficult to formulate a theory that was adequate to explain all the unusual aspects of the fragile X mutation. Several hypotheses were proposed regarding the molecular basis of the fra(X) mutation. Some suggested that transposable elements (Hoegerman and Rary, 1986) may be involved. Other suggested that modifier loci on autosomal chromosomes may affect expression (Steinbach, 1986; Israel, 1987). Pembrey *et al.* (1985) hypothesized that a premutation exists on the X chromosome of transmitting males. They proposed that this interacts with an enhancing sequence on the homologous X chromosome during oogenesis in their daughters to produce a definitive mutation. They subsequently elaborated on their hypothesis to take into account DNA marker linkage information (Winter and Pembrey, 1986). We argued that their hypothesis was inconsistent with our observed data because there was no evidence to suggest the homologous X chromosome plays any role (Brown *et al.*, 1987c).

A useful hypothesis by Nussbaum *et al.* (1986) suggested that the fragile X region involves a long pyrimidine-rich DNA sequence that undergoes unequal crossing-over. A precedent for unequal crossing-over in the distal X region had been described for the mutations underlying human X-linked color blindness (Nathans *et al.*, 1988). Unequal crossing-over could lead to rearrangement, amplification, or deletion of a sequence and this could affect the expression of nearby genes. An amplified sequence could lead to a region that would be late in replication and visible as a cytogenetic marker. However, this hypothesis does not in itself explain the altered segregation ratios seen in different generations of a family (Sherman *et al.*, 1984, 1985).

Perhaps the most interesting and comprehensive hypothesis was put forward by Laird (1987) and Laird *et al.* (1987). They proposed that fra(X) results from a mutation that locally blocks the complete reactivation of a previously inactivated region locally adjacent to fra(X). A block to reactivation during oogenesis of a previously inactivated X chromosome region could lead to decreased gene expression of nearby genes. The fra(X) chromosomes could be designated as either "mutated," i.e., an X chromosome with the potential to block the local reactivation at Xq27.3 of an X chromosome that had been inactivated, or "imprinted," i.e., a mutated fra(X) chromosome that had been through a cycle of inactivation and incomplete reactivation. Because DNA methylation is presumed to be involved in X inactivation and chromosome imprinting, Laird suggested that mutation may involve an abnormal methylation and thus the mutation would not necessarily reflect an underlying sequence variation.

Laird's hypothesis made predictions that were consistent with much of the unusual inheritance pattern seen in fra(X). It predicted the altered ratio of affected to unaffected offspring. However, as originally proposed, the theory did not appear to explain the altered segregation ratios seen among the offspring of the mothers of transmitting males as compared to the offspring of the daughters of transmitting males, the so-called Sherman paradox (Sherman *et al.*, 1984, 1985; Opitz *et al.*, 1988). To account for this paradox, Laird subsequently suggested that the ovary from which the stem cells for eggs are derived is mosaic in nature (Laird *et al.*, 1990). For female carriers whose ovaries had been populated by stem cells in which more than 50% of the cells had been inactivated, a fra(X) chromosome would have a frequency of chromosome imprinting correspondingly greater than 50%. Laird suggested the stem cell pool size from which the fra(X) chromosome-containing oocytes are derived may be as small as two cells. This led to the prediction that the ratio of affected to unaffected males born to a carrier would be highly variable, which appeared to offer an explanation for the Sherman paradox.

XII. APPROACHES TO DEFINE THE NATURE OF THE MUTATION

A promising approach to characterize the mutation had been the study of fra(X) translocations by Warren *et al.* (1987). They obtained translocations involving the fra(X) chromosome and rodent chromosome in somatic cell hybrids. These translocation chromosomes appeared to selectively involve the fra(X) locus based on DNA marker studies. Fragility at the human–X rodent translocation junction was observed in two cells, but at a reduced frequency relative to the parental fra(X) cells. Cloning and sequencing of the junctional DNA seemed an attractive way to proceed but this was found to be very difficult (Warren *et al.*, 1987, 1990, and personal communication). Another promising method was direct physical isolation and cloning of the locus. MacKinnon *et al.* (1990) perfected and applied a method of microdissecting small portions of chromosomes from the region surrounding the fra(X). They obtained a library of some 20,000 clones from a region within a few percent recombination of the fra(X).

To understand the nature of the fra(X) mutation, it was clear that a complete physical map of the region would be desirable. An approach to such complete mapping was to employ pulsed-field gel electrophoresis (PFGE) to map very large fragments—up to several million base pairs—of DNA. PFGE employs the use of special restriction enzymes, for example, *Not*I, which recognize rarely occurring DNA sequences, such as 8- to 12-bp-long sequences. If a PFGE fragment could be shown to contain several smaller probes known by linkage methods to be on opposite sides of fra(X), then such a fragment would contain the fra(X) mutation.

Detailed PFGE physical mapping of the distal X region surrounding

ST14 and DX13 was reported (Patterson *et al.*, 1987a; Bell *et al.*, 1989). These studies showed that ST14 (*DXS52*) and DX13 (*DXS15*) were within a PFGE fragment of 470 kb. Patterson *et al.* (1989) identified a probe, 1A1 (*DXS374*), which was proximal to *DXS52* at about 3% recombination. They showed that it was within a 2×10^6-bp (2-mbp) PFGE fragment that was not physically linked to the region containing *DXS52*. Subsequent PFGE studies (Feil *et al.*, 1990) physically mapped a 1.2-mbp region around ST14. They showed that the ST14 probe actually detects a family of *DXS52* loci that are dispersed within a 600-kb region. This region also included MN12 (*dxs33*), cpX6 (*DXS130*), cpX67 (*DXS134*), and G1.3c (*DXF22S3*). On the distal side of *DXS52*, PFGE mapping studies identified a 1.7-mbp region containing the X-linked forms of color-blindness cone pigment genes (*RCP* and *GCP*), *MD13*, *GdX* (*DXS254*), *G6PD*, *F8C*, *DXS115*, and *DXYS64* (Arveiler *et al.*, 1990). These three physical regions identified by PFGE on the distal side of fra(X) included about 4 mbp of DNA.

On the proximal side of *fra*(X), Patterson *et al.* (1987b) reported the physical linkage of 4D8 (*DXS98*), cX55.7 (*DXS105*), and cX33.2 (*DXS105/ dxs152*) on a 400-kb PFGE fragment. However, additional studies showed that *DSX105* lies within a 600-kb region that is physically distinct from the 400-kb fragment detected by 4D8 (*DXS98*) (Dobkin and Brown, 1988). This later study showed that different X chromosomes have PFGE DNA restriction fragment length polymorphisms of 270 kb around the *DXS105* locus (cX55.7). A 1.3-mbp physical map of the region surrounding *F9* was reported (Nguyen *et al.*, 1988). Thus, three physically distinct regions of approximately 2.3 mbp in the region proximal to *fra*(X) were defined by PFGE.

In the spring of 1991, the results of much intensive further work to define the nature of the fragile X mutation were published by groups working in the Netherlands, France, England, Australia, and the United States. First, Vincent *et al.* (1991) and Bell *et al.* (1991), using PFGE and probes that were apparently close to the fragile X locus, reported that there was a region that was rich in CpG dinucleotide sequences and had a high frequently of rare-cutter restriction enzyme sites (so-called CpG islands, which are often found near to expressed gene sequences). This region was overly methylated in affected fragile X males but was unmethylated in normal males or nonpenetrant fragile X trans-mitting males. These results were consistent with the Laird hypothesis.

Shortly thereafter, Heitz *et al.* (1991) reported the isolation of a yeast artificial chromosome (YAC) probe that was shown to span the *fra*(X) region. This 425-kb YAC was shown to contain their previously isolated probes St677 and 2-35, which were on the proximal side of *fra*(X), and Do33, which was on the distal side. Fluorescent *in situ* hybridization showed an even distribution across the *fra*(X) gap and on proximal and distal sites. Near the middle portion of this YAC clone was the CpG island, which showed hypermethylation in fragile X-positive males. Thus a major goal, the cloning of the region, had been achieved.

Then Oberlé *et al.* (1991) with a 7-kb subclone of a region adjacent to the CpG island region, and Yu *et al.* (1991), with a separate probe that also was found to lie just distal to the CpG island, showed that fragile X males also have a significant amplification of base sequences within a region closely adjacent to the CpG island detected by their probes. In contrast to normal males, who lack such an insertion, nonpenetrant transmitting males were shown to have an insertion of about 100 to 500 bp. They pass on this insertion to their normal daughters, who then can have affected sons, who appeared to have undergone a further stage of amplification such that the insertion was now typically in the range of 1000–4000 bp. In many subjects the size of the insertion was not constant but appeared as a smear, indicating underlying molecular heterogeneity. Thus the fragile X mutation appeared to involve first a small insertion (a "premutation") that did not affect methylation, but that would progress to a much larger insertion that did affect methylation. Thus aspects of both the amplification process proposed by Nussbaum and Ledbetter and Laird's hypothesis appeared to be reflected in the mutation.

Verkerk *et al.* (1991) independently isolated overlapping cosmid clones that were shown to span the *fra*(X) region. They were able to use one of these clones to isolate a complementary coding sequence from a fetal brain cDNA library. They reported the nucleotide sequence of 3.8 kb of this cDNA clone and also determined that the total message was about 4.8 kb. The sequence of this gene, which they termed *FMR-1* (fragile X mental retardation-1), had many interesting properties. It was expressed in brain and lymphocytes but not in liver, kidney, or lung. It was expressed at reduced levels or not at all in affected fragile X males. It was highly conserved across animal species. Near the beginning of the gene at the 5' end was a long string of the amino acid arginine. In fact, 28 out of 30 amino acids were arginine, with the underlying codon CGG. This predicted that the protein has a very basic region, similar to but longer than arginine stretches seen in histones and other nucleic acid-binding proteins. Thus the gene may have some nucleic acid regulatory role and may effect gene expression. The long stretch of CGGs also offered a possible site for amplification by a mechanism such as unequal recombination.

XIII. CONCLUSIONS

The fragile X syndrome shows a very unusual genetic inheritance pattern. It appears that a novel genetic mechanism may underlie the fragile X mutation. Because of recent reports, the unique genetic situation of the fragile X is now approaching a molecular explanation. Because fragile sites also may be involved in other types of conditions, such as cancer and the constitutive breakage of chromosomes, information about the basis of the fra(X) mutation may lead to new insights into genetic mechanisms of human inheritance and mutation.

References

Arveiler, B., Vincent, A., and Mandel, J.-L. (1990). Toward a physical map of the Xq28 region in man: Linking color vision, G6PD, and coagulation factor VIII genes to an X–Y homology region. *Genomics* **4**:460–471.

Bell, M. V., Patterson, M. N., Dorkins, H. R., and Davies, K. E. (1989). Physical mapping of DXS134 close to the DXS52 locus. *Hum. Genet.* **82**:27–30.

Bell, M. V., Hirst, M. C., Nakahori, Y., MacKinnon, R. N., Roche, A., Flint, T. J., Jacobs, P. A., Tommerup, N., Tranebjaerg, L., Froster-Iskenius, U., Kerr, B., Turner, G., Lindenbaum, R. H., Winter, R., Pembrey, M., Tibodeau, S., and Davies, K. E. (1991). Physical mapping across the fragile X: Hypermethylation and clinical expression of the fragile X syndrome. *Cell (Cambridge, Mass.)* **64**:861–866.

Blomquist, H. K., Gustavson, K. H., Nordenson, I., and Sweins, A. (1982). Fragile site X chromosomes and X-linked mental retardation in severely retarded boys in a northern Swedish county. A prevalence study. *Clin. Genet.* **60**:278–280.

Blomquist, H. K., Gustavson, K. H., Holgrem, G., Nordenson, I., and Palsson-Ostrae, U. (1983). Fragile X syndrome in mildly mentally retarded children in a northern Swedish county. A prevalence study. *Clin. Genet.* **24**:393–398.

Blomquist, H. K., Bohman, M., Edvinsson, S. O., Gillberg, C., Gustavson, K. H., Holmgren, G., and Wahlstrom, J. (1984). Frequency of the fragile X syndrome in infantile autism. A Swedish multicenter study. *Clin. Genet.* **27**:113–117.

Borghgraeg, M., Fryns, J. P., Dielkens, A., Pyck, K., and van den Bergh, H. (1987). Fragile (X) syndrome: A study of the psychological profile in 23 prepubertal patients. *Clin. Genet.* **32**:179–186.

Brookwell, R., and Turner, G. (1983). High resolution banding and the locus of the Xq fragile site. *Hum. Genet.* **63**:77.

Brown, W. T., Mezzacappa, P. M., and Jenkins, E. C. (1981). Screening for fragile X syndrome by testicular size measurement. *Lancet* **2**:1055.

Brown, W. T., Friedman, E., Jenkins, E. C., Brooks, J., Wisniewski, K., Raguthu, S., and French, J. H. (1982). Association of fragile X with autism. *Lancet* **1**:100.

Brown, W. T., Gross, A. C., Chan, C. B., and Jenkins, E. C. (1985). Genetic heterogeneity in the fragile X syndrome. *Hum. Genet.* **71**:11–18.

Brown, W. T., Jenkins, E. C., Cohen, I. L., Fisch, G. S., Wolf-Schein, E. G., Gross, A., Waterhouse, L., Fein, D., Mason-Brothers, A., Ritvo, E., Ruttenberg, B. A., Buckley, W., and Castells, S. (1986a). Fragile X and autism: A multicenter survey. *Am. J. Med. Genet.* **23**:334–352.

Brown, W. T., Gross, A. G., and Chan, C. B. (1986b). DNA linkage studies in the fragile X syndrome suggest heterogeneity. *Am. J. Med. Genet.* **23**:643–664.

Brown, W. T., Jenkins, E. C., Krawczun, M. S., Wisniewski, K., Rudelli, R., Cohen, I. L., Fisch, G., Wolf-Schein, E., Miezejeski, C., and Dobkin, C. (1987a). The fragile X syndrome. *Ann. N.Y. Acad. Sci.* **477**:129–150.

Brown, W. T., Wu, Y., Gross, A. C., Chan, C. B., Dobkin, C. S., and Jenkins, E. C. (1987b). RFLP for linkage analysis of the fragile X. *Lancet* **1**:280.

Brown, W. T., Sherman, S. L., and Dobkin, C. S. (1987c). Hypothesis regarding the nature of the fragile X mutation. A reply to Winter and Pembrey. *Hum. Genet.* **75**:294–295.

Brown, W. T., Jenkins, E. C., Gross, A. C., Chan, C. B., Krawczun, M. S., Duncan, C. J., Sklower, S. L., and Fisch, G. S. (1987d). Further evidence for genetic heterogeneity in the fragile X syndrome. *Hum. Genet.* **75**:311–321.

Brown, W. T., Jenkins, E. C., Gross, A. C., Chan, C. B., Krawczun, M. S., Alonso, M. L., Cantu, E. S., Davis, J. G., Hagerman, R. J., Laxova, R., Liebowitz, M., Penchaszadeh, V. B., Thibodeau, S., Willey, A. M., Williams, M. K., Willner, J. P., and Zellers, N. J. (1988a). Clinical use of DNA markers in the fragile (X) syndrome for carrier detection and prenatal diagnosis. *In* "Nucleic Acid Probes In Diagnosis of Human Genetic Diseases," pp. 11–34. Alan R. Liss, New York.

Brown, W. T., Gross, A., Chan, C., Jenkins, E. C., Mandel, J. L., Oberlé, I., Arveiler, B., Novelli, G., Thibodeau, S., Hagerman, R., Summers, K., Turner, G., White, B. N., Mulligan, L., Forster-Gibson, C., Holden, J. J. A., Zoll, B., Krawczak, M., Gonneardena, P., Gustavson, K. H., Petterson, U., Holmgren, G., Schwartz, C., Howard-Pebbles, P. N., Murphy, P., Breg, W. R., Veenema, H., and Carpenter, N. J. (1988b). Multi-locus analysis of the fragile X syndrome. *Hum. Genet.* **78**: 201–205.

Brown, W. T., Rudelli, R. D., and Wisniewski, H. M. (1988c). Fragile X syndrome: Neuropathology Center. *Am. J. Med. Genet.* **30**:201–205.

Brown, W. T., Gross, A. C., Goonewardena, P., Ferrando, C., Dobkin, C., and Jenkins, E. C. (1991). Detection of fragile X non-penetrant males by DNA marker analysis. *Am. J. Med. Genet.* **38**:292–297.

Camerino, G., Mattei, M. G., and Mattei, J. F. (1983). Close linkage of fragile X linked mental retardation syndrome to haemophilia B and transmission through a normal male. *Nature (London)* **306**:701–707.

Carpenter, N. J., Veenema, H., Bakker, E., Hofker, M. H., and Pearson, P. L. (1988). A new DNA probe proximal to and closely linked to fragile X. *Am. J. Med. Genet.* **27**:731–732.

Cohen, I. L., Fisch, G. S., Sudhalter, V., Wolf-Schein, E. G., Hanson, D., Hagerman, R., Jenkins, E. C., and Brown, W. T. (1988). Social gaze, social avoidance and repetitive behavior in fragile X males: A controlled study. *Am. J. Ment. Defic.* **92**:436–446.

Cohen, I. L., Brown, W. T., Jenkins, E. C., Krawczun, M. S., French, J. H., Raguthu, S., Wolf-Schein, E. G., Sudhalter, V., Fisch, G., and Wisniewski, K. (1989). Fragile X syndrome in females with autism. *Am. J. Med. Genet.* **34**:302–303.

Courchesne, E., Yeung-Courchesne, R., Press, G. A., Hesselink, J. R., and Jernigan, T. L. (1988). Hypoplasia of cerebellar vermal lobules VI and VII in autism. *N. Engl. J. Med.* **318**:1349–1354.

Dahl, N., Goonewardena, P., Malmgren, H., Gustavson, K.-H., Holmgren, G., Seemanova, G., Anneren, G., Flood, A., and Pettersson, U. (1989a). Linkage analysis of families with fragile-X mental retardation, using a novel RFLP marker (DXS304). *Am. J. Hum. Genet.* **45**:304–309.

Dahl, N., Hammarstrom-Heeroma, K., Goonewardena, P., Wadelius, C., Gustavson, K.-H., Holmgren, G., van Ommen, G. J. B., and Pettersson, U. (1989b). Isolation of a DNA probe of potential use for diagnosis of the fragile-X syndrome. *Hum. Genet.* **82**:216–218.

Davies, K. E., Mattei, M. G., Mattei, J. F., Veenema, H., McGlade, S., Harper, K., Tommerup, N., Nielsen, K. B., Mikkelsen, M., Beighton, P., Drayna, D., White, R., and Pembrey, M. E. (1985). Linkage studies of X-linked mental retardation: High frequency of recombination in the telomeric region of the human X chromosome. *Hum. Genet.* **70**:249–255.

Dobkin, C. S., and Brown, W. T. (1988). Pulsed-field gradient-gel studies around the fragile site. *Am. J. Med. Genet.* **30**:593–600.

Drayna, D., Davies, K. E., Hartley, D. A., Williamson, R., and White, R. (1984). Genetic mapping of the human X chromosome using restriction fragment length polymorphism. *Proc. Natl. Acad. Sci. U.S.A.* **81**:2836–2839.

Escalante, J. A., Grunspun, H., and Frosa-Pessoa, O. (1971). Severe sex-linked mental retardation. *J. Genet. Hum.* **19:**137–140.

Feil, R., Palmieri, G., d'Urso, M., Heilig, R., Oberlé, I., and Mandel, J. L. (1990). Physical and genetic mapping of polymorphic loci in Xq28 (DXS 15, DXS 52, and DXS 134): Analysis of a cosmid clone and a yeast artificial chromosome. *Am. J. Hum. Genet.* **46:** 720–728.

Fisch, G. S., Cohen, I. L., Gross, A. C., Jenkins, V., Jenkins, E. C., and Brown, W. T. (1988). Folic acid treatment of fragile X males: A further study. *Am. J. Med. Genet.* **30:**393–399.

Fryns, J.-P., and van den Bergh, H. (1988). Inactivation pattern of the fragile X in heterozygous carriers. *Am. J. Med. Genet.* **30:**401–406.

Giraud, F., Ayme, S., Mattei, J. F., and Mattei, M. G. (1976). Constitutional chromosomal breakage. *Hum. Genet.* **34:**125–136.

Gitscher, J., Drayna, D., Tuddenham, E. G. D., White, R. L., and Lawn, R. M. (1985). Genetic mapping and diagnosis of haemophilia A achieved through a BclI polymorphism in the factor VIII gene. *Nature (London)* **314:**738–740.

Glover, T. W. (1981). FUdR induction of the X chromosome fragile site: Evidence for the mechanism of folic acid and thymidine inhibition. *Am. J. Hum. Genet.* **33:**234–242, 1981.

Glover, T. W., and Stein, C. K. (1987). Induction of sister chromatic exchanges at common fragile sites. *Am. J. Hum. Genet.* **41:**5:882–890.

Glover, T. W., Berger, C., Colyle, J., and Echo, B. (1984). DNA polymerase alpha inhibition by aphidicolin induces gaps and breaks at common fragile sites in human chromosomes. *Hum. Genet.* **67:**136–142.

Goonewardena, P., Brown, W. T., Gross, A. C., Ferrando, C., Dobkin, C., Romano, V., Bosco, P., Ceratto, N., Dahl, N., and Pettersson, U. (1991). Linkage analysis of the fragile X syndrome using a new DNA marker U6.2 defining locus DXS304. *Am. J. Med. Genet.* **38:** 322–327.

Gustavson, K. H., Dahlbom, K., Flood, A., Holgrem, G., Blomquist, H. K., and Sanner, G. (1985). Effect of folic acid treatment in the fragile X syndrome. *Clin. Genet.* **27:**463–467.

Hagerman, R. J., Kemper, M., and Hudson, M. (1985). Learning disabilities and attentional problems in boys with the fragile X syndrome. *Am. J. Dis. Child* **139:**674–678.

Hagerman, R. J., Jackson, A. W., III, Levitas, A., Braden, M., McBogg, P., Kemper, M., McGavran, L., Berry, R., Matus, I., and Hagerman, P. J. (1986a). Oral folic acid versus placebo in the treatment of males with the fragile X syndrome. *Am. J. Med. Genet.* **23:**241–262.

Hagerman, R. J., Jackson, A. W., III, Levitas, A., Rimland, B., and Braden, M. (1986b). An analysis of autism in fifty males with the fragile X syndrome. *Am. J. Med. Genet.* **23:**359–374.

Hagerman, R. J., Murphy, M. A., and Wittenberger, M. D. (1988). A controlled trial of stimulant medication in children with the *fragile* X syndrome. *Am. J. Med. Genet.* **30:** 377–392.

Hanson, D. M., Jackson, A. W., III, and Hagerman, R. J. (1986). Speech disturbances (Cluttering) in mildly impaired males with the Martin–Bell/fragile X syndrome. *Am. J. Med. Genet.* **23:**195–206.

Harrison, C. J., Jack, E. M., Allen, T. D., and Harris, R. (1983). The fragile X: A scanning electron microscope study. *J. Med. Genet.* **20:**280–285.

Harvey, J., Judge, C., and Wiener, S. (1977). Familial X-linked mental retardation with an X chromosome abnormality. *J. Med. Genet.* **14:**46–50.

Heilig, R., Oberlé, I., Arveiler, B., Hanauer, A., Vidaud, M., and Mandel, J. L. (1988). Improved DNA markers for efficient analysis of fragile X families. *Am. J. Med. Genet.* **30:**543–550.

Heitz, D., Rousseau, F., Devys, D., Soccone, S., Abderrahim, H., LePalier, D., Cohen, D., Vincent, A., Toniolo, D., Della Valle, G., Johnson, S., Schlessinger, D., Oberlé, I., and Mandel, J. L. (1991). Isolation of sequences that span the fragile X and identification of a fragile-X related CpG island. *Science* **251:**1236–1239.

Hoegerman, S. F., and Rary, J. M. (1986). Speculation on the role of transposable elements in human genetic disease with particular attention to achondroplasia and the fragile X syndrome. *Am. J. Med. Genet.* **23**:685–699.

Hyland, V. J., Fernandez, K. E. W., Callen, D. F., MacKinnon, R. N., Baker, E. G., Friend, K., and Sutherland, G. R. (1989). Assignment of anonymous DNA probes to specific intervals of human chromosomes 16 and X. *Hum. Genet.* **83**:61–66.

Israel, M. H. (1987). Autosomal supressor gene for fragile-X: An hypothesis. *Am. J. Med. Genet.* **26**:19–31.

Jenkins, E. C., Brown, W. T., Duncan, C. J., Brooks, J., Duncan, C. J., Brooks, J., Ben-Yishay, M., Giordano, F. M., and Nitowsky, H. M. (1981). Feasability of fragile X chromosome prenatal diagnosis demonstrated. *Lancet* **1**:1291.

Jenkins, E. C., Brown, W. T., Brooks, J., Duncan, C. J., Sanz, M. M., Silverman, W. P., Lele, K. P., Masia, A., Katz, E., Lubin, R. A., and Nolin, S. L. (1986). Low frequencies of apparently fra X chromosomes in normal control cultures: A possible explanation. *Exp. Cell Biol.* **54**:40–48.

Jenkins, E. C., Brown, W. T., Krawczun, M. S., Duncan, C. J., Lele, K. P., Cantu, E., Schonberg, S., Golbus, M. S., Sekhon, G. S., Stark, S., Kunaporn, S., and Silverman, W. P. (1988). Recent experience in prenatal fra(X) detection. *Am. J. Med. Genet.* **30**:329–336.

Jenkins, E. C., Krawczun, M. S., Brooks, S. E., Sklower-Brooks, S. L., Sherman, S. L., and Brown, W. T. (1991). Laboratory aspects of prenatal fragile X diagnosis. *In* "Fragile X/Cancer Genetics" (A. M. Willey and P. D. Murphy, eds.), New York. Liss/Wiley, pp. 27–42.

Kemper, M. B., Hagerman, R. J., Ahmad, R. S., and Mariner, R. (1986). Cognitive profiles and the spectrum of clinical manifestations in heterozygous fra(X) females. *Am. J. Med. Genet.* **23**:139–156.

Krawczun, M. S., Jenkins, E. C., and Brown, W. T. (1985). Analysis of the fragile-X chromosome: Localization and detection of the fragile site in high resolution preparations. *Hum. Genet.* **69**:209–211.

Lachiewicz, A. M., Gullion, C. M., Spiridigliozzi, G. A., and Aylsworth, A. S. (1987). Declining IQs of young males with the fragile X syndrome. *Am. J. Ment. Retard.* **92**:272–278.

Laird, C. D. (1987). Proposed mechanism of inheritance and expression of the human fragile-X syndrome of mental retardation. *Genetics* **117**:587–599.

Laird, C. D., Jaffe, E., Karpen, G., Lamb, M., and Nelson, R. (1987). Fragile sites in human chromosomes as regions of late-replicating DNA. *Trends Genet.* **3**(10):274–281.

Ledbetter, D. H., Ledbetter, S. A., and Nussbaum, R. L. (1986). Implications of fragile X expression in normal males for the nature of the mutation. *Nature (London)* **324**:161–163.

Lehrke, R. (1972). A theory of X-linkage of major intellectual traits. *Am. J. Ment. Defic.* **76**:611–619.

LeJeune, J. (1982). Is the fragile X syndrome amenable to treatment? *Lancet* **1**:231–244.

MacKinnon, R. N., Hirst, M. C., Bell, M. V., Watson, J. E. V., Claussen, U., Ludecke, H. J., Senger, G., Horsthemke, B., and Davies, K. E. (1990). Microdissection of the fragile X region. *Am. J. Hum. Genet.* **47**:181–187.

Marlhens, F. W., Achkar, A. L., Aurias, A., Couturier, J., Dutrillaus, A. M., Gerbault-Sereau, M., Hoffschir, F., Lamoliatte, E., Lefrançois, D., Lombard, M., Muleris, M., Prieur, M., Prod'homme, M., Sabtier, L., Viegas-pequignot, E., Volobouen, V., and Dutrillaux, B. (1986). The rate of chromosome breakage is age dependent in lymphocytes of adult controls. *Hum. Genet.* **73**:290–297.

Martin, J. P., and Bell, J. (1943). A pedigree of mental defects showing sex linkage. *J. Neurol. Neurosurg. Psychiatry* **6**:154–157.

Miezejeski, C. M., Jenkins, E. C., Hill, A. L., Wisniewski, K., and Brown, W. T. (1984). Verbal vs. nonverbal ability, fragile X syndrome, and heterozygous carriers. *Am. J. Hum. Genet.* **36**:227–229.

Nathans, J., Piantanida, T. P., Eddy, R. L., Shows, T. B., and Hogness, D. S. (1988). Molecular genetics of inherited variation in human color vision. *Science* **232**:203–210.

Nguyen, C., Matte, M. G., Rey, J. A., Baeteman, M.-A., Matte, J.-F., and Jordan, B. R. (1988). Cytogenetic and physical mapping in the region of the X chromosome surrounding the fragile site. *Am. J. Med. Genet.* **30**: 601–612.

Nussbaum, R. L., Airhart, S. D., and Ledbetter, D. H. (1986). Recombination and amplification of pyrimidine-rich sequences may be responsible for initiation and progression of the Xq27 fragile site: An hypothesis. *Am. J. Med. Genet.* **23**:715–721.

Oberlé, I., Drayna, D., Camerino, G., Kloepfer, C., and Mandel, J. L. (1985). The telemeric region of the human X chromosome long arm: Presence of a highly polymorphic DNA marker and analysis of recombination frequency. *Proc. Natl. Acad. Sci. U.S.A.* **82**:2824–2828.

Oberlé, I., Rousseau, F., Heita, D., Kretz, C., Devys, D., Hanauer, A., Boué, J., Bertheas, M. F., and Mandel, J.-L. (1991). Instability of a 550-base pair DNA segment and abnormal methylation in fragile X syndrome. *Science* **252**:1097–1102.

Opitz, J. (1986). On the gates of hell and a most unusual gene. Editorial comment. *Am. J. Med. Genet.* **23**: 1–10.

Patterson, M., Kenwrick, S., Thibodeau, S., Faulk, K., Mattei, M. G., Mattei, J. F., and Davies, K. E. (1987a). Mapping of DNA markers close to the fragile site on the human X chromosome at Xq27.3. *Nucleic Acids Res.* **15**:2639–2651.

Patterson, M., Schwartz, C., Bell, M., Sauer, S., Hofker, M., Trask, B., van den Engh, G., and Davies, K. E. (1987b). Physical mapping studies on the human X chromosome in the region Xq27-Xqter. *Genomics* **1**:297–306.

Patterson, M. N., Bell, M. V., Bloomfield, J., Flint, T., Dorkins, H., Thibodeau, S. N., Schaid, D., Bren, G., Schwartz, C. E., Wieringa, B., Ropers, H. H., Collen, D. F., Sutherland, G. R., Froster-Iskenius, U., Vissing, H., and Davies, K. E. (1989). Genetic and physical mapping of a novel region close to the fragile X site on the human X chromosome. *Genomics* **4**:570–578.

Pembrey, M. E., and Winter, R. M., and Davies, K. E. (1985). A premutation that generates a defect at crossing over explains the inheritance of fragile X mental retardation. *Am. J. Med. Genet.* **21**:709–717.

Penrose, L. S. (1938). A clinical and genetic study of 1,280 cases of mental defect. *Med. Res. Coun. (G.B.), Spec. Rep. Ser.* **5RS-299.**

Pergolizzi, R., Brown, W. T., Goonewardena, P., Bhan, R., Dobkin, C., Dahl, N., and Pettersson, U. (1991) Molecular characterization of a DNA probe, U6.2, located close to the fragile X locus. *Am. J. Med. Genet.* **38**:380–383.

Reiss, A., Hagerman, R. J., Vinogradov, S., Abrams, M., and King, R. (1988). Psychiatric disability in female carriers of the fragile C chromosome. *Arch. Gen. Psychiatry* **45**:25–30.

Reiss, A. L., Aylward, E., Freund, L., Bryan, N., and Joshi, P. (1991). Neuroanatomy of fragile X syndrome: The posterior fossa. *Ann. Neurol.* **29**:26–32.

Richards, B. W., Sylvester, P. E., and Booker, C. (1981). Fragile X-linked mental retardation: The Martin–Bell syndrome. *J. Ment. Defic. Res.* **25**:253–256.

Rousseau, F., Vincent, A., Rivella, S., Heitz, D., Triboli, C., Maestrini, E., Warren, S. T., Suthers, G. K., Goodfellow, P., Mandel, J. L., Toniolo, D., and Oberlé, I. (1991). Four chromosomal breakpoints and four new probes mark out a 10-cM region encompassing the fragile-X locus (FRAXA). *Am. J. Hum. Genet.* **48**:108–116.

Rudelli, R. D., Brown, W. T., Wisniewski, K., Jenkins, E. C., Laure-Kamionowska, M., and Connell, F. (1983). Adult fragile X syndrome: Clinico-neuropathologic findings. *Acta Neuropathol.* **67**:289–295.

Shapiro, L. R., Wilmot, P. L., Brenholz, P., Lett, A., Martino, M., Harris, G., Mahoney, M. J., Hobbins, J. C. (1982). Prenatal diagnosis of *fragile* X chromosome. *Lancet* **1**: 99–100.

Sherman, S. L., Morton, N. E., Jacobs, P. A., and Turner, G. (1984). The marker (X) syndrome: A cytogenetic and genetic analysis. *Ann. Hum. Genet.* **48:**21–37.

Sherman, S. L., Jacobs, P. A., Morton, N. E., Froster-Iskenius, U., Howard-Peebles, P. N., Nielsen, K. B., Partington, M. W., Sutherland, G. R., Turner, G., and Wilson, M. (1985). Further segregation analysis of the fragile X syndrome with special reference to transmitting males. *Hum. Genet.* **69:**289–299.

Sklower-Brooks, S., Cohen, I., Ferrando, C., Jenkins, E. C., Brown, W. T., and Dobkin, C. (1991). Cytogenetic negative, linkage positive "Fragile X" syndrome. *Am. J. Med. Genet.* **38:**370–373.

Steinbach, P. (1986). Mental impairment in Martin–Bell syndrome is probably determined by interaction of several genes: Simple explanation of phenotypic differences between unaffected and affected males with the same X chromosome. *Hum. Genet.* **72:**248–252.

Sutherland, G. R. (1977a). Fragile sites on human chromosomes: Demonstration of their dependence on the type of tissue culture medium. *Science* **197:**265–266.

Sutherland, G. R. (1977b). Marker X chromosome and mental retardation. *N. Engl. J. Med.* **296:**1415.

Sutherland, G. R. (1983). The fragile X chromosome. *Int. Rev. Cytol.* **81:**107–143.

Sutherland, G. R., and Baker, E. (1990). The common fragile site in band q27 of the human X chromosome is not coincident with the fragile X. *Clin. Genet.* **37:**167–172.

Sutherland, G. R., and Hecht, F. (1985). "Fragile Sites on Human Chromosomes." Oxford Univ. Press, New York.

Sutherland, G. R., and Ledbetter, D. H. (1989). Report of the committee on cytogenetic markers. *Cytogenet. Cell Genet.* **51:**452–458.

Sutherland, G. R., Baker, E., and Fratini, A. (1985). Excess thymidine induces folate sensitive fragile sites. *Am. J. Med. Genet.* **22:**433–443.

Suthers, G. K., Callen, D. K., Hyland, V. J., Kozman, H. M., Baker, E., Eyre, H., Harper, P. S., Roberts, S. H., Hors-Cayla, M. C., Davies, K. E., Bell, M. V., and Sutherland, G. R. (1989). A new DNA marker tightly linked to the fragile X locus (FRAXA). *Science* **246:**1298–1300.

Suthers, G. K., Hyland, V. J., Callen, D. F., Oberlé, I., Rocchi, M., Thomas, N. S., Morris, C. P., Schwartz, C. E., Schmidt, M., Ropers, H. H., Baker, E., Oostra, B. A., Dahl, N., Wilson, P. J., Hopwood, J. J., and Sutherland, G. R. (1990). Physical mapping of new DNA probes near the fragile X mutation (FRAXA) by using a panel of cell lines. *Am. J. Hum. Genet.* **47:**187–195.

Tommerup, N., Sondergaard, F., Tonnesen, T., Kristensen, M., Arveiler, B., and Schnzel, A. (1985). First trimester prenatal diagnosis of a male fetus with fragile X. *Lancet* **1:**870.

Tuckerman, E., and Webb, T. (1989). The inactivation of the fragile X chromosome in female carriers of the Martin–Bell syndrome as studied by two different methods. *Clin. Genet.* **36:**25–30.

Tuckerman, E., Webb, T., and Bundey, S. E. (1985). Frequency and replication status of the fragile X, fra(X)(q27-28), in a pair of monozygotic twins of markedly differing intelligence. *J. Med. Genet.* **22:**85–91.

Turner, G., and Turner, B. (1974). X-linked mental retardation. *J. Med. Genet.* **11:**109–113.

Turner, G., Till, R., and Daniel, A. (1978). Marker X chromosomes, mental retardation and macroorchidism. *N. Engl. J. Med.* **299:**1472.

Turner, G., Brookwell, R., Daniel, A., Selikowitz, M., and Zilibowitz, M. (1980a). Heterozygous expression of X-linked mental retardation and X-chromosome marker fra(X) (q27). *N. Engl. J. Med.* **303:**662–664.

Turner, G., Daniel, A., and Frost, M. (1980b). X-linked mental retardation, macroorchidism, and the Xq27 fragile site. *J. Pediatr.* **96:**837–841.

Uchida, I. A., and Joyce, E. M. (1982). Activity of the fragile X in heterozygous carriers. *Am. J. Hum. Genet.* **34:**286–293.

Uchida, I. A., Freeman, V. C., Jamro, H., Partington, M. W., and Soltan, H. (1983). Additional evidence for fragile X activity in heterozygous carriers. *Am. J. Hum. Genet.* **35:**861–868.

Van Ostra, B. A., Hupkes, P. E., Perdon, L.F., Van Bennekom, C. A., Bakker, E., Halley, D. J. J., Schmidt, M., DuSart, D., Smits, A., Wieringa, B., and Van Oost, B. A. (1990). New polymorphic DNA marker close to the fragile site FRAXA. *Genomics* **6:** 129–132.

Verkerk, A. J. M. H., Pieretti, M., Sutcliffe, J. S., Fu, Y.-H., Kuhl, D. P. A., Pizzuti, A., Reiner, O., Richard, S., Victoria, M. F., Zhang, F., Eussen, B. E., van Ommen, G.-J. B., Blonden, L. A. J., Riggins, G. J., Chastain, J. L., Kunst, C. B., Galjaard, H., Caskey, C. T., Nelson, D. L., Oostra, B. A., and Warren, S. T. (1991). Identification of a gene (*FMR-1*) containing a CGG repeat coincident with a breakpoint cluster region exhibiting length variation in fragile X syndrome. *Cell (Cambridge, Mass.)* **65:**905–914.

Vincent, A., Heitz, D., Petit, C., Kretz, C., Oberlé, I., and Mandel, J.-L. (1991). Abnormal pattern detected in fragile-X patients by pulsed-field gel electrophoresis. *Nature (London)* **349:**624–626.

Voelckel, M. A., Philip, N., Piquet, C., Pellissier, M. C., Oberlé, I., Birg, F., Mattei, M. G., and Mattei, J. F. (1989). Study of a family with a fragile site of the X chromosome at Xq27-28 without mental retardation. *Hum. Genet.* **81:**353–357.

Warren, S. T., Zhang, F., Licamelli, G. R., and Peters, J. F. (1987). The fragile X site in somatic cell hybrids: An approach for molecular cloning of fragile sites. *Science* **237:**420–423.

Warren, S. T., Knight, S. J. L., Peters, J. F., Stayton, C. L., Consalez, G. G., and Zhang, F. (1990). Isolation of the human chromosomal band Xq28 within somatic cell hybrids by fragile X site breakage. *Proc. Natl. Acad. Sci. U.S.A.* **87:**3856–3860.

Webb, T. P., Bundey, S. E., Thake, A. I., and Todd, J. (1986). The frequency of the *fragile* X chromosome among school children in Coventry. *J. Med. Genet.* **23:** 396–398.

Webb, T. P., Bundey, S., and McKinley, M. (1989). Missed prenatal diagnosis of fragile X syndrome. *Prenatal Diagn.* **9:**777–781.

Weber, J. L., and May, P. E. (1989). Abundant class of human DNA polymorphisms which can be typed using the polymerase chain reaction. *Am. J. Hum. Genet.* **44:**388–396.

Winter, R. M., and Pembrey, M. E. (1986). Analysis of linkage relationships between genetic markers around the fragile X locus with special reference to the daughters of normal transmitting males. *Hum. Genet.* **74:**93–97.

Wisniewski, K. C., French, J. H., Fernando, S., Brown, W. T., Jenkins, E. C., Friedman, E., Hill, A. L., and Miezejeski, C. M. (1985). The fragile X syndrome: Associated neurological abnormalities and developmental disabilities. *Ann. Neurol.* **18:**665–669.

Wolff, P. H., Gardiner, J., Lappen, J., Paccia, J., and Meryash, D. (1988). Variable expression of the fragile X syndrome in heterozygous females of normal intelligence. *Am. J. Med. Genet.* **30:**213–225.

Wolf-Schien, E. G., Cohen, I. L., Fisch, G. S., Hanson, D., Pfadt, A. G., Hagerman, R., Jenkins, E. C., and Brown, W. T. (1987). Speech–language and the fragile X syndrome: Initial findings and directions for study. *J. Am. Speech Hear. Assoc.* **29:**35–38.

Yu, S., Pritchard, M., Kremer, E., Lynch, M., Nancarrow, J., Baker, E., Holman, K., Mulley, J. C., Warren, S. T., Schlessinger, D., Sutherland, G. R., and Richards, R. I. (1991). Fragile X genotype characterized by an unstable region of DNA. *Science* **252:**1179–1181.

3

Hepatitis B Virus Biology and Pathogenesis

Francis V. Chisari
Department of Molecular and Experimental Medicine
Division of Experimental Pathology
The Scripps Research Institute
La Jolla, California

I. OVERVIEW OF THE PROBLEM

The hepatitis B virus (HBV) is a small, enveloped, hepatotropic DNA virus (hepadnavirus) that causes acute and chronic liver disease and leads to the development of hepatocellular carcinoma (HCC) (Ganem and Varmus, 1987). The virus may exist either as an episome, replicating by a process involving reverse transcription of an RNA pregenome, or as a linear DNA molecule randomly integrated into the chromosomal DNA of the host. The pathogenetic mechanisms responsible for hepatocellular injury and malignant transformation in this disease are not well understood.

Transmission of HBV occurs principally by percutaneous and sexual exposure; however, the most prevalent mode of transmission worldwide is from infected mother to child, during or shortly after birth. Infection of immunocompetent adults by HBV usually leads to an acute, self-limited hepatitis that resolves with clearance of the virus. Most neonatal infections, however, persist for life, thereby creating the reservoir for spread of the virus.

The HBV reservoir now exceeds 300 million people worldwide, nearly 5% of the global population. Because chronic HBV infection is associated with more than a 100-fold increase in the risk of a highly lethal malignancy (Beasley et al., 1981), this virus causes more deaths each year throughout the world than any other infectious agent, except for malaria. Ironically, the size of the reservoir is increasing despite the existence of an effective, but expensive, vaccine.

II. DISCOVERY OF THE VIRUS

Because of the magnitude of the problem of hepatitis B virus infection, HBV has gained the attention of a global network of investigators. In the mid-1960s, Blumberg and colleagues discovered the first serological marker of HBV, an envelope determinant of the virus, which they termed the Australia antigen (Blumberg, 1976) and which is now known as hepatitis B surface antigen (HBsAg). That seminal discovery spawned a plethora of studies that established HBV as a major causative agent of acute and chronic viral hepatitis, connected it epidemiologically to hepatocellular carcinoma, identified the groups at high risk of infection and the routes of transmission, and laid the foundation for structural analysis of the viral particles and the subsequent development of an effective vaccine.

A. Structure of the virus

By the early 1970s, ultrastructural studies had revealed the polymorphic nature of HBV particles (Figure 3.1A), which consist of abundant 22-nm spheres, somewhat less abundant 22-nm filaments of variable length, and rare 42-nm complex particles containing an outer envelope and an inner core (Dane particle) (Dane et al., 1970). Identification of these complex particles as the infectious virion was achieved in a series of classic experiments in the mid-1970s by Robinson and colleagues (Robinson and Greenman, 1974; Robinson, 1977; Robinson et al., 1974; Kaplan et al., 1973; Hruska et al., 1977; Landers et al., 1977), who demonstrated that the inner component of the Dane particle represents the viral nucleocapsid. They demonstrated that the viral core particle is

Figure 3.1. Hepatitis B virus morphogenesis. (A) Circulating HBV particles consist of noninfectious 22-nm-diameter spheres and filaments consisting exclusively of viral envelope polypeptides. Spheres consist of the major and middle polypeptides whereas filaments also contain the large envelope polypeptide. Infectious HBV particles (Dane particles) consist of an envelope containing all three polypeptides surrounding a nucleocapsid containing the viral core antigen, DNA polymerase protein, and a circular, partially double-stranded DNA genome. (B) Spherical and filamentous particles are formed by the insertion of envelope polypeptides into the membrane of the endoplasmic reticulum (ER), followed by budding into the ER lumen. High molar ratios of the large envelope polypeptide relative to the middle and major polypeptides cause the formation of long, nonsecretable filamentous particles that accumulate within the cell. The pre-S region is designated p(S). (C) Presumptive interactions between nucleocapsid and envelope polypeptides lead to the formation of Dane particles at the ER membrane, with invagination and budding into the lumen and secretion via the Golgi apparatus. The viral precore nucleocapsid protein is directly translocated into the ER lumen, where it is processed and secreted as hepatitis Be antigen. RT, Reverse transcriptase.

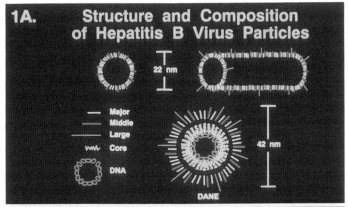

1A. Structure and Composition of Hepatitis B Virus Particles

22 nm

42 nm

— Major
— Middle
≡ Large
⌇ Core
⊚ DNA

DANE

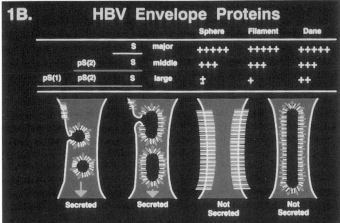

1B. HBV Envelope Proteins

				Sphere	Filament	Dane
		S	major	+++++	+++++	+++++
	pS(2)	S	middle	+++	+++	+++
pS(1)	pS(2)	S	large	±	+	++

Secreted | Secreted | Not Secreted | Not Secreted

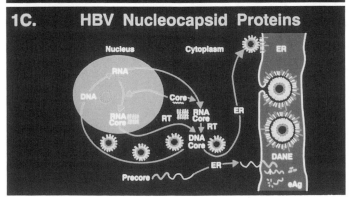

1C. HBV Nucleocapsid Proteins

Nucleus | Cytoplasm | ER

RNA

DNA

Core

RNA Core

RT | RNA Core

RT

DNA Core

ER

DANE

Precore

ER

eAg

itself quite complex, consisting of a 21-kD phosphoprotein termed hepatitis B core antigen (HBcAg), an endogenous DNA polymerase activity, and its template and product, both of which are also present within the viral core particles.

B. Structure of the viral genome

The structure of the viral genome was established in an elegant series of studies by Robinson and Summers and their colleagues (Robinson and Greenman, 1974; Robinson, 1977; Robinson et al., 1974; Kaplan et al., 1973; Hruska et al., 1977; Landers et al., 1977; Summers et al., 1975) in the middle to late 1970s. It was shown to be a small, relaxed, circular DNA molecule approximately 3200 nucleotides in length (Figure 3.2). Further, it was shown that the two DNA strands are unequal in length. The long (minus) strand is complete whereas the complementary (plus) strand is incomplete; its 5' end is fixed whereas the location of the 3' end is variable, creating a single-stranded gap that is repaired during the endogenous DNA polymerase reaction described above. A short cohesive overlap region at the 5' ends of the two strands is responsible for maintenance of the circular structure of the genome (Sattler and Robinson, 1979). Thus, it appears that the viral genome is packaged and exported from the infected cell before plus strand DNA synthesis is complete, yielding a partially duplex genome that is fully circularized only upon its entry into a newly infected cell, where the deoxynucleotides needed for completion of elongation of the plus strand are to be found.

Based upon these early discoveries, three critical developments occurred between the late 1970s and mid-1980s, providing unprecedented insight into the nature of the virus and laying the foundation for much of the exciting work that is currently underway in many laboratories throughout the world: first, the discovery of other members of the hepadnavirus family that infect other species; second, the cloning and sequencing of the hepadnaviral genome; and third, the elucidation of the replication strategy of HBV. These developments and selected highlights of the work that they spawned will now be discussed.

C. Hepadnaviruses of other species

Using the endogenous polymerase reaction coupled with agarose gel electrophoresis and autoradiography, Summers and his associates (1978) discovered the woodchuck hepatitis virus (WHV) in 1977 in a colony of marmots maintained in the Philadelphia zoo; these marmots had a high incidence of chronic hepatitis and HCC. Using a similar approach, Mason et al. (1980) and Marion et al. (1980) discovered the duck hepatitis B virus (DHBV) and the ground squirrel hepatitis virus (GSHV), respectively, and subsequently related viruses have been reported in the heron (Sprengel et al., 1988) and the tree squirrel (Feitelson et

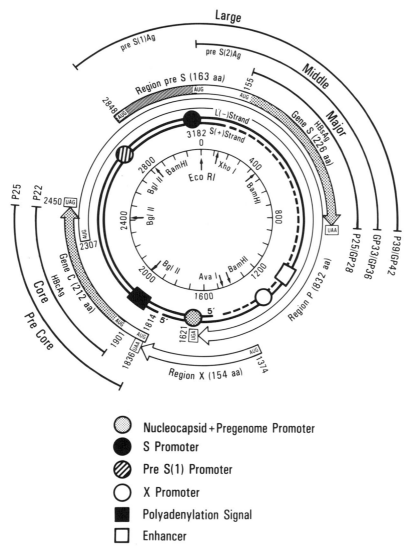

Nucleocapsid + Pregenome Promoter
S Promoter
Pre S(1) Promoter
X Promoter
Polyadenylation Signal
Enhancer

Figure 3.2. Map showing structure and organization of the HBV genome.

al., 1986). In terms of the genetic organization, tissue distribution, and expression of their genomes, and the natural history of the associated liver diseases, WHV and GSHV closely resemble HBV, whereas the avian hepadnavirus is more distantly related.

The existence of these animal models created the opportunity to directly investigate issues that are only indirectly approachable in humans. For example, Summers and Mason (1982) used the DHBV system to establish the replication strategy of hepadnaviruses (see below). Using the woodchuck model, Gerin and Tennant and their colleagues (Popper *et al.*, 1987) demonstrated the rapid development of HCC in chronically infected woodchucks, especially those experimentally infected at birth in captivity, corroborating the oncogenic potential of chronic HBV infection in humans. Importantly, chronically infected ground squirrels also develop HCC at high frequency (Marion *et al.*, 1986), and HCC develops in infected ducks as well (Omata *et al.*, 1987). More recently, Buendia and co-workers have demonstrated that insertional activation of the *myc* oncogene is a frequent occurrence in WHV-associated HCC (Fourel *et al.*, 1990; Hsu *et al.*, 1988; Moroy *et al.*, 1986), and that transgenic mice containing a cloned WHV integrant and flanking cellular sequences develop HCC. These fascinating results suggest, however, that the molecular pathogenesis of HCC may be somewhat different in the woodchuck and humans, because insertional activation of cellular protooncogenes appears to be an infrequent event in human hepatocellular carcinoma (Lee *et al.*, 1988).

These animal models have also been used to study the capacity of hepadnaviruses for extrahepatic replication. DHBV replication has been demonstrated in the spleen, kidney, pancreas, adrenal gland, and yolk sac (Halpern *et al.*, 1983, 1984; Jilbert *et al.*, 1987; Tagawa *et al.*, 1985), and a high level of extrahepatic WHV replication has been documented in the spleen and in mitogen-activated peripheral blood lymphocytes in chronically infected woodchucks (Korba *et al.*, 1987a,b, 1990) without apparent functional consequences. Although clearly establishing the existence of an extrahepatic life cycle for hepadnaviruses, which has been confirmed in human HBV infection (Yoffe *et al.*, 1990), the relevance of these fascinating observations to the biology and pathogenesis of hepadnavirus infection remains to be elucidated, because the functional consequences of viral replication in these tissues appear to be minimal.

III. GENETIC ORGANIZATION OF THE HBV GENOME

In the late 1970s and early 1980s several laboratories, including those of Murray (Pasek *et al.*, 1979), Rutter (Valenzuela *et al.*, 1980), Tiollais (Charnay *et al.*, 1979), Galibert *et al.*, (1979), Matsubara (Fujiyama *et al.*, 1983), Koike (Kobayashi and Koike, 1984), and Nishioka (Ono *et al.*, 1983), succeeded in the molecular cloning and analysis of the complete nucleotide sequence of HBV genomes derived from infectious virus particles. Comparison of these nucleotide sequences revealed an extraordinarily efficient organizational strategy that has permitted this smallest of genomes to become, at the same time, one of mankind's most successful parasites and one of its most deadly killers.

As previously reviewed (Chisari *et al.*, 1989a; Chisari, 1991), four promoter elements regulate expression of an equal number of HBV open reading frames (Figure 3.2). The nucleocapsid promoter encodes a greater-than-genome-length (3.5-kb) transcript that terminates at the single polyadenylation site in the HBV genome, which is located within the nucleocapsid open reading frame. Apparently the transcription apparatus ignores this transcription termination signal once in order to produce this transcript. In view of the importance of these transcripts and polypeptides in viral replication, this promoter is transcriptionally quite active in most HBV-infected tissue. Recent evidence suggests that elements within this promoter region exert a major influence on the tissue specificity of HBV gene expression (Yee, 1989) by virtue of their interaction with liver-specific transcription factors (Karpen et al., 1988; Yee, 1989; Honigwachs et al., 1989).

The 3.5-kb genomic RNA is heterogeneous at its 5' end. The longest constituent subspecies encode the viral precore polypeptide, and the shorter species serve as the RNA pregenome template for reverse transcription and production of DNA minus strands during viral replication (Summers and Mason, 1982; Rall et al., 1983; Buscher et al., 1985; Will et al., 1987); the shorter species also encode the viral core polypeptide and the viral polymerase (Enders et al., 1985, 1987; Ou et al., 1990). Recent evidence suggests that translation of the polymerase gene product is initiated by ribosomal entry at one or more internal AUGs within the 3.5-kb transcript, yielding two polypeptides with molecular masses of 90 and 70 kD (Jean-Jean et al., 1989; Bavand and Laub, 1988; Bavand et al., 1989; L-J. Chang et al., 1989; Schlicht et al., 1989). Additionally, a novel, apparently doubly spliced 2.2-kb HBV transcript detected in infected human liver may also serve to encode a truncated polymerase protein (Chen et al., 1989), although the functional capacity of this transcript has not yet been demonstrated.

The nucleocapsid open reading frame begins immediately downstream of this promoter. It contains two in-phase start codons that define two overlapping polypeptides. The shorter of these polypeptides (core, HBcAg) binds the viral RNA pregenome and assembles into viral core particles (Enders et al., 1987; Will et al., 1987; Junker-Niepmann et al., 1990; Birnbaum and Nassal, 1990) and, via nuclear translocation signals (Yeh et al., 1990; Eckhardt et al., 1991), apparently transports the replicating viral genome to the nucleus of the cell in the course of viral amplification. Its longer counterpart (precore) is a secreted, cytoplasmic, nuclear, and membrane protein (Ou et al., 1989; Schlicht and Schaller, 1989) that is not required for viral replication (C. Chang et al., 1987a). However, the highly conserved nature of the precore region suggests that it plays an important role in the viral life cycle. Based on considerable circumstantial clinical evidence, and an emerging immunological database, it is believed that a cellular immune response to the nucleocapsid antigens is an important factor in viral clearance in HBV infection (see below). Indeed, it has recently been recognized that during chronic HBV infection viral mutants occur that contain a translational stop codon within the precore region (Liang *et al.*, 1990; Takeda *et al.*, 1990; Tong *et al.*, 1990; Brunetto *et al.*, 1989), and it has been suggested that they are selected by virtue of their ability to escape cytolytic immunological pressure directed against nucleocapsid antigens in this disease.

The polymerase open reading frame overlaps all the others. It encodes a polyprotein that contains a 5' DNA-binding protein that is thought to serve as a primer for reverse transcription of the viral pregenome, as well as reverse transcriptase, DNA polymerase, and RNase H activities known to be essential for the multiple steps involved in viral genome replication (Mack *et al.*, 1988; Bosch *et al.*, 1988; Bavand and Laub, 1988; Bavand *et al.*, 1989; Schlicht *et al.*, 1989; Radziwill *et al.*, 1990). Recently, the polymerase gene product has also been shown to be structurally required for genomic RNA encapsidation within the viral nucleocapsid (Lavine *et al.*, 1989; Schlicht *et al.*, 1989; L.-J. Chang *et al.*, 1990; Hirsch *et al.*, 1990), and the encapsidation signal has been identified as a short sequence near the 5' end of the molecule (Junker-Niepmann *et al.*, 1990). Based on considerable experience in other viral systems (Gotch *et al.*, 1987; Bennink *et al.*, 1987), it is likely that a polymerase-specific T cell response occurs during HBV infection and that it may play an important role in viral clearance, although this remains speculative at present. However, antibodies to polymerase determinants have been detected in infected individuals (Feitelson *et al.*, 1988; Weimer *et al.*, 1989; Yuki *et al.*, 1990), attesting to their immunogenicity, at least at the B cell level, in man.

Two independent promoters control envelope gene expression. The pre-S promoter contains a canonical TATA sequence located just upstream of the first translational start codon in the envelope region, and it encodes a 2.4-kb transcript from which the large envelope polypeptide is produced. Transcription initiation from this promoter occurs preferentially in differentiated hepatoma cells by a process that appears to be regulated by the interaction of promoter sequences with a liver-specific transcription factor, hepatocyte nuclear factor 1 (HNF-1) (H. K. Chang and Ting, 1989; Raney *et al.*, 1990). This promoter is relatively silent transcriptionally in comparison with the core and S promoters (Buscher *et al.*, 1985; Ou and Rutter, 1985; Siddiqui *et al.*, 1986; Will *et al.*, 1987). Indeed, recent studies indicate that elements within the S promoter exert a strong negative influence on the activity of the pre-S promoter, such that deletion of these sequences results in a substantial enhancement of pre-S promoter activity. (Bulla and Siddiqui, 1988). The tight regulation of this promoter is not surprising because it appears to be critical for the morphogenesis of the complete HBV virion and in view of the structural and pathological consequences of its overproduction (see below).

The transcriptionally very active S promoter encodes a 2.1-kb transcript that, by virtue of microheterogeneity at its 5' end, controls production of the middle and major envelope polypeptides, both of which are integral components of the viral envelope. This promoter is located internally within the envelope-coding region just upstream of the translation start site of the middle envelope polypeptide (Rall et al., 1983; Enders et al., 1985, 1987; De-Medina et al., 1988; Raney et al., 1989). Important regulatory sequences that bind several nuclear transcription factors have been mapped just upstream of the transcription start sites of this promoter using cloned HBV genomes of the *ayw* (Raney et al., 1989) and *adw2* (De-Medina et al., 1988) subtypes. Interestingly, the identified functional and structural differences in these elements suggest that these two subtypes of HBV may have evolved sufficiently independently to display different regulatory mechanisms.

The envelope open reading frame contains three in-phase translation start codons that define the amino termini of three overlapping polypeptides, the expression of which is transcriptionally regulated (see above). The shortest envelope polypeptide, designated "major" based on its relative abundance, contains the group (a) and subtype (d/y, w/r) determinants of the hepatitis B surface antigen. It represents the dominant constituent in all currently available HBV vaccines. The middle envelope polypeptide contains the entire amino acid sequence and antigenic determinants of the major envelope polypeptide plus an extra 55 N-terminal amino acids containing the pre-S(2) antigen. The large envelope polypeptide contains the entire middle polypeptide plus an additional 108–119 N-terminal amino acids (depending on subtype) containing the pre-S(1) antigen. The two pre-S antigens are highly immunogenic neutralization epitopes at the B cell and T cell level in experimental animals (Milich, 1987) and in humans (Ferrari et al., 1989), and efforts are being made to incorporate one or both of these domains into the next generation of vaccines.

Like the pre-S promoter, the X gene promoter appears to be transcriptionally quite silent *in vivo*, because X-specific transcripts usually represent less than 1% of the total viral RNA in the infected liver (Kaneko and Miller, 1988). Alternatively, X-specific transcripts could be unstable in the naturally infected liver, because in some experimental systems the X promoter has been shown to be transcriptionally quite active (Raney et al., 1990; Treinin and Laub, 1987). Because the X open reading frame encodes a transcriptional trans-activating protein that positively regulates transcription from HBV and other viral and cellular promoters (Twu and Schloemer, 1987; Spandau and Lee, 1988; Seto et al., 1988; Twu et al., 1989; Colgrove et al., 1989), it is quite possible that strict regulation of X gene expression might be required for the orderly replication of the virus and the normal homeostasis of the infected cell. Current data suggests that the X gene product can transactivate a broad assortment of promoters in many cell types and that it may operate in a fashion reminiscent of the adenovirus E1A transactivator, by influencing the transcription process in a general fashion rather than by directly binding target sequences (Colgrove et al.,

1989). Indeed, recent evidence from Robinson's group indicates that the X gene product is a novel serine/threonine protein kinase (Wu et al., 1990). Because of these properties it has been proposed that dysregulated expression of the X gene product may be involved in hepatocarcinogenesis in chronic HBV infection (Wollersheim et al., 1988).

An enhancer element is present between the envelope and X open reading frames; the enhancer increases the level of HBV promoter activity and viral replication in liver cells (Shaul et al., 1985; Tur-Kaspa et al., 1986; Roossinck et al., 1986; Karpen et al., 1988; Antonucci and Rutter, 1989), although recent evidence indicates that the enhancer is active in many other cell types as well (Vannice and Levinson, 1988) and that the liver specificity of HBV expression may be determined primarily by a regulatory element within the nucleocapsid promoter region (Yee, 1989). Recently, a second enhancer has been identified within the X gene (J. Wang et al., 1990; Yuh and Ting, 1990; Zhou and Yen, 1990). Both enhancers have been shown to bind or to contain binding sites for several general and liver-specific transcription factors such as NF-1, HNF-1, c/EBP, EBP-1, and EF-C (Roossinck et al., 1986; Karpen et al., 1988; Patel et al., 1989; Ostapchuk et al., 1989; Wang et al., 1990; Yuh and Ting, 1990; Zhou and Yen, 1990; Dikstein et al., 1990a,b). The enhancer element also displays glucocorticoid inducibility together with a glucocorticoid response element located elsewhere in the genome (Tur-Kaspa et al., 1986).

IV. VIRAL MORPHOGENESIS

The morphogenesis, transport, and secretion of viral envelope particles appear to involve a process in which newly formed envelope polypeptides are partially translocated across the endoplasmic reticulum (ER) membrane, where they become integral membrane proteins (Eble et al., 1986, 1987). Based on in vitro translation studies (Eble et al., 1986) a model has emerged wherein the membrane-bound envelope polypeptides form aggregates that bud into the lumen of the ER (Figure 3.1B) as viral and subviral spherical and filamentous particles (Eble et al., 1986, 1987). The viral polypeptides within these particles undergo glycosylation in the ER, where they remain until they are transported (presumably via transport vesicles) to the Golgi apparatus to undergo oligosaccharide processing (Patzer et al., 1984b) followed by rapid secretion by the cell. Based on this model it has been suggested that the rate-limiting step in viral particle secretion may be the transfer of particles from the ER to the Golgi apparatus (Patzer et al., 1984a,b). In the context of this model, events that prolong this rate-limiting step may lead to accumulation of viral particles within the cell. It has been observed that incorporation of the pre-S(1)-containing large envelope polypeptide into the ER membrane-bound aggregate, at a relatively high molar ratio with respect to the other envelope polypeptides, exerts major structural constraints on particle formation, leading to the formation of extremely long (over 1000 nm), branching filaments that became trapped in the dilated ER compartment of the hepatocyte; the filaments fail to be transported to the Golgi and are thus not secreted (Chisari *et al.*, 1987). These entrapped filaments appear to contribute to the morphological and ulstrastructural changes seen in "ground glass" hepatocytes found in chronic carriers (Stein *et al.*, 1972; Hadziyannis *et al.*, 1973; Gerber *et al.*, 1974a,b, 1975) and they may contribute to the death of the hepatocyte if intracellular HBsAg concentrations rise to very high levels, as seen in certain transgenic mice (Chisari *et al.*, 1987).

A. Viral replication and life cycle

While other investigators were delineating the structure and organization of the HBV genome, Summers and Mason focused on the mechanism responsible for HBV replication. In a series of seminal experiments, they demonstrated that the replication of HBV is unique among DNA viruses in that it involves reverse transcription of an RNA pregenome (Summers and Mason, 1982). Based on this observation and subsequent studies from several other laboratories (Summers and Mason, 1982; Mason *et al.*, 1982; Rosenthal *et al.*, 1983; Miller *et al.*, 1984a,b; Molnar-Kimber *et al.*, 1984; Seeger *et al.*, 1986; Lien *et al.*, 1986; Tuttleman *et al.*, 1986b; Will *et al.*, 1987), a model of the HBV life cycle within the hepatocyte has emerged (Robinson *et al.*, 1987).

As recently reviewed (Chisari *et al.*, 1989a; Chisari, 1991), following entry into susceptible cells (by a currently poorly defined mechanism), viral plus-strand DNA synthesis is completed and the processing and joining of minus and plus strands yields a covalently closed circular DNA molecule that reaches the nucleus, where it serves as the viral transcriptional template and is ultimately translated to produce the various viral gene products (Figure 3.3). The RNA pregenome is also transported to the cytoplasm, where, together with newly formed viral polymerase, it becomes encapsidated by the core protein to form immature core particles. Within these particles new DNA minus strands are synthesized by reverse transcription, which is initiated within the DR1 sequence, near the 3' end of the RNA template, utilizing a protein primer that is derived from the amino-terminal domain of the viral polymerase polyprotein. Newly formed DNA minus strands serve as the template for DNA plus-strand synthesis, which is initiated at the nucleotide adjoining the 3' end of DR2, near the 5' end of the minus strand. Plus-strand elongation past the 5' end of the minus strand, using the 3' end as a template, converts the linear DNA intermediates into a relaxed circular double-stranded molecule. Some of these core particles are transported back to the nucleus where the relaxed circular viral DNA is converted into covalently closed circular DNA, which effectively am-

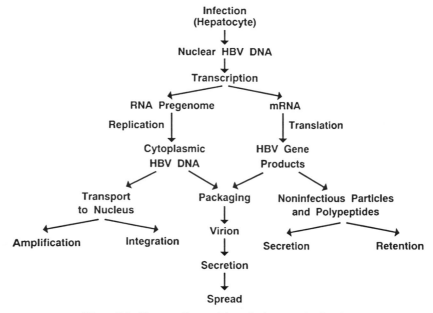

Figure 3.3. Hepatitis B virus life cycle (see text for details).

plifies the pool of HBV genomes within the cell (Tuttleman *et al.*, 1986a). Other core particles are packaged into viral envelopes and secreted (Figure 3.1C). After many such cycles (as might occur during chronic infection), the viral DNA may integrate into the host genome. Integration can be associated with extensive rearrangement of viral and host flanking sequences with attendant modulation of expression of viral and host genes (see below). The similarity between hepadnaviral and retroviral replication strategies, as well as striking homologies between conserved regions of hepadnaviral and retroviral genomes, have led to the suggestion that HBV and retroviruses may have a common evolutionary origin (Miller and Robinson, 1986).

B. Immunobiology of HBV and pathogenesis of liver cell injury

Much has been learned about the HBV structural antigens due to the production of recombinant envelope and nucleocapsid polypeptides in bacteria, yeast, mammalian, and insect cells and due to the availability of synthetic peptides derived from the nucleotide sequence of the HBV structural genes. As with other antigens, the envelope and nucleocapsid polypeptides contain domains (epitopes) that are recognized by antibody (B cell determinants) and other, sometimes overlapping, domains that are recognized by T cells (T cell determinants).

Starting in the early 1980s, extensive analysis of the immune response to the HBV structural polypeptides in mice by Milich and his colleagues, and in humans by Ferrari and his colleagues, and other groups, has led to development of several important insights into the immunogenicity and structural determinants of these antigens.

The envelope antigens are T cell dependent (Milich and Chisari, 1982; Milich et al., 1985a, 1986); i.e., production of antienvelope (HBs, pre-S) antibodies by immunization with the corresponding envelope polypeptides requires the presence of T cells capable of recognizing and responding to specific determinants within the envelope polypeptides. T cell recognition requires the presentation of these antigenic determinants to T cells by antigen-presenting cells (APCs) in association with gene products of the major histocompatibility complex (MHC; HLA in humans). Therefore a normal T cell-dependent response requires that an immunogen must contain T cell determinants that are appropriately processed by an APC (e.g., macrophage or B cell). It also requires that the host phenotype includes MHC polypeptides (restriction elements) capable of efficient intracellular binding of the T cell determinants and displaying them on the surface of the APC. It further requires that the T cell repertoire of the host includes functional T cell receptors that can bind to the antigen–MHC complex. If all these conditions are met, the antigen-activated T cell must then deliver positive regulatory signals to antigen-specific B cells that recognize conformational B cell determinants on native (not processed) antigen via B cell surface immunoglobulin receptors, if antibody formation is to occur. Superimposed on this model is the fact that not all T cell determinants are equal as immunogens. Indeed, with respect to the HBV envelope antigens, the pre-S region T cell determinants display enhanced immunogenicity with respect to the HBs region determinants (Milich et al., 1985b).

Because T cell-dependent immune responses are MHC restricted, it follows that the immune response to each of the three envelope antigens [HBs, pre-S(1), and pre-S(2)] varies according to the MHC phenotype of the recipient and is independently regulated at the T cell level (Milich and Chisari, 1982; Milich et al., 1985a, 1986). Consequently, HBsAg nonresponder mice that fail to mount an anti-HBs response following immunization with the major envelope polypeptide, due to the absence of MHC restriction elements required for T cell recognition of HBsAg, can be induced to produce anti-HBs by immunization with the middle or large envelope polypeptides via their independent recognition of the pre-S T cell determinants on these molecules (Milich et al., 1985b, 1986, 1987a; Milich, 1987). Based on the foregoing, it is likely that vaccines that include pre-S determinants may provide a greater degree of protection than those consisting of HBsAg alone, because they might reduce the number of

HBsAg nonresponders and they will induce responses to the pre-S antigens that are also highly represented on the infectious HBV virion. Indeed, immunization with a synthetic pre-S(2) peptide vaccine has been shown to be protective in chimpanzees (Itoh et al., 1986).

Recently, several groups have demonstrated the induction of HBV envelope-specific T cell proliferative responses at the clonal level in human HBsAg vaccine recipients and in a patient with chronic HBV infection (Jin et al., 1988; Celis et al., 1988; Ferrari et al., 1989; Barnaba et al., 1989). HBs-, pre-S2-, and pre-S(1)-specific T cell lines and clones derived from these vaccine recipients display MHC class I or class II restriction as well as the ability to recognize exogenous and endogenously synthesized antigen, and have been used to begin to map the fine specificity of the T cell response to these antigens in humans. The continuation of such studies in the context of the extensive database generated in the murine system should contribute significantly to a better understanding of the regulation, fine specificity, and biological significance of the envelope-specific immune response in vaccine recipients and during acute and chronic HBV infection.

The nucleocapsid antigens differ considerably from the envelope antigens in many respects. In particular, in inbred mice, hepatitis B core antigen is a T cell-independent as well as a T cell-dependent antigen, and the T cell response to HBcAg is quite strong (Milich and McLachlan, 1986). These observations help to explain why the anti-HB core response is much more vigorous than the anti-HBs response during natural infection in humans. Importantly, HBcAg-specific T cells can provide help for the induction of antienvelope antibodies in experimental animals (Milich et al., 1987b). This mechanism may be responsible for the protection against HBV infection observed after immunization of chimpanzees with HBcAg (Murray et al., 1987; Tabor and Gerety, 1984). In view of this phenomenon, as well as the superior immunogenicity of HBcAg T cell determinants, and the demonstrated carrier effect of HBcAg with respect to the response to other antigens (Milich et al., 1988; Clarke et al., 1987), it has been suggested that these properties of the core polypeptide or its T cell determinants might be exploited to enhance the immune response to HBV and possibly other viral vaccines in the future (Milich et al., 1988).

The T cell response to HBcAg is also quite vigorous during natural HBV infection in humans. Indeed, recent studies by Ferrari and colleagues (1990) have demonstrated a strong HBcAg-specific helper T cell response in the peripheral blood of patients with acute viral hepatitis, whereas patients with chronic hepatitis responded weakly or not at all. Additionally, they have shown (Ferrari et al., 1992) that the onset of this response corresponded temporally with clearance of virus markers from the circulation, suggesting a cause-and-effect relationship between these events. Importantly, fine specificity analysis revealed that over 95% of patients with acute hepatitis responded to a single antigenic determinant (epitope) located between residues 50 and 69 of the core molecule, irrespective of their HLA haplotype. These results may be highly significant in terms of development of therapeutic strategies for termination of chronic HBV infection and for the design of complex synthetic vaccines. If this epitope can be used to induce a strong HBcAg-specific T cell response in chronic carriers, one might anticipate that it would be followed by viral clearance in these patients, as is seen during acute infection. Similarly, if it can serve as a strong helper determinant for induction of an antienvelope antibody response, its inclusion in a complex HBc/HBenv synthetic vaccine might yield a more rapid and higher titer antienvelope response with fewer nonresponders than the current vaccines, which are based solely on the less immunogenic envelope antigens of the virus.

Obviously, no analysis of the immune response to HBV can be complete without consideration of the role played by the classical HLA class I-restricted, CD8$^+$, virus-specific cytotoxic T cell (CTL) in viral clearance and hepatocellular injury. Unfortunately, the experimental systems necessary for the precise identification and characterization of this response have not been available until recently; hence, little definitive information is available. Barnaba *et al.* (1990) have identified HBV envelope-specific, HLA class I-restricted CTLs in the liver of a patient with chronic active hepatitis. Although these studies clearly demonstrate the capacity of humans to produce a CD8$^+$ CTL response to HBV-encoded antigens, the pathogenetic implications of these observations are limited because of the small number of individuals studied and because of the technical requirement, faced by these investigators, to focus their attention at the clonal level, which precluded clinical correlation with disease activity.

The only experimental evidence of HBV-specific CTLs cytotoxic for infected liver cells is quite indirect. It derives from the pioneering observations of Mondelli and Eddleston and their colleagues (Mondelli *et al.*, 1982), who demonstrated that hepatocytes derived from liver biopsies of patients with chronic active hepatitis lose their adherence to plastic culture dishes when incubated in the presence of autologous peripheral blood T cells, and that this effect could be blocked by incubation of the hepatocytes with antibodies to HBcAg but not by antibodies to HBsAg. Clearly, less cumbersome methods must be developed to examine sequentially the polyclonal CTL response to HBV-encoded antigens in large numbers of patients in order to evaluate the potential importance of this response in HBV clearance and pathogenesis. Such studies are currently in progress in several laboratories, and this important aspect of HBV immunobiology should be forthcoming in the near future.

If clearance of infected hepatocytes is mediated by a virus-specific cytotoxic T lymphocyte response, it is imperative that immunogenic viral antigens be appropriately processed and displayed on the surface of infected hepatocytes in association with products of the major histocompatibility complex, and that they be recognized by corresponding T cell receptors on cytotoxic T cells. As discussed above, this has not yet been convincingly demonstrated in man; however, we have recently shown that HBV-specific, MHC class I-restricted cytotoxic T cells do cause liver cell injury when introduced into transgenic mice that express the homologous antigen in their hepatocytes (Moriyama *et al.*, 1990). The data indicate that endogenously synthesized HBV-encoded antigens can be expressed at the liver cell surface in a form that is recognized by classical virus-specific CTLs. These studies establish the scientific basis for the hypothesis that HBV-induced liver disease may be immunologically mediated.

Based on the foregoing results and on the natural history and clinical course of HBV infection, and precedent from other viral systems, a working hypothesis of HBV immunopathogenesis has emerged (Figure 3.4). According to this hypothesis, following infection of the hepatocyte, HBV particles and proteins are secreted into the blood, where they may be phagocytosed or otherwise internalized by antigen-presenting cells such as macrophages and B cells, within which they are processed and associate with MHC class II molecules and are delivered to the cell surface in a form that is recognizable by the T cell receptor of antigen-specific, CD4$^+$ helper T cells. These T cells proliferate and secrete various cytokines that provide help for the maturation and proliferation of antigen-specific B cells and cytotoxic T cells. Antigen-specific B cells bind antigen directly via surface immunoglobulin, which triggers the production of neutralizing antibody that contributes to clearance of circulating virus particles. CTLs recognize endogenously synthesized viral antigen present on the surface of infected hepatocytes in association with MHC class I molecules. This results in the destruction of infected cells, simultaneously causing liver cell injury and, if the response is adequate, viral clearance. It is thought that a suboptimal helper

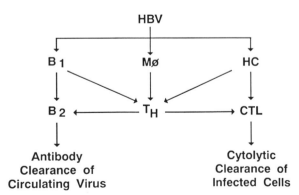

Figure 3.4. Hypothetical concept of hepatitis B virus immunopathogenesis (see text for details).

and cytotoxic T cell response may be responsible for failure to clear all infected cells, resulting in persistent infection and chronic liver disease. Although the foregoing hypothesis is fairly widely accepted, the component parameters have not been testable until very recently, so it should be considered speculative at present pending the outcome of studies currently underway in several laboratories here and abroad.

V. HEPATOCELLULAR CARCINOMA

The mechanism(s) responsible for malignant transformation in chronic HBV infection is (are) also incompletely defined. Because the interval between infection and hepatoma is usually several decades, it appears that HBV is neither directly nor acutely oncogenic.

Several independent but interrelated mechanisms have been identified as having the potential to contribute to hepatocarcinogenesis in chronic HBV. infection (Table 3.1). For example, analysis of the integrated viral and flanking sequences of a large number of human hepatomas reveals, in a few cases, that integration has occurred in the vicinity of genes associated with growth control and differentiation (retinoic acid receptor, cyclin A) (J. Wang *et al.*, 1990; de

Table 3.1. Mechanisms of Hepatocarcinogenesis in HBV Infection

Mechanism	Reference
Insertional activation of dominant oncogenes	
c-myc	Fourel *et al.* (1990)
Retinoic acid receptor	de Thé *et al.* (1987)
Cyclin A	J. Wang *et al.* (1990)
Inactivation of recessive oncogenes	
Loss of heterozygosity (1p, 4q, 11p, 13q, 16p, 17p)	Buetow *et al.* (1989), H. P. Wang and Rogler *et al.* (1988), Smith *et al.* (1986), Slagle *et al.* (1991), Simon *et al.* (1988)
Abnormal *p53* structure and expression	Hsu *et al.* (1991), Bressac *et al.* (1991), Slagle *et al.* (1991)
Viral trans-activation	
HBV X gene transgenic mice	Kim *et al.* (1991)
Truncated HBV *env* gene	Kekule *et al.* (1990)
Cellular response to chronic liver cell injury	
HBV *env* gene transgenic mice	Chisari *et al.* (1985, 1986, 1987)

Thé *et al.*, 1987). In the majority of cases of human HCC, such insertional events have not been identified. In the woodchuck model, however, insertional activation of c-*myc* and N-*myc* genes is a common event (Fourel *et al.*, 1990; Hsu *et al.*, 1988), suggesting that the mechanisms responsible for hepatocarcinogenesis in these two species may be quite different.

As recently reviewed by Chisari (1992), there is evidence that loss of antioncogene function may be operative in this process, because loss of heterozygosity at chromosomes 4q, 8q, 11p, 13q, 16p, and 17p appears to be quite common in HBV-induced HCC (Buetow *et al.*, 1989; H. P. Wang and Rogler, 1988; Smith *et al.*, 1986; Slagle *et al.*, 1991). More specifically, abnormalities of the structure and expression of the *p53* gene have been observed in several continuous HCC cell lines (Bressac *et al.*, 1990). Interestingly, point mutations in *p53* codon 249 have recently been identified in several cases of primary hepatocellular carcinoma from areas where HBV infection and aflatoxin exposure are common (Hsu *et al.*, 1991; Bressac *et al.*, 1991). The widespread chromosomal instability in HCC raises the possibility that DNA-damaging agents may be generated during chronic hepatitis, contributing to the process. The nature and identity of these putative events have not been established, nor have they been widely studied up to this point.

Despite the foregoing, the pathogenetic mechanisms responsible for liver cell injury and hepatocellular carcinoma in HBV infection have not yet been entirely elucidated. With the advent of embryo microinjection technology, however, it became evident that many questions relating to HBV pathogenesis, as well as more fundamental aspects of HBV biology and gene regulation, might be directly examined by introduction of partial or complete copies of the HBV genome into transgenic mice. In order to address these issues, several groups of investigators generated lineages of transgenic mice containing HBV sequences. The results of these studies will now be discussed, with particular emphasis on the insight they have yielded into mechanisms of viral pathogenesis.

A. Transgenic models of HBV gene expression and disease pathogenesis

Using constructs containing only HBV-derived regulatory sequences, Pourcel (Babinet *et al.*, 1985) and Burk *et al.* (1988) produced several lineages of transgenic mice that demonstrate preferential synthesis in the liver and kidney of the major and the middle envelope polypeptides of HBV. These results indicate that HBV contain cis-acting regulatory elements that are responsible for the predominant expression of HBV in the liver and kidney, and they help to explain the relative tissue specificity of the virus during natural infection. Subsequently, however, evidence from Pourcel (Farza *et al.*, 1988) and Yamamura (Araki *et al.*, 1989) suggested that other factors are also important determinants of the species and tissue specificities of HBV. Following microinjection of constructs capable of encoding the entire HBV RNA pregenome, they obtained evidence of HBV gene expression and DNA replication in liver, kidney, and heart. In conjunction with mounting evidence of extrahepatic virus expression in each of the hepadnavirus models (reviewed in Korba et al., 1986), these data strongly suggest that the relative liver specificity of HBV is a reflection of multiple constraints at the levels of viral entry, replication, and gene expression, and that none of these constraints is absolutely specific for the human hepatocyte.

One of the characteristics of HBV infection is its relative prevalence among males. Several groups (Farza et al., 1987; DeLoia et al., 1989) have shown that HBV envelope expression is much greater in male than in female transgenic mice, and that castration of both sexes causes a decline in expression that is reversible by administration of androgens or estrogens. Furthermore, Farza et al. (1987) and Chisari et al. (1986) have shown in transgenic mice that HBV gene expression is also regulated by glucocorticoids, as had been previously demonstrated in transfected cell lines (Tur-Kaspa et al., 1986). Thus, HBV gene expression is hormonally regulated in vivo. One might conclude from these data that the male prevalence of HBV infection in the natural setting is at least partially determined at this level.

Because the HBV X gene product displays transcriptional trans-activating properties (see above), it has been suggested that unregulated expression of this gene may contribute to the malignant transformation of the infected hepatocyte. In support of this hypothesis it appears that persistent expression of the HBV X gene may lead to HCC in transgenic mice (Kim et al., 1991). In contrast, however, Butel and colleagues (Lee et al., 1990) concluded that the X gene product is not tumorigenic in transgenic mice. Further studies will be needed to resolve this issue.

Our own studies (Chisari et al., 1985, 1986, 1987) have focused primarily on questions related to the pathogenesis of liver cell injury and malignant transformation. We have used constructs in which a subgenomic fragment containing the entire HBV envelope-coding region has been placed under the transcriptional control of relatively liver-specific regulatory elements that are either inducible (metallothionein; MT) or highly constitutively active (albumin; Alb) in the mouse (Chisari et al., 1985, 1986, 1987, 1989b; Dunsford et al., 1990). Normally, the HBV pre-S(1) promoter directs expression of the large envelope polypeptide, whereas an internal promoter in the pre-S(2) region directs expression of the middle and major polypeptides (see Figure 3.1). The internal promoter is present in our transgenic mice, but the endogenous pre-S(1) promoter has been replaced by the exogenous MT or Alb promoters (Chisari et al., 1986, 1987), therefore providing an opportunity to study the consequences of dysregulated HBV large envelope gene expression in this system. One lineage that contains the metallothionein–HBV envelope (MT–env) construct and 10 lineages that contain the albumin–HBV envelope (Alb–env) construct have been produced and characterized.

We have demonstrated that the large envelope polypeptide exerts significant structural constraints on HBsAg particle formation (Chisari et al., 1986, 1987). When the middle and major envelope polypeptides are produced in excess, they assemble into small (22-nm), spherical particles that are formed by internal budding into the lumen of the endoplasmic reticulum; these particles are readily secreted (Eble et al., 1987; Simon et al., 1988). When produced at a roughly equimolar ratio with respect to the other envelope polypeptides, the large envelope polypeptide prevents the formation of small spherical HBsAg particles and causes the formation of long, branching HBsAg filaments (containing all three envelope polypeptides), which become trapped in the endoplasmic reticulum of the hepatocyte, thereby inhibiting HBsAg secretion by the cell. This negative effect on secretion has also been observed by other investigators in cell culture systems (Standring et al., 1986; McLachlan et al., 1987; Cheng et al., 1986; Molnar-Kimber et al., 1988), but the structural basis for this effect was uniquely defined by the transgenic mouse model, which permitted expression in the primary hepatocyte, the normal target of HBV, in vivo.

During natural HBV infection, all three envelope polypeptides (large, middle, and major) are present on the surface of the relatively rare infectious virions and on short subviral filamentous forms present in the circulation (Heermann et al., 1984; Takahashi et al., 1986). In contrast, only the middle and major envelope polypeptides are present on the abundant subviral spherical forms, which represent over 90% of the circulating HBV-derived particles. This suggests that the large envelope polypeptide influences viral particle structure and secretion in some poorly defined fashion. From the experimental observations described above, it is conceivable that the structure and the relative rarity of complete virus particles in the circulation during HBV infection in humans may relate, at least partially, to their content of the large envelope polypeptide, which promotes retention of HBsAg within the hepatocyte.

We have shown that the progressive accumulation of large amounts of these subviral filamentous particles leads to a dramatic expansion of the endoplasmic reticulum of the hepatocyte (Chisari et al., 1987), eventually causing the ultrastructural and histologic changes characteristic of "ground glass" hepatocytes (Gerber et al., 1974a,b) that are observed in the liver of patients with chronic HBV infection and integrated HBV DNA. The similarities between human and transgenic mouse "ground glass" cells are so strong that it is likely that they share a common molecular pathogenesis. This raises the possibility that the "ground glass" cell merely represents one point on a continuous spectrum and that some of the pathological manifestations of HBV infection might be due to aberrant regulation of HBV gene expression, with overproduction of the large envelope polypeptide.

Along these lines, we have shown that prolonged storage of high concentrations of these long subviral filaments is directly cytotoxic to hepatocytes, initiating a lesion characterized by chronic hepatocellular necrosis and a secondary inflammatory and regenerative response in transgenic mice (Chisari et al., 1987). These data demonstrate that HBV has the potential to be directly cytotoxic to the hepatocyte under certain conditions and they raise the possibility that similar mechanisms might contribute to the pathogenesis of liver cell injury in natural infection. Although we do not understand the pathophysiological basis for the death of the hepatocyte in this model, it is possible that normal detoxification processes of the endoplasmic reticulum may be compromised.

In this model, severe, prolonged hepatocellular injury initiates a programmed response within the liver (Table 3.1), characterized by inflammation, Kupffer cell hyperplasia, hepatocellular regenerative hyperplasia, transcriptional deregulation, and aneuploidy, that inexorably progresses to HCC (Chisari et al., 1989b; Dunsford et al., 1990). Thus, the inappropriate expression of a single structural viral gene is sufficient to set in motion a complex series of events that ultimately lead to malignant transformation. The incidence of hepatocellular carcinoma in this model corresponds to the frequency, severity, and age of onset of liver cell injury, factors that correspond to the intrahepatic concentration of HBsAg and are influenced by genetic background and sex.

In view of the prolonged antecedent injury and regeneration, the early development of aneuploidy, and the altered transcriptional state (decreased HBsAg, increased alpha-fetoprotein, AFP) of the regenerating and transformed hepatocytes, it is likely that transformation occurs via a multistep process in our transgenic model. Because transformation was observed in two independent lineages, without evidence of transgene rearrangement or instability, direct insertional activation of a cellular oncogene is not likely. Rather, we suspect that it involves activating or inactivating mutations in multiple cellular genes that are spatially and functionally independent of the integrated HBV sequences.

To search for candidate cellular genes that might be so altered we have analyzed over 40 tumors to date for evidence of amplification and transcriptional activation of a representative panel of cellular oncogenes and antioncogenes (Pasquinelli et al., 1992). We have detected evidence of transcriptional activation of insulin-like growth factor-II (IGF-II) and mdr III gene expression in the majority of hepatomas, but not during the preneoplastic phase of the disease, suggesting that these represent late changes associated with tumor progression but not with tumor initiation in this model. The importance of these findings is underscored by the contrasting fact that we have detected no changes in p53 RB-1, Ha-ras, Ki-ras, N-ras, c-myc, N-myc, erb-A, erb-B, src, mos, abl, sis, fms, fes, fos, jun, TGF-α, TGF-β, PDGF-α, PDGF-β, EGF receptor, retinoic acid receptor-β, HNF-1, c/EBP, or CREB DNA copy number, gene structure, steady-state RNA levels, or protein content in any of the tumors. Obviously, the cellular genome is vast, as are the opportunities for growth-promoting mutations and chromosomal abnormalities outside of the loci we have examined thus far.

The pathogenetic importance of injury with respect to hepatocarcinogenesis is strengthened by the development of nodular regenerative activity and hepatocellular carcinoma in livers of transgenic mice sustaining neonatal hepatitis as a consequence of the hepatocellular retention of α_1-antitrypsin (Dycaico et al., 1988; J. Sorge, personal communication). Additional support for this hypothesis is the fact that human hepatocellular carcinoma occurs in the context of necrosis, inflammation, and regeneration (cirrhosis) in several diseases other than hepatitis B (Figure 3.5; Table 3.2), such as chronic non-A/non-B hepatitis (reviewed in Alter, 1988), alcoholism (Lieber et al., 1986), hemochromatosis (Niederau et al., 1985), glycogen storage disease (Limmer et al., 1988), α_1-antitrypsin deficiency (Carlson and Eriksson, 1985; Eriksson et al., 1986), and primary biliary cirrhosis (Melia et al., 1984).

It is likely that mutational activation of one or more dominant oncogenes, or mutational inactivation of one or more recessive oncogenes, or both, will ultimately prove to be the terminal events responsible for acquisition of the malignant phenotype in this model (and probably also in humans). We do not know, however, whether the presumptive increase in mutational frequency in our model is due solely to the increased number of cells at risk (i.e., regenerating hepatocytes) or whether there are enhanced levels of mutagens in the injured liver, or whether the capacity of the injured liver to inactivate the

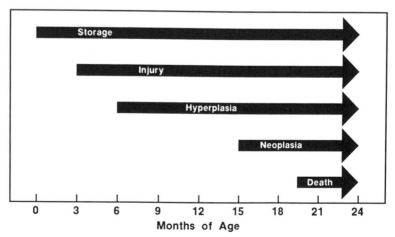

Figure 3.5. Summary of the natural history of liver disease in
          HBV envelope transgenic mice.

Table 3.2. Liver Cell Injury Precedes Hepatocellular
Carcinoma in Many Diseases

Injury	Reference
Chronic HBV infection	Beasley *et al.* (1981)
Chronic HCV infection	Alter *et al.* (1988)
Alcoholism	Lieber *et al.* (1986)
Hemochromatosis	Niederau *et al.* (1985)
Glycogen storage disease	Limmer *et al.* (1988)
Primary biliary cirrhosis	Melia *et al.* (1984)
α_1-Antitrypsin deficiency	Erikson *et al.* (1986)
	J. Sorge, personal communication

putative mutagens or to repair the ensuing DNA damage is compromised, or indeed whether all of these events are operational. The results suggest that severe, prolonged hepatocellular injury induces a preneoplastic proliferative and inflammatory response that places the dividing hepatocyte at risk of developing multiple random mutations or other chromosomal changes, including viral integration, some of which program the cell for unrestrained growth. In the current transgenic mouse model, injury is secondary to the overproduction of a viral gene product. Although this process may occur during viral infection, it is more likely that immunological mechanisms play a dominant role in humans. Irrespective of etiology or pathogenesis, however, we propose (Figure 3.6) that chronic liver cell injury is a premalignant condition that initiates a cascade of events characterized by increased rates of cellular DNA synthesis and production of endogenous mutagens coupled with compromised cellular detoxification and repair functions that eventually cooperate to increase the mutation rate to a level statistically compatible with the acquisition of the several independent mutations necessary to transform one or a few of the hepatocytes in the human liver.

The nature of the transforming mutations responsible for hepatocarcinogenesis in this model and in human chronic hepatitis is still poorly defined. It is clear, however, that the mutations must be multiple and that they may differ from tumor to tumor. In patients, viral DNA sequences frequently integrate into the host genome and occasionally they insertionally activate cellular growth control genes. Conceivably, mutational activation of viral trans-activating sequences may contribute to the process in isolated instances. It would appear, however, that genetic and chromosomal lesions such as point mutations, loss of heterozygosity, gene amplification, mitotic recombination, gene conversion, nondysjunction, etc. unrelated to the integrated viral genome are much more

HYPOTHESIS

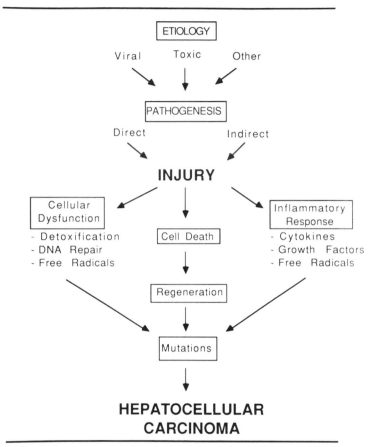

Figure 3.6. Hypothetical mechanism whereby severe chronic liver cell injury initiates a sequence of events that cooperate to transform the hepatocyte.

likely to contribute to hepatocarcinogenesis in the setting of human chronic hepatocellular injury.

B. Alternative model systems

One should not overlook the contribution made to our understanding of HBV biology by the introduction of viral DNA into susceptible cultured cells by transfection, by microinjection, or by infection using infectious recombinant viral vectors carrying HBV DNA sequences. Much has been learned using these systems with regard to the regulation of HBV gene expression (Spandau and Lee, 1988; Shaul et al., 1985; Tur-Kaspa et al., 1986; Treinin and Laub, 1987; H. K. Chang et al., 1987; Elfassi, 1987; Ganem and Varmus, 1987; Siddiqui et al., 1987; Tognoni et al., 1985) and particle structure, assembly, and transport (Ou et al., 1986; Roossinck et al., 1986; Uy et al., 1986; McLachlan et al., 1987; Schlicht et al., 1987; C. Chang et al., 1987a; Persing et al., 1986; Ou and Rutter, 1987; Molnar-Kimber et al., 1988; Cheng and Moss, 1987; Cheng et al., 1986; Marquardt et al., 1987; Moss et al., 1984; Standring et al., 1986; Yaginuma et al., 1987). Furthermore, among these systems are those that have opened the door for development of alternative vaccines (Heermann et al., 1984; Moss et al., 1984) and for production of immunological models to study the immunopathogenesis of HBV-induced liver cell injury in humans (McLachlan et al., 1987). Until recently, however, these in vitro systems did not support viral replication, thereby limiting their experimental value and restricting in vitro analysis of viral replication to the primary duck hepatocyte system described above (Tuttleman et al., 1986a,b). Because of the difficulties inherent in primary hepatocyte cell culture, it is not surprising that considerable effort was made to establish a system for viral replication in continuous cell lines.

Indeed, several laboratories have demonstrated that cloned, tandemly repeated, multimers of hepadnavirus genomes transfected into human hepatocellular carcinoma cell lines yield transformed cellular clones that support viral replication (Yaginuma et al., 1987; C. Chang et al., 1987b; Sells et al., 1987; Sureau et al., 1986; Tsurimoto et al., 1987) and produce complete HBV viral particles that are infectious in chimpanzees (Acs et al., 1987). The morphology, kinetics, and distribution of infectious HBV particles, subviral particles, and antigens can be examined using this system. Such studies also demonstrate the presence of HBV nucleocapsid as well as envelope antigens on the cell surface membrane, where they are in a position to be recognized by the immune system and possibly contribute to the pathogenesis of liver cell injury (Schlicht and Schaller, 1989; Michalak and Churchill, 1988). Additionally, although naked core particles are free in the cytoplasm and nucleoplasm, enveloped complete virions are located within cytoplasmic vesicles. This supports the emerging concept that the endoplasmic reticulum membrane forms an integral component of the viral envelope (Eble et al., 1986; Patzer et al., 1984a,b).

Importantly, the ability to establish a model of hepadnavirus replication by transfection of cloned viral genomes into continuous cell lines opens the door for several other lines of investigation. For example, by employing mutant viral genomes this new modality permits definitive identification of HBV DNA sequences essential for replication. Perhaps most importantly, a manipulable system is now at hand to evaluate the effect of candidate antiviral agents on HBV replication under controllable and reproducible *in vitro* conditions. The recent report by Petit's group (Bchini *et al.*, 1990) that HBV can infect HepG2 cells *in vitro* may represent a major advance in this area, especially if the conditions necessary for high-efficiency infection can be identified.

VI. FUTURE PROSPECTS, OPPORTUNITIES, AND CHALLENGES

The involved scientific community, collectively, has reason to be proud of the progress it has made toward an understanding of the structure, organization, expression, life cycle, pathogenesis, and immunological response to HBV and related hepadnaviruses since the discovery of the Australia antigen some 25 years ago. Nonetheless, there is much that remains to be done. A nonexclusive list of unfinished business and projects not yet begun should assure all of these investigators, and their students, that many interesting and important questions remain to be tackled.

A few examples should make the point. Virtually nothing is known about the early events involved in the attachment, entry, and intracellular trafficking of HBV within the hepatocyte, or other susceptible cells, or the cellular and viral structures and functions responsible for these processes. The three-dimensional structure of the viral envelope and nucleocapsid, and the functional correlates of these undiscovered structures, are entirely unexplored. The capacity of infected cells to actively abort viral gene expression and genome replication has not been touched despite provocative clinical evidence that such mechanisms probably exist. The functional domains of the viral polymerase protein, the mechanisms involved in viral transactivation, and the complex and dynamic interactions involved in viral particle assembly have barely been explored. The immunological determinants responsible for viral clearance are only beginning to be unraveled; hence, the physiological basis for viral persistence is entirely unknown (is it mediated by host factors, viral mutants, or both?). The molecular basis for malignant transformation is not understood, and many other interesting and important questions remain to be examined.

Two questions, however, remain paramount for all of us, irrespective of our scientific interests or orientation. First, how can we eradicate the virus from the 300,000,000 people alive today, who constitute its reservoir, or at least protect them from the late consequences of chronic HBV infection? Second, how can we protect the uninfected population, especially newborns, from becoming infected at all?

The answer to the first question will be difficult because of the complexity of the underlying science, because of the heterogeneity of the subjects at risk, and in no small way because of economic conditions that preclude the delivery of expensive medical care to indigent populations in Third World nations. The answer to the second question will be slightly easier because the scientific barriers have been largely overcome with the development of an effective vaccine. The economic questions remain, nonetheless, in this instance too. Until we find answers to these difficult socioeconomic and political questions, however, our efforts to understand the molecular genetics and biology of this fascinating and dangerous virus will stop short of the medical objectives we all should hope to achieve.

References

Acs, G., Sells, M. A., Purcell, R. H., Price, P., Engle, R., Shapiro, M., and Popper, H. (1987). Hepatitis B virus produced by transfected HepG2 cells causes hepatitis in chimpanzees. *Proc. Natl. Acad. Sci. U.S.A.* **84**:4641–4644.

Alter, H. J. (1988). Transfusion-associated non-A, non-B hepatitis: The first decade. In "Viral Hepatitis and Liver Disease" (A. J. Zuckerman, ed.), pp. 534–542. Alan R. Liss, New York.

Antonucci, T. K., and Rutter, W. J. (1989). Hepatitis B virus (HBV) promoters are regulated by the HBV enhancer in a tissue-specific manner. *J. Virol.* **63**:579–583.

Araki, K., Miyazaki, J.-I., Hino, O., Tomita, N., Chisaka, O., Matsubara, K., and Yamamura, K.-I. (1989). Expression and replication of hepatitis B virus genome in transgenic mice. *Proc. Natl. Acad. Sci. U.S.A.* **86**:207–211.

Babinet, C., Farza, H., Morello, D., Hadchouel, M., and Pourcel, C. (1985). Specific expression of hepatitis B surface antigen (HBsAg) in transgenic mice. *Science* **230**:1160–1163.

Barnaba, V., Franco, A., Alberti, A., Balsano, C., Benvenuto, R., and Balsano, F. (1989). Recognition of hepatitis B virus envelope proteins by liver-infiltrating T lymphocytes in chronic HBV infection. *J. Immunol.* **143**:2650–2655.

Barnaba, V., Franco, A., Alberti, A., Benvenuto, R., and Balsano, F. (1990). Selective killing of hepatitis B envelope antigen-specific B cells by class I-restricted, exogenous antigen-specific T lymphocytes. *Nature (London)* **345**:258–260.

Bavand, M. R., and Laub, O. (1988). Two proteins with reverse transcriptase activities associated with hepatitis B virus-like particles. *J. Virol.* **62**:626–628.

Bavand, M. R., Feitelson, M., and Laub, O. (1989). The hepatitis B virus-associated reverse transcriptase is encoded by the viral *pol* gene. *J. Virol.* **63**:1019–1021.

Bchini, R., Capel, F., Dauguet, C., Dubanchet, S., and Petit, M.-A. (1990). In vitro infection of human hepatoma (HepG2) cells with hepatitis B virus. *J. Virol.* **64**:3025–3032.

Beasley, R. P., Lin, C.-C., Hwan, L. Y., and Chen, C.-S. (1981). Hepatocellular carcinoma and hepatitis B virus. A prospective study of 22,707 men in Taiwan. *Lancet* **2**:1129–1132.

Bennink, J. R., Yewdell, J. W., Smith, G. L., and Moss, B. (1987). Anti-influenza virus cytotoxic T lymphocytes recognize the three viral polymerases and a nonstructural protein: Responsiveness to individual viral antigens is major histocompatibility complex controlled. *J. Virol.* **61**:1098–1102.

Birnbaum, F., and Nassal, M. (1990). Hepatitis B virus nucleocapsid assembly: Primary structure requirements in the core protein. *J. Virol.* **64**:3319–3330.

Blumberg, B. S. (1976). Australia antigen and the biology of hepatitis B. *Science* **197**:17–25.

Bosch, V., Bartenschlager, R., Radziwill, G., and Schaller, H. (1988). The duck hepatitis B virus P-gene codes for protein strongly associated with the 5'-end of the viral DNA minus strand. *Virology* **166**:475–485.

Bressac, B., Galvin, K. M., Liang, T. J., Isselbacher, K. J., Wands, J. R., and Ozturk, M. (1990). Abnormal structures and expression of p53 gene in human hepatocellular carcinoma. *Proc. Natl. Acad. Sci. U.S.A.* **87**:1973–1977.

Bressac, B., Kew, M., Wands, J., and Ozturk, M. (1991). Selective G to T mutations of p53 in hepatocellular carcinoma from southern Africa. *Nature (London)* **350**:429–431.

Brunetto, M. R., Stemler, M., Schodel, F., Will, H., Otttobrelli, A., Rizzetto, M., Berme, G., and Bonino, F. (1989). Identification of HBV variants which cannot produce precore derived HBeAg and may be responsible for severe hepatitis. *Scand. J. Gastroenterol.* **21**:151–154.

Buetow, K. H., Murray, J. C., Israel, J. L., London, W. T., Smith, M., Kew, M., Blanquet, V., Brechot, C., Redeker, A., and Govindarajah, S. (1989). Loss of heterozygosity suggests tumor suppressor gene responsible for primary hepatocellular carcinoma. *Proc. Natl. Acad. Sci. U.S.A.* **86**:8852–8856.

Bulla, G., and Siddiqui, A. (1988). Negative regulation of the hepatitis B virus pre-S1 promoter by internal DNA sequences. *In* "Abstracts of Papers Presented at the 1988 Meeting on Molecular Biology of Hepatitis B Virus," p. 64. University of California San Diego, La Jolla.

Burk, R. D., DeLoia, J. A., El-Awady, M. K., and Gearhart, J. D. (1988). Tissue preferential expression of hepatitis B virus (HBV) surface antigen gene in two lines of HBV transgenic mice. *J. Virol.* **62**:649–654.

Buscher, M., Reiser, W., Will, H., and Schaller, H. (1985). Transcripts and the putative RNA pregenome of duck hepatitis B virus: Implications for reverse transcription. *Cell (Cambridge, Mass.)* **40**:717–724.

Carlson, J., and Eriksson, S. (1985). Chronic "cryptogenic" liver disease and malignant hepatoma in intermediate alpha-1-antitrypsin deficiency identified by a pi z-specific monoclonal antibody. *Scand. J. Gastroenterol.* **20**:835–841.

Celis, E., Ou, D., and Otvos, L. (1988). Recognition of hepatitis B surface antigen by human T lymphocytes. Proliferative and cytotoxic responses to a major antigenic determinant defined by synthetic peptides. *J. Immunol.* **140**:1808–1815.

Chang, C., Enders, G., Sprengel, R., Peters, N., Varmus, H. E., and Ganem, D. (1987a). Expression of the precore region of an avian hepatitis virus is not required for viral replication. *J. Virol.* **61**:3322–3325.

Chang, C., Jeng, K.-S., Hu, C.-P., Lo, S. J., Su, T. S., Ting, L. P., Chou, C. K., Han, S. H., Pfaff, E., and Salfeld, J. (1987b). Production of hepatitis B virus *in vitro* by transient expression of cloned HBV DNA in a hepatoma cell line. *EMBO J.* **6**:675–680.

Chang, H.-K., and Ting, L. P. (1989). The surface gene promoter of the human hepatitis B virus displays a preference for differentiated hepatocytes. *Virology* **170**:176–183.

Chang, H.-K., Chou, C. K., Chang, C., Su, T. S., Hu, C., Yoshida, M., and Ting, L. P. (1987). The enhancer sequence of human hepatitis B virus can enhance the activity of its surface gene promoter. *Nucleic Acids Res.* **15**:2261–2268.

Chang, L.-J., Pryciak, P., Ganem, D., and Varmus, H. E. (1989). Biosynthesis of the reverse transcriptase of hepatitis B viruses involves *de novo* translational initiation not ribosomal frameshifting. *Nature (London)* **337**:364–368.

Chang, L.-J., Hirsch, R. C., Ganem, D., and Varmus, H. E. (1990). Effects of insertional and point mutations on the functions of the duck hepatitis B virus polymerase. *J. Virol.* **64**:5553–5558.

Charnay, P., Pourcel, C., Louise, A., Fritsch, A., and Tiollais, P. (1979). Cloning in *Escherichia coli* and physical structure of hepatitis B virion DNA. *Proc. Natl. Acad. Sci. U.S.A.* **76**:2222–2226.

Chen, P.-J., Chen, C.-R., Sung, J.-L., and Chen, D.-S. (1989). Identification of a doubly spliced viral transcript joining the separated domains for putative protease and reverse transcriptase of hepatitis B virus. *J. Virol.* **63**:4165–4171.

Cheng, K.-C., and Moss, B. (1987). Selective synthesis and secretion of particles composed of the hepatitis B virus middle surface protein directed by a recombinant vaccinia virus: Induction of antibodies to pre-S and S epitopes. *J. Virol.* **61:**1286–1290.

Cheng, K.-C., Smith, G. L., and Moss, B. (1986). Hepatitis B virus large surface protein is not secreted but is immunogenic when selectively expressed by recombinant vaccinia virus. *J. Virol.* **60:**337–344.

Chisari, F. V. (1991). Analysis of hepadnavirus gene expression, biology and pathogenesis in the transgenic mouse. *Curr. Top. Microbiol. Immunol.* **168:**85–101.

Chisari, F. V. (1992). Multistage hepatocarcinogenesis in hepatitis B virus transgenic mice. *In* "Origins of Human Cancer" (E. Harlow, J. Brugge, T. Curran, and F. McCormick, eds.). Cold Spring Harbor Lab., Cold Spring Harbor, New York (in press).

Chisari, F. V., Pinkert, C. A., Milich, D. R., Filippi, P., McLachlan, A., Palmiter, R. D., and Brinster, R. L. (1985). A transgenic mouse model of the chronic hepatitis B surface antigen carrier state. *Science* **230:**1157–1160.

Chisari, F. V., Filippi, P., McLachlan, A., Milich, D. R., Riggs, M., Lee, S., Palmiter, R. D., Pinkert, C. A., and Brinster, R. L. (1986). Expression of hepatitis B virus large envelope polypeptide inhibits hepatitis B surface antigen secretion in transgenic mice. *J. Virol.* **60:**880–887.

Chisari, F. V., Filippi, P., Buras, J., McLachlan, A., Popper, H., Pinkert, C. A., Palmiter, R. D., and Brinster, R. L. (1987). Structural and pathological effects of synthesis of hepatitis B virus large envelope polypeptide in transgenic mice. *Proc. Natl. Acad. Sci. U.S.A.* **84:**6909–6913.

Chisari, F. V., Ferrari, C., and Mondelli, M. U. (1989a). Hepatitis B virus structure and biology. *Microb. Pathog.* **6:**311–325.

Chisari, F. V., Klopchin, K., Moriyama, T., Pasquinelli, C., Dunsford, H. A., Sell, S., Pinkert, C. A., Brinster, R. L., and Palmiter, R. D. (1989b). Molecular pathogenesis of hepatocellular carcinoma in hepatitis B virus transgenic mice. *Cell (Cambridge, Mass.)* **59:**1145–1156.

Clarke, B. E., Newton, S. E., Carroll, A. R., Francis, M. J., Appleyard, G., Syred, A. D., Highfield, P. E., Rowlands, D. J., and Brown, F. (1987). Improved immunogenicity of a peptide epitope after fusion to hepatitis B core protein. *Nature (London)* **330:**381–384.

Colgrove, R., Simon, G., and Ganem, D. (1989). Transcriptional activation of homologous and heterologous genes by the hepatitis B virus X gene product in cells permissive for viral replication. *J. Virol.* **63:**4019–4026.

Dane, D. S., Cameron, C. H., and Briggs, M. (1970). Virus-like particles in serum of patients with Australia-antigen-associated hepatitis. *Lancet* **1:**695–698.

DeLoia, J. A., Burk, R. D., and Gearhart, J. D. (1989). Developmental regulation of hepatitis B surface antigen expression in two lines of hepatitis B virus transgenic mice. *J. Virol.* **63:**4069–4073.

De-Medina, T., Faktor, O., and Shaul, Y. (1988). The S promoter of hepatitis B virus is regulated by positive and negative elements. *Mol. Cell. Biol.* **8:**2449–2455.

de Thé, H., Marchio, A., Tiollais, P., and Dejean, A. (1987). A novel steroid thyroid hormone receptor-related gene inappropriately expressed in human hepatocellular carcinoma. *Nature (London)* **330:**667–670.

Dikstein, R., Faktor, O., Ben-Levy, R., and Shaul, Y. (1990a). Functional organization of the hepatitis B virus enhancer. *Mol. Cell. Biol.* **10:**3683–3689.

Dikstein, R., Faktor, O., and Shaul, Y. (1990b). Hierarchic and cooperative binding of the rat liver nuclear protein C/EBP at the hepatitis B virus enhancer. *Mol. Cell. Biol.* **10:**4427–4430.

Dunsford, H. A., Sell, S., and Chisari, F. V. (1990). Hepatocarcinogenesis due to chronic liver cell injury in hepatitis B virus transgenic mice. *Cancer Res.* **50:**3400–3407.

Dycaico, M. J., Grant, S. G. N., Felts, K., Nichols, W. S., Geller, S. A., Hager, J. H., Pollard,

A. J., Kohler, S. W., Short, H. P., Jirik, F. R., Hanahan, D., and Sorge, J. A. (1988). Neonatal hepatitis induced by alpha 1-antitrypsin: A transgenic mouse model. *Science* **242:**1409–1412.

Eble, B. E., Lingappa, V. R., and Ganem, D. (1986). Hepatitis B surface antigen: An unusual secreted protein initially synthesized as a transmembrane polypeptide. *Mol. Cell. Biol.* **6:**1454–1463.

Eble, B. E., MacRae, D. R., Lingappa, V. R., and Ganem, D. (1987). Multiple topogenic sequences determine the transmembrane orientation of hepatitis B surface antigen. *Mol. Cell. Biol.* **7:**3591–3601.

Eckhardt, S. G., Milich, D. R., and McLachlan, A. (1991). Hepatitis B virus core antigen has two nuclear localization sequences in the arginine-rich carboxyl terminus. *J. Virol.* **65:**575–582.

Elfassi, E. (1987). Broad specificity of the hepatitis B enhancer function. *Virology* **160:**259–262.

Enders, G. H., Ganem, D., and Varmus, H. (1985). Mapping the major transcripts of ground squirrel hepatitis virus: The presumptive template for reverse transcriptase is terminally redundant. *Cell (Cambridge, Mass.)* **42:**297–308.

Enders, G. H., Ganem, D., and Varmus, H. E. (1987). 5'-Terminal sequences influence the segregation of ground squirrel hepatitis virus RNAs into polyribosomes and viral core particles. *J. Virol.* **61:**35–41.

Eriksson, S., Carlson, J., and Velez, R. N. (1986). Risk of cirrhosis and primary liver cancer in alpha-1-antrypsin deficiency. *N. Engl. J. Med.* **314:**736–740.

Farza, H., Salmon, A. M., Hadchouel, M., Moreau, J. L., Babinet, C., Tiollais, P., and Pourcel, C. (1987). Hepatitis B surface antigen gene expression is regulated by sex steroids and glucocorticoids in transgenic mice. *Proc. Natl. Acad. Sci.U.S.A.* **84:**1187–1191.

Farza, H., Hadchouel, M., Scotto, J., Tiollais, P., Babinet, C., and Pourcel, C. (1988). Replication and gene expression of hepatitis B virus in a transgenic mouse that contains the complete viral genome. *J. Virol.* **62:**4144–4152.

Feitelson, M. A., Millman, I., Halbherr, T., Simmons, H., and Blumberg, B. S. (1986). A newly identified hepatitis B type virus in tree squirrels. *Proc. Natl. Acad. Sci. U.S.A.* **83:**2232–2237.

Feitelson, M. A., Millman, I., Duncan, G. D., and Blumberg, B. S. (1988). Presence of antibodies to the polymerase gene product(s) of hepatitis B and woodchuck hepatitis virus in natural and experimental infections. *J. Med. Virol.* **24:**121–136.

Ferrari, C., Penna, A., Bertoletti, A., Cavalli, A., Valli, A., Schianchi, C., and Fiaccadori, F. (1989). The preS1 antigen of hepatitis B virus is highly immunogenic at the T cell level in man. *J. Clin. Invest.* **84:**1314–1319.

Ferrari, C., Penna, A., Bertoletti, A., Valli, A., Antoni, A. D., Giuberti, T., Cavalli, A., Petit, M.-A., and Fiaccadori, F. (1990). Cellular immune response to hepatitis B virus-encoded antigens in acute and chronic hepatitis B virus infection. *J. Immunol.* **145:**3442–3449.

Ferrari, C., Bertoletti, A., Penna, A., Cavalli, A., Valli, A., Missale, G., Pilli, M., Fowler, P., Giuberti, T., Chisari, F. V., and Fiaccadori, F. (1991). Identification of immunodominant T cell epitopes of the hepatitis B virus nucleocapsid antigen. *J. Clin. Invest.* **88:** 214–222.

Fourel, G., Trepo, C., Bougueleret, L., Henglein, B., Ponzetto, A., Tiollais, P., and Buendia, M.-A. (1990). Frequent activation of N-*myc* genes by hepadnavirus insertion in woodchuck liver tumours. *Nature (London)* **347:**294–298.

Fujiyama, A., Miyanohara, A., Nozaki, C., Yoneyama, T., Ohtomo, N., and Matsubara, K. (1983). Cloning and structural analyses of hepatitis B virus DNAs, subtype adr. *Nucleic Acids Res.* **11:**4601–4610.

Galibert, F., Mandart, E., Fitoussi, F., Tiollais, P., and Charnay, P. (1979). Nucleotide sequence of the hepatitis B virus genome (subtype ayw) cloned in *E. coli. Nature (London)* **281:**646–650.

Ganem, D., and Varmus, H. E. (1987). The molecular biology of the hepatitis B virus. *Annu. Rev. Biochem.* **56:**651–693.

Gerber, M. A., Hadziyannis, S., Vissoulis, C., Schaffner, F., Paronetto, F., and Popper, H. (1974a).

Hepatitis B antigen: Nature and distribution of cytoplasmic antigen in hepatocytes of carriers (37912). *Proc. Soc. Exp. Biol. Med.* **145:**863–867.

Gerber, M. A., Hadziyannis, S., Vissoulis, C., Schaffner, F., Paronetto, F., and Popper, H. (1974b). Electron microscopy and immunoelectronmicroscopy of cytoplasmic hepatitis B antigen in hepatocytes. *Am. J. Pathol.* **75:**489–502.

Gerber, M. A., Hadziyannis, S., Vernace, S., and Vissoulis, C. (1975). Incidence and nature of cytoplasmic hepatitis B antigen in hepatocytes. *Lab. Invest.* **32:**251–256.

Gotch, F., McMichael, A., Smith, G., and Moss, B. (1987). Identification of viral molecules recognized by influenza-specific human cytotoxic T lymphocytes. *J. Exp. Med.* **165:**408–416.

Hadziyannis, S., Gerber, M. A., Vissoulis, C., and Popper, H. (1973). Cytoplasmic hepatitis B antigen in "ground glass" hepatocytes of carriers. *Arch. Pathol.* **96:**327–330.

Halpern, M. S., England, J. M., Deery, D. T., Petcu, D. J., Mason, W. S., and Molnar-Kimber, K. L. (1983). Viral nucleic acid synthesis and antigen accumulation in pancreas and kidney of Pekin ducks infected with duck hepatitis B virus. *Proc. Natl. Acad. Sci. U.S.A.* **80:**4865–4869.

Halpern, M. S., Egan, J., Mason, W. S., and England, J. M. (1984). Viral antigen in endocrine cells of the pancreatic islets and adrenal cortex of Pekin ducks infected with duck hepatitis B virus. *Virus Res.* **1:**213–223.

Heermann, K. H., Goldmann, U., Schwartz, W., Seyffarth, T., Baumgarten, H., and Gerlich, W. H. (1984). Large surface proteins of hepatitis B virus containing the pre-S sequence. *J. Virol.* **52:**396–402.

Hirsch, R. C., Lavine, J. E., Chang, L.-J., Varmus, H. E., and Ganem, D. (1990). Polymerase gene products of hepatitis B viruses are required for genomic RNA packaging as well as for reverse transcription. *Nature (London)* **344:**552–555.

Hirsch, R. C., Lavine, J. E., Chang, L.-J., Varmus, H. E., and Ganem, D. (1990). Polymerase gene products of hepatitis B viruses are required for genomic RNA packaging as well as for reverse transcription. *Nature (London)* **344:**552–555.

Honigwachs, J., Faktor, O., Dikstein, R., Shaul, Y., and Laub, O. (1989). Liver-specific expression of hepatitis B virus is determined by the combined action of the core gene promoter and the enhancer. *J. Virol.* **63:**919–924.

Hruska, J. F., Clayton, D. A., Rubenstein, J. L. R., and Robinson, W. S. (1977). Structure of hepatitis B Dane particle DNA before and after the Dane particle DNA polymerase reaction. *J. Virol.* **21:**666–672.

Hsu, I. C., Metcalf, R. A., Sun, T., Welsh, J. A., Wang, N. J., and Harris, C. C. (1991). Mutational hotspot in the p53 gene in human hepatocellular carcinomas. *Nature (London)* **350:**427–428.

Hsu, T-Y., Moroy, T., Etiemble, J., Louise, A., Trepo, C., Tiollais, P., and Buendia, M.-A. (1988). Activation of c-myc by woodchuck hepatitis virus insertion in hepatocellular carcinoma. *Cell (Cambridge, Mass.)* **55:**627–635.

Itoh, Y., Takai, E., Ohnuma, H., Kitajima, K., Tsuba, F., Machida, A., Mishiro, S., Nakamura, T., Miyakawa, Y., and Mayumi, M. (1986). A synthetic peptide vaccine involving the product of the pre-S(2) region of the hepatitis B virus DNA: Protective efficacy in chimpanzees. *Proc. Natl. Acad. Sci. U.S.A.* **83:**9174–9178.

Jean-Jean, O., Weimer, T., de Recondo, A.-M., Will, H., and Rossignol, J.-M. (1989). Internal entry of ribosomes and ribosomal scanning involved in hepatitis B virus P gene expression. *J. Virol.* **63:**5451–5454.

Jilbert, A. R., Freiman, J. S., Gowans, E. J., Holmes, M., Cossart, Y. E., and Burrell, C. J. (1987). Duck hepatitis B virus DNA in liver, spleen and pancreas. Analysis by *in situ* and Southern blot hybridization. *Virology* **158:**330–338.

Jin, Y., Shih, J. W.-K., and Berkower, I. (1988). Human T cell response to the surface antigen of hepatitis B virus (HBsAg). *J. Exp. Med.* **168:**293–306.

Junker-Niepmann, M., Bartenschlager, R., and Schaller, H. (1990). A short cis-acting sequence is required for HBV pregenome encapsidation and sufficient for packaging of foreign DNA. *EMBO J.* **9:**3389–3396.

Kaneko, S., and Miller, R. H. (1988). X-Region-specific transcript in mammalian hepatitis B virus-infected liver. *J. Virol.* **62:**3979–3984.

Kaplan, P. M., Greenman, R. L., Gerin, J. L., Purcell, R. J., and Robinson, W. S. (1973). DNA polymerase associated with human hepatitis B antigen. *J. Virol.* **12:**995–1005.

Karpen, S., Banerjee, R., Zelent, A., Price, P., and Acs, G. (1988). Identification of protein-binding sites in the hepatitis B virus enhancer and core promoter domains. *Mol. Cell. Biol.* **8:**5159–5165.

Kekule, A., Lauer, U., Meyer, M., Caselmann, W. H., Hufschneider, P. H., and Koshy, R. (1990). The pre S 2/5 region of integrated hepatitis B virus DNA encodes a transcriptional transactivator. *Nature (London)* **343:**457–461.

Kim, C.-M., Koike, K. Saito, I., Miyamura, T., and Jay, G. (1991). HBx gene of hepatitis B virus induces liver cancer in transgenic mice. *Nature (London)* **351:**317–320.

Kobayashi, M., and Koike, K. (1984). Complete nucleotide sequence of hepatitis B virus DNA of subtype *adr* an its conserved gene organization. *Gene* **30:**227–232.

Korba, B. E., Wells, F., Tennant, B. C., Yoakum, G. H., Purcell, R. H., and Gerin, J. L. (1986). Hepadnavirus infection of peripheral blood lymphocytes *in vivo:* Woodchuck and chimpanzee models of viral hepatitis. *J. Virol.* **58:**1–8.

Korba, B. E., Tennant, B. C., Gowans, E., Cote, P. J., Wells, F., Baldwin, B., and Gerin, J. L. (1987a). Infection and tissue tropism of WHV during the natural course of viral infection of woodchucks. *In* "Hepadnaviruses" (W. Robinson, K. Koike, and H. Will, eds.), pp. 419–428. Alan R. Liss, New York.

Korba, B. E., Wells, F., Tennant, B. C., Cote, P. J., and Gerin, J. L. (1987b). Lymphoid cells in the spleens of woodchuck hepatitis virus-infected woodchucks are a site of active viral replication. *J. Virol.* **61:**1318–1324.

Korba, B. E., Brown, T. L., Wells, F. V., Baldwin, B., Cote, P. J., Steinberg, H., Tennant, B. C., and Gerin, J. L. (1990). Natural history of experimental woodchuck hepatitis virus infection: Molecular virologic features of the pancreas, kidney, ovary, testis. *J. Virol.* **64:**4499–4506.

Landers, T. A., Greenberg, H. B., and Robinson, W. S. (1977). Structure of hepatitis B Dane particle DNA and nature of the endogenous DNA polymerase reaction. *J. Virol.* **23:**368–376.

Lavine, J., Hirsch, R., and Ganem, D. (1989). A system for studying the selective encapsidation of hepadnavirus FNA. *J. Virol.* **63:**4257–4263.

Lee, H.-S., Rajagopalan, M. S., and Vyas, G. N. (1988). A lack of direct role of hepatitis B virus in the activation of *ras* and c-*myc* oncogenes in human hepatocellular carcinogenesis. *Hepatology* **8:**1116–1120.

Lee, T.-H., Finegold, M. J., Shen, R.-F., DeMayo, J. L., Woo, S. L., and Butel, J. S. (1990). Hepatitis B virus transactivator X protein is not tumorigenic in transgenic mice. *J. Virol.* **64:**5939–5947.

Liang, T. J., Blum, H. E., and Wands, J. R. (1990). Characterization and biological properties of a hepatitis B virus isolated from a patient without hepatitis B virus serologic markers. *Hepatology* **12:**204–212.

Lieber, C. S., Garro, A., Leo, M. A., Mak, K. M., and Worner, T. (1986). Alcohol and cancer. *Hepatology* **6:**1005–1019.

Lien, J.-M., Aldrich, C. E., and Mason, W. S. (1986). Evidence that a capped oligoribonucleotide is the primer for duck hepatitis B virus plus-strand DNA synthesis. *J. Virol.* **57:**229–236.

Limmer, J., Fleig, W. E., Leupold, D., Bittner, R., Ditschuneit, H., and Beger, H.-G. (1988). Hepatocellular carcinoma in type I glycogen storage disease. *Hepatology* **8:**531–537.

Mack, D. H., Bloch, W., Nath, N., and Sninsky, J. J. (1988). Hepatitis B virus particles contain a polypeptide encoded by the largest open reading frame: A putative reverse transcriptase. *J. Virol.* **62**:4786–4790.

Marion, P. L., Oshiro, L. S., Regnery, D. S., Scullard, G. H., and Robinson, W. S. (1980). A virus in Beechey ground squirrels which is related to hepatitis B virus of man. *Proc. Natl. Acad. Sci. U.S.A.* **77**:2941–2945.

Marion, P. L., Van Davelaar, M. J., Knight, S. S., Salazar, F. H., Garcia, G., Popper, H., and Robinson, W. S. (1986). Hepatocellular carcinoma in ground squirrels persistently infected with ground squirrel hepatitis virus. *Proc. Natl. Acad. Sci. U.S.A.* **83**:4543–4546.

Marquardt, O., Heermann, K. H., Seifer, M., and Gerlich, W. H. (1987). Cell type specific expression of pre S 1 antigen and secretion of hepatitis B virus surface antigen. Brief report. *Arch. Virol. (Chicago)* **96**:249–256.

Mason, W. S., Seal, S., and Summers, J. (1980). Virus of Pekin ducks with structural and biological relatedness to human hepatitis B virus. *Proc. Natl. Acad. Sci. U.S.A.* **36**:829–836.

Mason, W. S., Aldrich, C., Summers, J., and Taylor, J. M. (1982). Asymmetric replication of duck hepatitis B virus DNA in liver cells (free minus-strand DNA). *Proc. Natl. Acad. Sci. U.S.A.* **79**:3997–4001.

McLachlan, A., Milich, D. R., Raney, A. K., Riggs, M. G., Hughes, J. L., Sorge, J., and Chisari, F. V. (1987). Expression of hepatitis B virus surface and core antigens: Influences of pre-S and precore sequences. *J. Virol.* **61**:683–692.

Melia, W. M., Johnson, P. J., and Neuberger, J. (1984). Hepatocellular carcinoma in primary biliary cirrhosis: Detection of α-fetoprotein estimation. *Gastroenterology* **87**:660–663.

Michalak, T. I., and Churchill, N. D. (1988). Interaction of woodchuck hepatitis virus surface antigen with hepatocyte plasma membrane in woodchuck chronic hepatitis. *Hepatology* **8**:499–506.

Milich, D. R. (1987). Immunological responses to pre-S antigens of the hepatitis B virus. *Viral Immunol.* **1**:83–96.

Milich, D. R., and Chisari, F. V. (1982). Genetic regulation of the immune response to hepatitis B surface antigen (HBsAg). I. H-2 regulation of the murine humoral immune response to the a and d determinants of HBsAg. *J. Immunol.* **129**:320–420.

Milich, D. R., and McLachlan, A. (1986). The nucleocapsid of hepatitis B virus is both a T-cell-independent and a T-cell dependent antigen. *Science* **234**:1398–1401.

Milich, D. R., McNamara, M., McLachlan, A., Thornton, G., and Chisari, F. V. (1985a). Distinct H-2-linked regulation of T cell responses to the pre-S and S regions of the same HBsAg polypeptide allows circumvention of S region non-responsiveness. *Proc. Natl. Acad. Sci. U.S.A.* **82**:8168–8172.

Milich, D. R., Thornton, G. B., Neurath, A., Kent, S., Michel, M., Tiollais, P., and Chisari, F. V. (1985b). Enhanced immunogenicity of the pre-s region of hepatitis B surface anigen. *Science* **228**:1195–1199.

Milich, D. R., McLachlan, A., Chisari, F. V., Kent, S. B. H., and Thornton, G. B. (1986). Immune response to the pre-S(1) region of the hepatitis B surface anigen (HBsAg): A pre-S(1)-specific T cell response can bypass nonresponsiveness to the pre-S(2) and s regions of the HBsAg. *J. Immunol.* **137**:315–322.

Milich, D. R., McLachlan, A., Moriatry, A., Thornton, G., and Chisari, F. V. (1987a). A single 10-residue pre-s(1) peptide can prime T cell help for antibody production to multiple epitopes within the pre-S(1), pre-S(2) and S regions of HBsAg. *J. Immunol.* **138**:4457–4465.

Milich, D. R., McLachlan, A., Thornton, G. B., and Hughes, J. L. (1987b). Antibody production to the nucleocapsid and envelope of the hepatitis B virus primed by a single synthetic T cell site. *Nature (London)* **329**:547–549.

Milich, D. R., Hughes, J. L., McLachlan, A., Thornton, G. B., and Moriarty, A. (1988). Hepatitis

B synthetic immunogen comprised of nucleocapsid T-cell sites and an envelope B-cell epitope. *Proc. Natl. Acad. Sci. U.S.A.* **85:**1610–1614.

Miller, R. H., and Robinson, W. S. (1986). Common evolutionary origin of hepatitis B virus and retroviruses. *Proc. Natl. Acad. Sci. U.S.A.* **83:**2531–2535.

Miller, R. H., Tran, C.-T., and Robinson, W. S. (1984a). Hepatitis B virus particles of plasma and liver contain viral DNA–RNA hybrid molecules. *Virology* **139:**53–63.

Miller, R. H., Marion, P. L., and Robinson, W. S. (1984b). Hepatitis B viral DNA–RNA hybrid molecules in particles from infected liver are converted to viral DNA molecules during an endogenous DNA polymerase reaction. *Virology* **139:**64–72.

Molnar-Kimber, K. L., Summers, J. W., and Mason, W. S. (1984). Mapping of the cohesive overlap of duck hepatitis B virus DNA and of the site of initiation of reverse transcription. *J. Virol.* **51:**181–191.

Molnar-Kimber, K. L., Jarocki-Witek, V., Dheer, S. K., Vernon, S. K., Conley, A. J., Davis, A. R., and Hung, P. P. (1988). Distinctive properties of the hepatitis B virus envelope proteins. *J. Virol.* **62:**407–416.

Mondelli, M., Mieli-Vergani, G., Alberti, A., Vergani, D., Portmann, B., Eddleston, A. L., and Williams, R. (1982). Specificity of T lymphocyte cytotoxicity to autologous hepatocytes in chronic hepatitis B virus infection: Evidence that T cells are directed against HBV core antigen expressed on hepatocytes. *J. Immunol.* **129:**2773–2778.

Moriyama, T., Guilhot, S., Moss, B., Pinkert, C. A., Palmiter, R. D., Brinster, R. L., Klopchin, K., and Chisari, F. V. (1990). Immunobiology and pathogenesis of hepatocellular injury in hepatitis B virus transgenic mice. *Science* **248:**361–364.

Moroy, T., Marchio, A., Etiemble, J., Trepo, C., Tiollais, P., and Buendia, M.-A. (1986). Rearrangement and enhanced expression of c-myc in hepatocellular carcinoma of hepatitis virus infected woodchucks. *Nature (London)* **324:**276–279.

Moss, B., Smith, G. L., Geriin, J. L., and Purcell, R. H. (1984). Live recombinant vaccina virus protects chimpanzees against hepatitis B. *Nature (London)* **301:**490–495.

Murray, K., Bruce, S. A., Wingfield, P., van Eerd, P., de Reus, A., and Schellekens, H. (1987). Protective immunization against hepatitis B with an internal antigen of the virus. *J. Med. Virol.* **23:**101–107.

Niederau, C., Fischer, R., Sonnenberg, A., Stremmel, W., Trampisch, H. J., and Strohmeyer, G. (1985). Survival and causes of death in cirrhotic and in noncirrhotic patients with primary hemochromatosis. *N. Engl. J. Med.* **313:**1256–1262.

Omata, M., Zhou, Y.-Z., Uchiumi, K., Hirota, K., Ito, Y., Yokosuka, O., and Okuda, K. (1987). Hepatitis B virus DNA, antigen and liver pathology in ducks: An animal model of human liver disease. *In* "Hepadnaviruses" (W. S. Robinson, K. Koike, and H. Will, eds.), pp. 349–356. Alan R. Liss, New York.

Ono, Y., Onda, H., Sasada, R., Igarashi, K., Sugino, Y., and Nishioka, K. (1983). The complete nucleotide sequences of the cloned hepatitis B virus DNA; subtype are and adw. *Nucleic Acids Res.* **11:**1747–1757.

Ostapchuk, P., Scheirle, G., and Hearing, P. (1989). Binding of nuclear factor EF-C to a functional domain of the hepatitis B virus enhancer region. *Mol. Cell. Biol.* **9:**2787–2797.

Ou, J.-H., and Rutter, W. J. (1985). Hybrid hepatitis B virus-host transcripts in a human hepatoma cell. *Proc. Natl. Acad. Sci. U.S.A.* **82:**83–87.

Ou, J.-H., and Rutter, W. J. (1987). Regulation of secretion of the hepatitis B virus major surface antigen by the PreS-1 protein. *J. Virol.* **61:**782–786.

Ou, J.-H., Laub, O., and Rutter, W. J. (1986). Hepatitis B gene function: The precore region targets the core antigen to cellular membranes and causes the secretion of e-antigen. *Proc. Natl. Acad. Sci. U.S.A.* **83:**1578–1582.

Ou, J.-H., Yeh, C. T., and Yen, T. S. B. (1989). Transport of hepatitis B virus precore protein into the nucleus after cleavage of its signal peptide. *J. Virol.* **63**:5238–5243.

Ou, J.-H., Bao, H., Shih, C., and Tahara, S. M. (1990). Preferred translation of human hepatitis B virus polymerase 4 from core protein- but not from precore protein-specific transcript. *J. Virol.* **64**:4578–4581.

Pasek, M., Goto, T., Gilbert, W., Zink, B., Schaller, H., Mackay, P., Leadbetter, G., and Murray, K. (1979). Hepatitis B virus genes and their expression in *E. coli. Nature (London)* **282**:575–579.

Pasquinelli, C., Bhavani, K., Wen, L., Hagen, T., Ames, B., Schirmacher, P., Rogler, C., and Chisari, F. V. (1992). Chromosomal instability, DNA damage and altered cellular and viral gene expression in hepatocellular carcinoma in hepatitis B virus transgenic mice. In preparation.

Patel, N. U., Jameel, S., Isom, H., and Siddiqui, A. (1989). Interactions between nuclear factors and the hepatitis B virus enhancer. *J. Virol.* **63**:5293–5301.

Patzer, E. J., Nakamura, G. R., and Yaffe, A. (1984a). Intracellular transport and secretion of hepatitis B surface antigen in mammalian cells. *J. Virol.* **51**:346–353.

Patzer, E. J., Nakamura, G. R., Simonsen, C. C., and Levinson, A. D. (1984b). Intracellular assembly and packaging of hepatitis B surface antigen particles occur in the endoplasmic reticulum. *J. Virol.* **58**:884–892.

Persing, D. H., Varmus, H. E., and Ganem, D. (1986). Inhibition of secretion of hepatitis B surface antigen by a related presurface polypeptide. *Science* **234**:1388–1391.

Popper, H., Roth, L., Purcell, R. H., Tennant, B. C., and Gerin, J. L. (1987). Hepatocarcinogenicity of the woodchuck hepatitis virus. *Proc. Natl. Acad. Sci. U.S.A.* **84**:866–870.

Radziwill, G., Tucker, W., and Schaller, H. (1990). Mutational analysis of the hepatitis B virus P gene product: Domain structure and RNase H activity. *J. Virol.* **64**:613–620.

Rall, L. B., Standring, D. N., Laub, O., and Rutter, W. J. (1983). Transcription of hepatitis B virus by RNA polymerase II. *Mol. Cell. Biol.* **3**:1766–1773.

Raney, A. K., Milich, D. R., and McLachlan, A. (1989). Characterization of hepatitis B virus major surface antigen gene transcriptional regulatory elements in differentiated hepatoma cell lines. *J. Virol.* **63**:3919–3925.

Raney, A. K., Milich, D. R., Easton, A. J., and McLachlan, A. (1990). Differentiation-specific transcriptional regulation of the hepatitis B virus large surface antigen gene in human hepatoma cell lines. *J. Virol.* **64**:2360–2368.

Robinson, W. S. (1977). The genome of hepatitis B virus. *Annu. Rev. Microbiol.* **31**:357–377.

Robinson, W. S., and Greenman, R. L. (1974). DNA polymerase in the core of the human hepatitis B virus candidate. *J. Virol.* **13**:1231–1236.

Robinson, W. S., Clayton, D. A., and Greenman, R. L. (1974). DNA of a human hepatitis B virus candidate. *J. Virol.* **14**:384–391.

Robinson, W. S., Miller, R. H., and Marion, P. L. (1987). Hepadnaviruses and retroviruses share genome homology and features of replication. *Hepatology* **7**:64S–73S.

Roosinck, M. J., Jameel, S., Loukin, S. H., and Siddiqui, A. (1986). Expression of hepatitis B viral core region in mammalian cells. *Mol. Cell. Biol.* **6**:1393–1400.

Rosenthal, N., Kress, M., Gruss, P., and Khoury, G. (1983). BK viral enhancer element and a human cellular homolog. *Science* **222**:749–755.

Sattler, F., and Robinson, W. S. (1979). Hepatitis B viral DNA molecules have cohesive ends. *J. Virol.* **32**:226–233.

Schlicht, H. J., and Schaller, H. (1989). The secretory core protein of human hepatitis B virus is expressed on the cell surface. *J. Virol.* **63**:5399–5404.

Schlicht, H. J., Salfeld, J., and Schaller, H. (1987). The duck hepatitis B virus pre-C region encodes a signal sequence which is essential for synthesis and secretion of processed core proteins but not for virus formation. *J. Virol.* **61**:3701–3709.

Schlicht, H. J., Radziwill, G., and Schaller, H. (1989). Synthesis and encapsidation of duck hepatitis B virus reverse transcriptase do not require formation of core-polymerase fusion proteins. *Cell (Cambridge, Mass.)* **56**:85-92.

Seeger, C., Ganem, D., and Varmus, H. E. (1986). Biochemical and genetic evidence for the hepatitis B virus replication strategy. *Science* **232**:477-484.

Sells, M. A., Chen, M. L., and Asc, G. (1987). Production of hepatitis B virus in HepG2 cells transfected with cloned hepatitis B virus DNA. *Proc. Natl. Acad. Sci. U.S.A.* **84**:1005-1009.

Seto, E., Yen, T. S., Peterlin, B. M., and Ou, J. H. (1988). Trans-activation of the human immunodeficiency virus long terminal repeat by the hepatitis B virus X protein. *Proc. Natl. Acad. Sci. U.S.A.* **85**:8286-8290.

Shaul, Y., Rutter, W. J., and Laub, O. (1985). A human hepatitis B viral enhancer element. *EMBO J.* **4**:427-430.

Siddiqui, A., Jameel, S., and Mapoles, J. (1986). Transcriptional control elements of hepatitis B surface antigen gene. *Proc. Natl. Acad. Sci. U.S.A.* **83**:566-570.

Siddiqui, A., Jameel, S., and Mapoles, J. (1987). Expression of the hepatitis B virus X gene in mammalian cells. *Proc. Natl. Acad. Sci. U.S.A.* **84**:2513-2517.

Simon, K., Lingappa, V. R., and Ganem, D. J. (1988). Secreted hepatitis B surface antigen polypeptides are derived from a transmembrane precursor. *J. Cell Biol.* **107**:2163-2168.

Slagle, B. L., Zhou, Y.-Z., and Butel, J. S. (1991). Hepatitis B virus integration event in human chromosome 17p near the p53 gene identifies the region of the chromosome commonly deleted in virus-positive hepatocellular carcinomas. *Cancer Res.* **51**:49-51.

Smith, M., Hiroshige, S., and Murray, J. (1986). Evidence in human hepatomas for structural chromosome changes and alteration in the expression of genes in the region 4q21-4q27. *Am. J. Hum. Genet.* **39**:A220 (abstr.).

Spandau, D. F., and Lee, C.-H. (1988). Trans-activation of viral enhancers by the hepatitis B virus X protein. *J. Virol.* **62**:427-434.

Sprengel, R., Kaleta, E. F., and Will, H. (1988). Isolation and characterization of a hepatitis B virus endemic in herons. *J. Virol.* **62**:3832-3839.

Standring, D. N., Ou, J. H., and Rutter, W. J. (1986). Assembly of viral particles in *Xenopus* oocytes: Pre-surface-antigens regulate secretion of the hepatitis viral surface envelope particle. *Proc. Natl. Acad. Sci. U.S.A.* **83**:9338-9342.

Stein, O., Fainaru, M., and Stein, Y. (1982). Visualization of virus-like particles in ednoplasmic reticulum of hepatocytes of Australia antigen carriers. *Lab. Invest.* **26**:262-269.

Summers, J., and Mason, W. S. (1982). Replication of the genome of a hepatitis B-like virus by reverse transcription of an RNA intermediate. *Cell (Cambridge, Mass.)* **29**:403-415.

Summers, J., O'Connell, A., and Millman, I. (1975). Genome of hepatitis B virus: Restriction enzyme cleavage and structure of DNA extracted from Dane particles. *Proc. Natl. Acad. Sci. U.S.A.* **72**:4597-4601.

Summers, J., Smolec, J., and Snyder, R. (1978). A virus similar to human hepatitis B virus associated with hepatitis and hepatoma in woodchucks. *Proc. Natl. Acad. Sci. U.S.A.* **75**:4533-4537.

Sureau, C., Romet-Lemonne, J.-L., Mullins, J. I., and Essex, M. (1986). Production of hepatitis b virus by a differentiated human hepatoma cell line after transfection with cloned circular HBV DNA. *Cell (Cambridge, Mass.)* **47**:37-47.

Tabor, E., and Gerety, R. J. (1984). Possible role of immune responses to hepatitis B core antigen in protection against hepatitis B infection [letter]. *Lancet* **1**:172.

Tagawa, M., Omata, M., Yokosuka, O., Uchiumi, K., Imazeki, F., and Okuda, K. (1985). Early events in duck hepatitis B virus infection. Sequential appearance of viral deoxyribonucleic acid in liver, pancreas, kidney and spleen. *Gastroenterology* **89**:1224-1229.

Takahashi, K., Kishimoto, S., Ohnuma, H., Machida, A., Takai, E., Tsuda, F., Miyamoto, H.,

Tanaka, T., Matsushita, K., Oda, K., Miyakawa, Y., and Mayumi, M. (1986). Polypeptides coded for by the region pre-S and gene S of hepatitis virus DNA with the receptor for polymerized human serum albumin expression on hepatitis B particles produced in the HBeAg or anti-HBe phase of hepatitis B virus infection. *J. Immunol.* **136**:3467–3472.

Takeda, K., Akahane, Y., Suzuki, H., Okamoto, H., Tsuda, F., Miyakawa, Y., and Mayumi, M. (1990). Defects in the precore region of the HBV genome in patients with chronic hepatitis B after sustained seroconversion from HBeAg to anti-HBe induced spontaneously or with interferon therapy. *Hepatology* **12**:1284–1289.

Tognoni, A., Cattaneo, R., Serfling, E., and Schaffner, W. A. (1985). A novel expression selection approach allows precise mapping of the hepatitis B virus enhancer. *Nucleic Acids Res.* **13**:7457–7472.

Tong, S., Li, J., Vitvitski, L., and Trepo, C. (1990). Active hepatitis B virus replication in the presence of anti-HBe is associated with viral variants containing an inactive pre-C region. *Virology* **176**:596–603.

Treinin, M., and Laub, O. (1987). Identification of a promoter element located upstream from the hepatitis B virus X gene. *Mol. Cell. Biol.* **7**:545–548.

Tsurimoto, T., Fujiyama, A., and Matsubara, K. (1987). Stable expression and replication of hepatitis B virus genome in an integrated state in a human hepatoma cell line transfected with cloned viral DNA. *Proc. Natl. Acad. Sci. U.S.A.* **84**:444–448.

Tur-Kaspa, R., Burk, R. D., Shaul, Y., and Shafritz, D. A. (1986). Hepatitis B virus contains a glucocorticoid-responsive element. *Proc. Natl. Acad. Sci. U.S.A.* **83**:1627–1631.

Tuttleman, J., Pourcel, C., and Summers, J. (1986a). Formation of the pool of covalently closed circular viral DNA in hepadnavirus infected cells. *Cell (Cambridge, Mass.)* **47**:451–460.

Tuttleman, J., Pugh, J., and Summers, J. (1986b). *In vitro* experimental infection of primary duck hepatocyte cultures with duck hepatitis B virus. *J. Virol.* **58**:17–25.

Twu, J.-S., and Schloemer, R. H. (1987). Trancriptional trans-activating function of hepatitis B virus. *J. Virol.* **61**:3448–3453.

Twu, J.-S., Chu, K., and Robinson, W. S. (1989). Hepatitis B virus X gene activates kB-like enhancer sequences in the long terminal repeat of human immunodeficiency virus 1. *Proc. Natl. Acad. Sci. U.S.A.* **86**:5168–5172.

Uy, A., Bruss, V., Gerlich, W. H., Kochel, H. G., and Thomssen, R. (1986). Precore sequence of hepatitis B virus inducing e antigen and membrane association of the viral core protein. *J. Virol.* **61**:683–92.

Valenzuela, P., Quiroga, M., Zalfivar, J., Gray, P., and Rutter, W. J. (1980). The nucleotide sequence of the hepatitis B genome and the identification of the major viral genes. *In* "Animal Virus Genetics" (B. N. Fields and R. Jaenisch, eds.), pp. 57–70. Academic Press, New York.

Vannice, J. L., and Levinson, A. D. (1988). Properties of the human hepatitis B virus enhancer: Position effects and cell-type nonspecificity. *J. Virol.* **62**:1305–1313.

Wang, H. P., and Rogler, C. E. (1988). Deletions in chromosome arms 11p and 13q in hepatocellular carcinomas. *Cytogenet. Cell Genet.* **48**:72–78.

Wang, J., Chenivesse, X., Henglein, B., and Brechot, C. (1990). Hepatitis B virus integration in a cyclin A gene in a hepatocellular carcinoma. *Nature (London)* **343**:555–557.

Wang, Y., Chen, P., Wu, X., Sun, Z.-L., Wang, H., Zhu, Y.-A., and Li, Z.-P. (1990). A new enhancer element, ENII, identified in the X gene of hepatitis B virus. *J. Virol.* **64**:3977–3981.

Weimer, T., Weimer, K., Tu, Z.-X., Jung, M.-C., Pape, G. R., and Will, H. (1989). Immunogenicity of human hepatitis B virus P-gene derived proteins. *J. Immunol.* **143**:3750–3756.

Will, H., Reiser, W., Weimer, T., Pfaff, E., Buscher, M., Sprengel, R., Cattaneo, R., and Schaller, H. (1987). Replication strategy of human hepatitis B virus. *J. Virol.* **61**:904–911.

Wollersheim, M., Debelka, U., and Hofschneider, P. H. (1988). A transactivating function encoded in the hepatitis B virus X gene is conserved in the integrated state. *Oncogene* **3**:545–552.

Wu, J. Y., Zhou, Z.-Y., Judd, A., Cartwright, C. A., and Robinson, W. S. (1990). The hepatitis B virus-encoded transcriptional *trans*-activator hbx appears to be a novel protein serine/threonine kinase. *Cell (Cambridge, Mass.)* **63**:687–695.

Yaginuma, K., Shirakata, Y., Kobayashi, M., and Koike, K. (1987). Hepatitis B virus (HBV) particles are produced in a cell culture system by transient expression of transfected HBV DNA. *Proc. Natl. Acad. Sci. U.S.A.* **84**:2678–2682.

Yee, J. K. (1989). A liver-specific enhancer in the core promoter region of human hepatitis B virus. *Science* **246**:658–661.

Yeh, C.-T., Liaw, Y.-F., and Ou, J.-H. (1990). The arginine-rich domain of hepatitis B virus precore and core proteins contains a signal for nuclear transport. *J. Virol.* **64**:6141–6147.

Yoffe, B., Burns, D. K., Bhatt, H. S., and Combes, B. (1990). Extrahepatic hepatitis B virus DNA sequences in patients with acute hepatitis B infection. *Hepatology* **12**:187–192.

Yuh, C.-H., and Ting, L.-P. (1990). The genome of hepatitis B virus contains a second enhancer: Cooperation of two elements within this enhancer is required for its function. *J. Virol.* **64**:4281–4287.

Yuki, N., Hayashi, N., Kasahara, A., Katayama, K., Ueda, K., Fusamoto, H., and Kamada, T. (1990). Detection of antibodies against the polymerase gene product in hepatitis B virus infection. *Hepatology* **12**:193–198.

Zhou, D.-X., and Yen, T. S. B. (1990). Differential regulation of the hepatitis B virus surface gene promoters by a second viral enhancer. *J. Biol. Chem.* **265**:20731–20734.

4

The Molecular Genetics
of Down Syndrome

David M. Holtzman
Department of Neurology
University of California, San Francisco
San Francisco, California

Charles J. Epstein
Department of Pediatrics and
Department of Biochemistry and Biophysics
University of California, San Francisco
San Francisco, California

I. INTRODUCTION

Down syndrome (DS), or trisomy 21, is one of the most frequently occurring chromosomal abnormalities in man. This aneuploid condition occurs with a frequency of between 1:700 and 1:1000 births and is the most common identified cause of mental retardation. Based on clinical observations in both humans and mice, it is clear that there is a definite relationships between the genetic structure of an unbalanced chromosomal region and the phenotypic consequences resulting from its imbalance (Epstein, 1986). For example, trisomy 21 results in a specific phenotype that is quite distinct from that seen in other human trisomies. It is characterized by certain dysmorphic features of the face and head, dermatoglyphic changes, congenital anomalies of the heart, immunodeficiency, and mental retardation. In addition, the neuropathology of Alzheimer's disease (AD) is seen in 100% of patients by age 40 (Malamud, 1972).

    With the development of recombinant DNA technology, major advances have occurred that have led to a better understanding of the molecular biology of DS. In this article, we shall discuss three general topics and how they may relate to the genetics of DS and its phenotype: (1) the concept of gene dosage effects, (2) molecular definition of the DS region of human chromosome

21, and (3) future approaches toward understanding the DS genotype and phenotype using animal models.

II. GENE DOSAGE EFFECTS

Ultimately, it should be possible to relate the phenotype of DS and other aneuploid conditions (trisomies) to the presence of extra copies of specific genes and their regulatory sequences. Central to an understanding of the mechanism by which aneuploidy leads to particular phenotypes is the question of how gene dosage affects gene expression. There are two general possibilities (Figure 4.1). The first is based on the concept of gene dosage effects. This concept holds that the synthesis and hence the concentration of a primary gene product is directly proportional to the number of genes coding for its synthesis. A primary gene product refers to a protein or RNA for which the structural gene is present on the chromosome in question. In DS, this concept would predict that each chromosome 21-specific locus is operative and expressing equally. Thus, each chromosome 21 (HSA-21) gene product in a tissue or group of cells would be

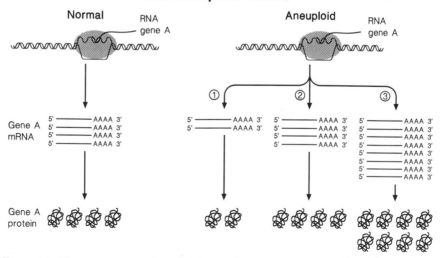

Gene Expression per Chromosome in Normal and Aneuploid States

Figure 4.1. There are two general possibilities as to how gene expression is affected by aneuploidy. The first possibility, represented by pathway 2, illustrates the concept of gene dosage effects in which, per chromosomal locus, each gene is expressed equally, whether in an aneuploid or diploid cell. The second possibility is shown in pathways 1 and 3; here gene dosage effects are not obeyed.

present at a level 1.5 times more than that present in appropriate diploid controls. In addition, genes located on nontrisomic chromosomes would in general be expected to be expressed at levels similar to those seen in controls, although these levels could be altered as secondary effects of the primary gene dosage effects.

The other general possibility is that the gene dosage effect concept is not operative for all loci in aneuploid cells (Figure 4.1). Thus genes may be expressed per chromosomal locus at some level that is greater than or less than that predicted on the basis of gene dosage. In DS, HSA-21 gene products could be present at a level greater than or less than 1.5 times diploid controls. Once again, gene products encoded on other chromosomes could be present at levels greater or less than controls.

Numerous gene products have been examined in aneuploid humans and mice. Until recently, the analysis of most gene products in DS and other aneuploidies has been accomplished by measuring specific protein levels or enzyme activities. In general, this large body of data supports the gene dosage effect concept for trisomy 21 and other aneuploid states (Epstein, 1986). Most gene products studied to date have been enzymes or housekeeping genes. In addition, the analyses of these products have been carried out with blood cells or fibroblasts. There are comparatively few quantitative data on a large variety of other cellular components in a variety of tissue types.

Recent data from patients with DS have suggested that, at the level of mRNA, one gene and several chromosome 21-specific sequences may not obey gene dosage effects. It has been reported that mRNA for the amyloid precursor protein (APP) was overexpressed an average of fourfold in three fetal DS brains (Neve et al., 1988). Another group examined the expression of four different human chromosome 21-specific sequences in DS fetal brain and liver and age-matched controls (Stefani et al., 1988). The identity of the gene or genes encoded by the sequences examined was unknown, but two sequences were expressed at a 5 times greater level in DS brain as assessed by Northern analysis. This contrasted with the expression of the same sequences in liver in which no differences were seen between DS and control samples.

To evaluate further whether gene dosage effects are operative in aneuploidy, animal models of DS have been employed. The most thoroughly studied model has been mouse trisomy 16 (Ts 16) (Section IV). Although larger than HSA-21, mouse chromosome 16 (MMU-16) contains a large conserved region located on the distal portion of HSA-21. To date, in addition to anonymous DNA sequences, several genes have been localized to this region, including *App*, *Sod-1*, *Ets-2*, *Ifnar*, *Prgs*, *Mx-1*, and *Mx-2* (Lin et al., 1980; Cox et al., 1980; Cox and Epstein, 1985; Lovett et al., 1987; Reeves et al., 1987, 1988, 1989; Cheng et al., 1988).

Recent studies with fetal Ts 16 mice have also suggested that strict gene dosage effects are not seen at the level of APP mRNA. When examined in embryonic day (ED) 15 mouse brain, the expression of two developmentally regulated genes on MMU-16 did not obey gene dosage efects (O'Hara et al., 1989). GAP-43 mRNA was increased 2.1 times and APP mRNA was increased 1.96 times; both values were significantly different from 1.5. Further analysis of these animals revealed that there is altered developmental and tissue-specific regulation of App gene expression (Holtzman et al., 1990). APP mRNA levels were examined in several organs at ED 15 and ED 17 from both Ts 16 and control littermates (Figures 4.2 and 4.3). The ratio of APP mRNA in Ts 16 versus control organs was tissue dependent. In ED 15 skin, there was no significant difference between Ts 16 and controls, whereas in heart there was a 2.7-fold increase in Ts 16 (Figure 4.2). Brain, skin, lung, and placenta APP mRNA levels all showed greater than a twofold increase in Ts 16. At ED 17 (Figure 4.3), as compared to ED 15, the ratios of APP mRNA in Ts 16 versus controls dramatically increased in both skin (Ts 16, 3.65 ± 0.30; controls, 1.25 ± 0.28) and placenta (Ts 16, 4.95 ± 0.43; controls, 2.38 ± 0.09). All numbers represent means ± 1 SD. If similar dysregulation of APP and other genes on HSA-21 as well as on other chromosomes occurs in DS, then understanding the mechanisms underlying various DS phenotypes may be even more complicated than the myriad of changes that can theoretically be induced by a straightforward gene dosage effect (Epstein, 1986).

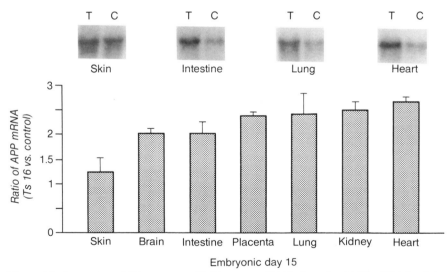

Figure 4.2. In a variety of different mouse Ts 16 organs at ED 15, the ratio of APP mRNA levels in Ts 16 (T) versus controls (C) is tissue specific as determined by quantitative Northern analysis. Values from each organ represent mean ± 1 SD; N = 3 or more for each group of pooled organ samples (n = 10–30 for each organ sample).

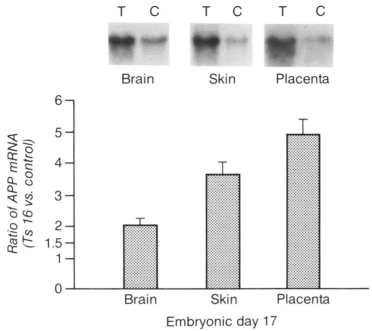

Figure 4.3. At ED 17 the ratio of APP mRNA in Ts 16 (T) versus control organs (C) is not predicted by gene dose. For example, in skin and placenta, the ratios are both greater than three.

One potential explanation for an alteration in gene dosage effects in DS and Ts 16 mice is a delay in normal development. For example, the expression of the thymocyte surface antigens, Thy-1, CD4, CD8, and Ly-1, in Ts 16 fetal thymocytes indicates that there is approximately a 2-day developmental delay in the maturation of these cells (Berger and Epstein, 1989). This is quite a significant period of time, as there are only 15 days between implantation and birth in the mouse. The ontogeny of DS fetal thymocytes has not been similarly studied; however, the thymocytes of young DS patients undergoing heart surgery show an abnormal pattern of expression for the CD3–T cell receptor complex (Murphy and Epstein, 1990). However, overexpression of APP mRNA in fetal DS and Ts 16 mouse brain cannot be interpreted in a similar manner. APP mRNA is expressed in neurons and is developmentally regulated in the brain (Neve et al., 1988; Mobley et al., 1988). During early brain development, it is expressed at relatively low levels that steadily increase and then plateau in the adult. APP mRNA levels appear to be increased beyond gene dosage effects in both fetal DS and Ts 16 brain. This could imply that, at the level of the expression of these genes, both DS and Ts 16 brains are developmentally ahead of schedule. However, this is not the case at the histologic level. During growth of the central nervous system, neurons migrate from the germinal zone adjacent to the ventricular surface to the overlying cortex. In Ts 16, as compared to controls, there is a thicker germinal zone with a thinner overlying cortex (Singer et al., 1984). Thus, although at the level of App gene expression there might appear to be "accelerated" brain development, there is delayed development at the morphologic level. A detailed dissection of cis- or trans-acting factors responsible for regulating important genes during organogenesis may lead to a more clear understanding of the abnormal molecular events occurring during DS development that ultimately lead to recognizable phenotypes.

The finding of gene product levels different from 1.5-times normal in DS or Ts 16 fetuses does not necessarily mean that the principle of gene dosage has been completely violated. In fact, what may be occurring is the superimposition of a secondary regulatory disturbance on a primary gene dosage effect. Such secondary dysregulation might be expected to affect products of chromosomes other than HSA-21 or MMU-16. A situation of this type has long been recognized to occur in DS red cells, in which the activities of several non-HSA-21 enzymes are elevated about 1.5-fold (Epstein, 1986).

III. MOLECULAR DEFINITION OF THE DS REGION OF HSA-21

Most cases of DS are caused by the presence of an extra copy of HSA-21 in its entirety. As previously discussed, the mechanism by which the presence of an extra copy of normal genes leads to particular phenotypes remains unknown. Interestingly, molecular analysis of a subset of patients with DS reveals that triplication of only part of HSA-21 is required to visualize aspects of the DS phenotype. This suggests that a detailed knowledge of a much smaller region of this chromosome may be able to shed new light and generate new hypotheses on the molecular basis of the several components of the phenotype of DS.

A small portion (1–5%) of individuals with DS have a partial unbalanced translocation of the long arm of HSA-21, band q22 (Epstein, 1986). This band has been called the "DS region," as defined by the presence of a subset of the major phenotypic features of the syndrome. These include mental retardation, congenital heart disease, the characteristic facial appearance, the hand anomalies, and dermatoglyphic changes. It has been suggested that subband 21q22.1 and possibly subband 21q22.2 may generate most of these abnormalities. Recently, several groups have described rare individuals who have an apparently normal karyotype but harbor a small amount of extra material from HSA-21. Recent molecular analyses of a Japanese family with "partial" trisomy 21 have been particularly revealing (Korenberg et al., 1990). Phenotypic features of affected family members included characteristic DS facies, endocardial

cushion defects, hand anomalies, and mental retardation. Quantitative Southern analysis revealed that the triplicated region excluded sequences mapping in
21q21 (APP, D21S46) and in 21q22.1 (SOD1, D21S47, and SF57), but included DNA sequences probably mapping in band 21q22.3 (D21S39, D21S43,
and D21S43). This region is likely to include the marker D21S85 (Rahmani et
al., 1989). In another report, a single patient with mental retardation and the
DS facial phenotype had a triplication of the region from 21q22.1 to 21qter,
whereas APP and SOD1 were present in only two copies (McCormick et al.,
1989).

    Further confirming the specificity of band 21q22 to at least part of the
DS phenotype is the description of several patients with triplication of a large
region of the proximal long arm of HSA-21, including most, if not all, of band
21q21. Interestingly, duplication of 21pter–proximal q21 may be associated with
a normal physical phenotype, whereas duplication of 21pter through all of band
q21 has resulted in severe mental retardation without typical facial or cardiac
abnormalities associated with DS (Park et al., 1987). This implies there are at
least two regions on HSA-21 that, when present in triplicate, can result in
mental retardation: the region causing the visible DS phenotype in q22, as well
as a portion of band q21. These and further studies will be crucial in determining
essential HSA-21 regions and genes relevant to particular features seen in DS.
However, careful interpretation and more detailed analyses of patients and families with partial trisomy 21 will be essential.

    The phenotype of DS includes a large array of both minor and major
malformations and biochemical abnormalities. All individuals do not display the
entire range of physical features. Although studies to define further the "DS"
region of HSA-21 appear to have localized the facial appearance and congenital
heart defect of the endocardial cushion type to a region clearly involving
21q22.2–q22.3, which may include the very distal part of 21q22.1 (Korenberg et
al., 1990), several questions remain to be answered. One of the most interesting
aspects of DS is the increased frequency of phenotypic abnormalities that have
high prevalence rates in the general population. These include immune defects,
susceptibility to leukemia, and the premature development of Alzheimer's disease (AD). It remains unknown as to whether patients who possess three copies
of what is currently felt to be the minimal DS region will also develop any of
these phenotypic features, including AD.

    AD is of particular interest because of a myriad of recent molecular
studies that point to HSA-21 regions as being of potential importance in its
pathogenesis (for review, see Holtzman and Mobley, 1991). One of the hallmarks of this pathology is the diffuse deposition within the brain of a 39- to 42-
amino acid amyloidogenic peptide termed β/A4. Deposition of this peptide can
be found in some DS brains as early as the second decade. Whether β/A4 serves
solely as an AD marker or is also involved in the pathogenesis of dementia

remains unclear. It is derived through abnormal proteolytic processing from a much larger precursor protein, APP, which, as has been noted, is encoded on HSA-21. It has been hypothesized that overexpression of APP mRNA in DS secondary to increased gene dose results in the premature development of AD neuropathology. As it appears that *APP* is not included in the minimal DS region seen in several patients with partial trisomy 21, it will be interesting to learn whether such patients prematurely develop the neuropathology of AD. If such pathology were found, it would prove that cellular and molecular abnomalities required to accelerate AD were initiated by an excess of genes, excluding *APP*. It would not, however, exclude that overexpression of *APP* or other genes was occurring in these patients. The complexities of this single DS phenotypic manifestation illustrate the difficulty in understanding the effects of increased gene dosage. Therefore, to adequately test various hypotheses regarding the effects of three copies of single or multiple genes or chromosomal regions, animal models, in conjunction with further human studies, are essential.

IV. ANIMAL MODELS OF DOWN SYNDROME

The study of Down syndrome has and will be greatly facilitated by the study of animal models (for review, see Epstein, 1986). The most easily studied genetic models are in mice. As mentioned in Section II, a large conserved region exists between the distal portion of HSA-21 and mouse chromosome 16 (Figure 4.4). Five known genes are located on both HSA-21 and MMU-16. These include *APP, SOD1, ETS2, IFNAR, MX1, MX2,* and *PRGS* (*App, Sod-1, Ets-2, Ifnar, Mx-1, Mx-2,* and *Prgs*) (for references, see Section II). In addition, DNA segments *D21S13* and *DS1S52* as well as the locus encoding the neurological mutant weaver (*wv*) are all present on both MMU-16 and HSA-21 (MacDonald and Cox, 1989; Reeves *et al.*, 1989). Because of their relative size differences, with MMU-16 comprising about 4% of the mouse genome and HSA-21 only about 2% of the human genome, MMU-16 contains genes also located on other human chromosomes. Ideally, one would want to study a mouse model with only the excess genetic material obligate for the DS phenotype (see Section III). In the future, this may be possible. Despite the differences between MMU-16 and HSA-21, these chromosomes possess the largest region of conserved synteny between the two species that is currently known (Searle *et al.*, 1989).

Based on comparative mapping studies, mouse Ts 16 has been identified as an animal model of DS. These mice can be generated using Robertsonian translocation-carrying strains of mice in which a high rate of meiotic nondisjunction is observed (Gropp *et al.*, 1975). By utilizing strains in which each MMU-16 is fused to a different mouse chromosome, one can generate animals monosomic or trisomic for MMU-16. In practice, about 17% of the embryos produced in this manner are trisomic, with the same percentage being mono-

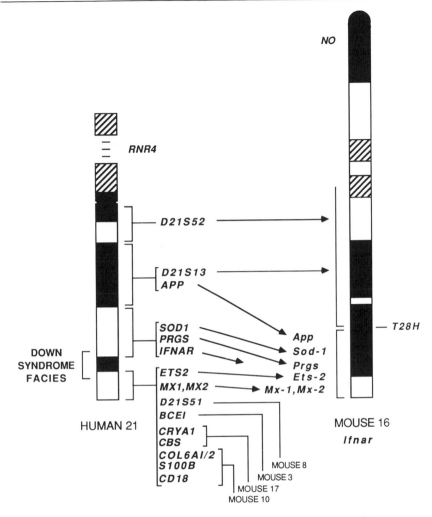

**LOCATION OF HUMAN CHROMOSOME 21 GENES
IN THE MOUSE GENOME**

Figure 4.4. Comparative map of mouse chromosome 16 and human chromosome 21. Reprinted by permission from Epstein *et al.* (1990).

somic (Magnuson *et al.*, 1985). The monosomies do not survive the implantation stage, whereas Ts 16 fetuses develop to term but rarely survive birth (Epstein, 1986).

There are many phenotypic features of the Ts 16 fetus that are similar to those seen in DS. These features are seen in many organ systems. There is a short, thick neck and flat snout along with marked midgestational edema that diminishes with later development. These findings are reminiscent of those seen in DS (Epstein, 1986).

In the nervous system, in addition to a number of nonspecific abnormalities such as decreased brain weight, Ts 16 fetuses possess some specific abnormalities also seen in DS. For example, there are decreased cholinergic, noradrenergic, and serotonergic markers, whereas other neurotransmitter systems appear normal (Coyle et al., 1988). In mammals, cholinergic neurons of the basal forebrain are the major source of acetylcholine for both the neocortex and hippocampus. These neurons have been shown to be decreased in numbers in young DS patients and are particularly vulnerable to undergoing degeneration in AD (Coyle et al., 1983; Casanova et al., 1985). Interestingly, two groups have shown that Ts 16 embryos also show a decreased density of cholinergic basal forebrain neurons (Sweeney et al., 1989; Kiss et al., 1989). In recent studies, it has been shown that these neurons can be "rescued" through the use of neurotransplantation. It appears that over a 6-month period of time, Ts 16 cholinergic neurons undergo selective atrophy as is seen in AD (Holtzman et al., 1991).

Numerous aberrations of the hematologic, cardiovascular, and immunologic system have been described in DS. Thymic abnormalities with marked lymphoid depletion and abnormally large Hassal's corpuscles have been noted (Epstein, 1986). In DS, abnormal T cell development may lead secondarily to other immunological disorders such as an increased susceptibility to infections and possibly leukemia. Studies with Ts 16 fetuses have revealed the thymus to be severely hypoplastic and, as previously mentioned (Section II), there is a developmental delay in the ontogeny of T cell markers. Congenital cardiac malformations are seen in approximately 40% of patients with DS, with the most prominent abnormality being some form of endocardial cushion defect (Epstein, 1986). Although almost 100% of Ts 16 fetuses have abnormalities of the great vessels, more than 50% also have endocardial cushion defects (Epstein, 1986; Bacchus et al., 1987). In sum, many specific phenotypic features seen in DS are also seen in mouse Ts 16. Some of these abnormalities are likely to be a direct result of the similar excess genetic material seen in both HSA-21 and MMU-16. Future molecular studies of mechanisms involved in abnormal organogenesis in Ts 16 will likely give new insights into the origins of abnormal phenotypes in DS and other aneuploidies.

A major problem arises in studying Ts 16 mice in that they undergo late fetal demise. The use of Ts 16 ↔ 2N chimeras (mosaics) has been one way to circumvent this problem. Successful production of Ts 16 ↔ 2N chimeras has been accomplished by two groups (Cox et al., 1984; Gearhart et al., 1986). Some organs, such as the brain, tend to have a much larger trisomic component than others. Preliminary studies with a small number of animals have revealed that there may be subtle behavioral abnormalities (Gearhart *et al.*, 1986). Furthermore, Ts 16 ↔ 2N chimeras are more susceptible to infection with the infectious scrapie agent (prions), which causes a neurodegenerative disease (Epstein *et al.*, 1991). Ts 16 ↔ 2N chimeras inoculated intracerebrally with prions had a significantly shorter survival time as compared to control chimeras. This may have been due to factors such as altered nervous system development in these animals. Further study of these animals seems warranted for many reasons, among which is the fact that human trisomy 21 mosaics may possess many, if not all, features of DS, including the neuropathology of AD. Analysis with Ts 16 ↔ 2N chimeras has been limited by the difficulty in producing large numbers of animals by aggregation of diploid four- or eight-cell-stage embryos with Ts 16 embryos. In the future, embryonic stem (ES) cells could be used to replace one of the partners used to form chimeras (Robertson, 1987). In addition to obtaining a higher efficiency of chimera production, a trisomic ES cell line offers the potential of assessing the effects of varying amounts of trisomic cells on organogensis and on the overall viability of the animals. Last, the addition of exogenous genes to ES cells or the removal of endogenous gene activity by homologous recombination (Doetschmann *et al.*, 1988) enables one to ask questions concerning the function of specific genes in the trisomic state.

Because the phenotype of DS results from the presence of an extra copy of a region of genetic material, it remains unclear as to the role excessive dose for a particular gene may play in generating this phenotype. It may be that through the addition of specific genes, one could dissect which HSA-21 genes are responsible for various phenotypes. Technological advances that have paved the way for the development of transgenic mice and cultured ES cells have allowed for such studies to commence.

The first successful HSA-21 gene to be studied in transgenic mice was the gene for human CuZn superoxide dismustase (*SOD1*) (Epstein *et al.*, 1987). In DS and Ts 16 mice, strict gene dosage effects for this gene have been observed in many different cells and tissue types (Epstein, 1986). As the steady-state equilibrium of oxygen free radicals may be disrupted by an increased *SOD1* gene dose, it is conceivable that oxidative damage to important biological molecules may occur in DS. Transgenic mice that overexpress *SOD1* do not share any of the obvious phenotypic features of DS or mouse Ts 16. Careful analysis, however, has revealed that, as in DS and aged mice, they do share similar pathological abnormalities of the tongue neuromuscular junction (Groner *et al.*, 1990). These include decreased numbers of terminal axons and an increase in degenerated membranes, vacuoles, and filaments. Such abnormalities may contribute to muscle and tongue hypotonia in DS. PC12 cells transfected with *SOD1* have been shown to have impaired uptake of the neurotransmitters, dopamine and norepinephrine (Elroy-Stein and Groner, 1988). Furthermore, *SOD1* transgenic mouse platelets have a decreased uptake of serotonin, as do DS platelets (Groner *et al.*, 1990). A diminished transmembrane pH gradient has been identified as the defect in these cells that leads to these abnormalities. Overexpression of *SOD1* may be a reason why DS patients have alterations in these neurotransmitter systems. In addition to these deleterious effects, the brain of *SOD1* transgenic mice appears to actually be more resistant to ischemic changes and the development of edema following traumatic injury (Kinouchi *et al.*, 1990; Chan *et al.*, 1991). Both edema and chronic infarction resulting from cold trauma or vascular occlusion were significantly reduced in *SOD1* transgenic mice as compared to controls. It is thought that, following a variety of pathological insults, including brain ischemia and trauma, overproduction of superoxide radicals plays a role in mediating neuronal damage. These studies indicate cellular overexpression of *SOD1* may be directly protective from such insults. Whether detrimental, protective, or other effects of increased superoxide dismutase occur in DS remains to be answered.

As mentioned, another HSA-21 gene that has evoked widespread attention is *APP*. Several groups have attempted to determine *in vivo* whether increased expression of this gene can directly lead to the neuropathological changes seen in AD and DS. One group has reported the successful production of transgenic mice that express the human form of *APP* under the control of the human metallothionein-IIa promoter (Beer *et al.*, 1990). Although overproduction of APP was found in neurons, β/A4 production and other AD neuropathology were not seen. However, another group using human β-APP 751 cDNA under control of the rat neural-specific enolase promoter, has observed both diffuse and compact extracellular β-amyloid immunoreactive deposits in the cortex and hippocampus of transgenic animals (Quon *et al.*, 1991). Whether overproduction of APP is even required or if additional cellular abnormalities play more important roles in the generation of AD neuropathology remains unknown.

It may be that overexpression of several HSA-21 genes together is required to produce particular phenotypic features in DS. Attempts are now in progress to generate mice that overexpress several HSA-21 genes. Because many genes in the obligate DS region are still unknown, a more thorough knowledge of HSA-21 may be required before this can be accomplished.

One of the limitations of conventional cloning techniques in the development of animal models of DS is that the size of the DNA that can be introduced is generally less than 50 kb. This results in insertional site-dependent expression of most transgenes in transgenic mice, and, therefore, the number of copies introduced does not necessarily correlate with expression. Ideally, one might want to insert large pieces of genomic DNA obligate for the DS phenotype. In this way, each gene would be under its normal regulatory control and its copy number and expression would be increased to the same extent as in DS. The normal order of different genes within a chromosomal region may also be quite important in obtaining normal patterns of gene expression from a region of genetic material. Several systems for obtaining large DNA fragments have now been developed and may enable the injection of a chromosome fragment of interest into mouse pronuclei. These systems include yeast artificial chromosome cloning (Burke *et al.*, 1987), reconstruction of large DNA fragments from smaller pieces via homologous recombination (O'Connor *et al.*, 1989), and dissection of chromosome fragments from human metaphase spreads (Richa and Lo, 1989). In addition to aiding in the development of transgenic mice with extra copies of large DNA segments of interest, these techniques will also speed up the cloning of other genes on HSA-21 within regions obligate for different DS features. It may be that currently known genes are only the "tip of the iceberg" in terms of understanding which genes, when present in triplicate, lead to the DS phenotype.

V. SUMMARY

Major advances have occurred in the understanding of the genetics of DS since the discovery a little more than 30 years ago that it resulted from an extra copy of HSA-21. It has been learned that only a small region of HSA-21 is required in triplicate to produce at least some of the DS phenotype. Future work will clarify which regions are responsible for particular phenotypes of interest. The mechanisms by which extra genetic material leads to phenotypic abnormalities in DS and other aneuploidies appear to be complex. Although gene dosage effects are operative for many loci, they do not appear to be strictly operative for all genes. A more thorough understanding of the effects of aneuploidy on gene expression is needed. To understand adequately the mechanisms by which extra genetic material leads to particular phenotypic features will require the use of animal models. The trisomy 16 mouse, as well as new transgenic and partial trisomic mouse lines currently being developed, may be of particular help in this endeavor.

Acknowledgments

Preparation of this review was supported by National Institutes of Health Grants AG00445 (D.M.H.) and AG08938 (C.J.E.). D.M.H. is also supported by a research fellowship award from the American Academy of Neurology. The authors also wish to thank Dr. William Mobley and Dr. Christopher Berger for their support and advice during preparation of this manuscript.

References

Bacchus, C., Sterz, H., Buselmaier, W., Sahai, S., and Winking, H. (1987). Genesis and systematization of cardiovascular anomalies and analysis of skeletal malformations in murine trisomy 16 and 19. *Hum. Genet.* **77**:12–22.
Beer, J., Salbaum, J. M., Schlichtmann, Hoppe, P., Earley, S., Masters, C. L., Carlson, G. A., and

Beyreuther, K. (1990). Transgenic mice and Alzheimer's disease. *Neurobiol. Aging* **11**:327 (abstr.).

Berger, C. N., and Epstein, C. J. (1989). Delayed thymocyte maturation in the trisomy 16 mouse fetus. *J. Immunol.* **143**:389–396.

Burke, D. T., Carle, G. F., and Olson, M. V. (1987). Cloning of large segments of exogenous DNA into yeast by means of artificial chromosome vectors. *Science* **236**:806–812.

Casanova, M. F., Walker, L. C., Whitehouse, P. J., and Price, D. L. (1985). Abnormalities of the nucleus basalis in Down's syndrome. *Ann. Neurol.* **18**:310–313.

Chan, P. H., Yang, G. Y., Chen, S. F., Carlson, E., and Epstein, C. J. (1991). Cold-induced brain edema and infarction are reduced in transgenic mice overexpressing CuZn superoxide dismutase. *Ann. Neurol.* **29**:482–486.

Cheng, S. V., Nadeau, J. H., Tanzi, R. E., Watkins, P. C., Jagadesh, J., Taylor, B. A., Haines, J. L., Sacchi, N., and Gusella, J. F. (1988). Comparative mapping of DNA markers from familial Alzheimer's disease and Down syndrome regions of human chromosome 21 to mouse chromosome 16 and 17. *Proc. Natl. Acad. Sci. U.S.A.* **85**:6032–6036.

Cox, D. R., and Epstein, C. J. (1985). Comparative gene mapping of human chromosome 21 and mouse chromosome 16. *Ann. N. Y. Acad. Sci.* **450**:169–177.

Cox, D. R., Epstein, L. B., and Epstein, C. J. (1980). Genes coding for sensitivity to interferon (IfRec) and soluble superoxide dismutase (SOD-1) are linked in mouse and man and map to mouse chromosome 16. *Proc. Natl. Acad. Sci. U.S.A.* **77**:2168–2172.

Cox, D. R., Smith, S. A., Epstein, L. B., and Epstein, C. J. (1984). Mouse trisomy 16 as an animal model of human trisomy 21 (Down syndrome): Production of viable trisomy 16 ↔ diploid mouse chimeras. *Dev. Biol.* **101**:416–424.

Coyle, J. T., Price, D. F., and DeLong, M. R. (1983). Alzheimer's disease: A disorder of cortical cholinergic innervation. *Science* **219**:1184–1190.

Coyle, J. T., Oster-Granite, M. L., Reeves, R. H., and Gearhart, J. D. (1988). Down syndrome, Alzheimer's disease, and the trisomy 16 mouse. *Trends Neurosci.* **11**:390–394.

Doetschman, T., Maeda, N., and Smithies, O. (1988). Targeted mutation of the *Hprt* gene in mouse embryonic stem cell. *Proc. Natl. Acad. Sci. U.S.A.* **85**:8583–8587.

Elroy-Stein, O., and Groner, Y. (1988). Impaired neurotransmitter uptake in PC12 cells overexpressing human Cu/Zn-superoxide dismutase—Implication for gene dosage effects in Down syndrome. *Cell (Cambridge, Mass.)* **52**:259–267.

Epstein, C. J. (1986). "The Consequences of Chromosome Imbalance: Principles, Mechanisms, and Models." Cambridge Univ. Press, New York.

Epstein, C. J., Avraham, K. B., Lovett, M., Smith, S., Elroy-Stein, O., Rotman, G., Bry, C., and Groner, Y. (1987). Transgenic mice with increased Cu/Zn superoxide dismutase activity: Animal model of dosage effects in Down syndrome. *Proc. Natl. Acad. Sci. U.S.A.* **84**:8044–8048.

Epstein, C. J., Berger, C. N., Carlson, E. J., Chan, P. H., and Huang, T. T. (1990). Models for Down syndrome: Chromosome-21 specific genes in mice. *In* "Molecular Genetics of Chromosome 21 and Down Syndrome" (D. Patterson and C. J. Epstein, eds.), pp. 215–232. Wiley-Liss, New York.

Epstein, C. J., Foster, D. B., DeArmond, S. J., and Prusiner, S. B. (1991). Acceleration of scrapie in trisomy 16 ↔ diploid aggregation chimeras. *Ann. Neurol.* **29**:95–97.

Gearhart, J. D., Singer, H. S., Moran, T. H., Tiemeyer, M. C., Oster-Granite, M. L., and Coyle, J. T. (1986). Mouse chimeras composed of trisomy 16 and normal (2*n*) cells: Preliminary studies. *Brain Res. Bull.* **16**:815–824.

Groner, Y., Avraham, K. B., Schickler, M., Yarom, R., and Knobler, H. (1990). Clinical symptoms of Down syndrome are manifested in transgenic mice overexpressing the human Cu/Zn-superoxide dismutase gene. *In* "Molecular Genetics of Chromosome 21 and Down Syndrome" (D. Patterson and C. J. Epstein, eds.), pp. 233–262. Wiley-Liss, New York.

Gropp, A., Kolbus, U., and Giers, D. (1975). Systematic approach to the study of trisomy in the mouse. II. *Cytogenet. Cell Genet.* **14**:42–62.

Holtzman, D. M., and Mobley, W. C. (1991). Molecular studies in Alzheimer's disease. *Trends Biochem. Sci.* **16**:140–144.

Holtzman, D. M., Bayney, R., Berger, C., Epstein, C. J., and Mobley, W. C. (1990). Altered developmental and tissue specific regulation of gene expression in mouse trisomy 16. *Soc. Neurosci. Abstr.* **16**:1138.

Holtzman, D. M., Li, Y. W., Gage, F. H., DeArmond, S. J., Epstein, C. J., McKinley, M. P., and Mobley, W. C. (1991). Modeling cholinergic abnormalities in Down syndrome and Alzheimer's disease. *In* "The Morphogenesis of Down Syndrome" (C. J. Epstein, ed.), pp. 189–202. Wiley-Liss, New York.

Kinouchi, H., Imaizumi, S., Carlson, E., Epstein, C. J., and Chan, P. H. (1990). Focal cerebral ischemic infarction and brain edema are reduced in transgenic mice overexpressing human superoxide dismutase. *Soc. Neurosci. Abstr.* **16**:276 (abstr.).

Kiss, J., Schlumpf, M., and Balazs, R. (1989). Selective retardation of the development of the basal forebrain cholinergic and pontine catecholaminergic nuclei in the brain of trisomy 16 mouse, an animal model of Down syndrome. *Dev. Brain Res.* **50**:251–264.

Korenberg, J. R., Kawashima, H., Pulst, S. M., Ikeuchi, T., Ogasawara, N., Yamamoto, K., Schonberg, A., West, R., Allen, L., Magenis, E., Ikawa, K., Taniguchi, N., and Epstein, C. J. (1990). Molecular definition of a region of chromosome 21 that causes features of the the Down syndrome phenotype. *Am. J. Hum. Genet.* **47**:236–246.

Lin, P. F., Slate, D. L., Lawyer, F. C., and Ruddle, F. H. (1980). Assignment of the murine interferon sensitivity and cytoplasmic superoxide dismutase genes to chromosome 16. *Science* **209**:285–287.

Lovett, M., Goldgaber, D., Ashley, P., Cox, D. R., Gajdusek, D. C., and Epstein, C. J. (1987). The mouse homolog of the human amyloid beta protein (AD-AP) gene is located on the distal end of mouse chromosome 16: Further extension of the homology between human chromosome 21 and mouse chromosome 16. *Biochem. Biophys. Res. Commun.* **144**:1069–1075.

MacDonald, G. P., and Cox, D. R. (1989). The mouse T28H translocation break point occurs in a region of chromosome 16 homologous to human chromosome 21, separating sequences D21S13 and D21S52 from *App*, *Sod*-1, and *Ets*-2. *Am. J. Hum. Genet.* **45**, A149 (abstr.).

Magnuson, T., Debrot, S., Dimpfl, J., Zamora, T., and Epstein, C. J. (1985). The early lethality of autosomal monosomy in the mouse. *J. Embryol. Exp. Morphol.* **69**:223–236.

Malamud, N. (1972). Neuropathology of organic brain syndromes associated with aging. *In* "Aging and the Brain" (C. M. Gartz, ed.), Vol. 3, pp. 63–87. Plenum, New York.

McCormick, M. K., Schinzel, A., Petersen, M. B., Stetten, G., Driscoll, S., Cantu, E. S., Tranebjaerg, L., Mikkelsen, M., Watkins, P. C., and Antonarakis, S. E. (1989). Molecular genetic approach to the characterization of the "Down syndrome region" of chromosome 21. *Genomics* **5**:325–331.

Mobley, W. C., Neve, R. L., Prusiner, S. B., and McKinley, M. P. (1988). Nerve growth factor increases mRNA levels for the prion protein and the β-amyloid protein precursor in developing hamster brain. *Proc. Natl. Acad. Sci. U.S.A.* **85**:9811–9815.

Murphy, M., and Epstein, L. B. (1990). Down syndrome thymuses have a decreased proportion of cells expressing high levels of TCR alpha, beta, and CD3. A possible mechanism for diminished T cell function in Down syndrome. *Clin. Immunol. Immunopathol.* **55**:453–467.

Neve, R. L., Finch, E. A., and Dawes, L. P. (1988). Expression of the Alzheimer amyloid precursor gene transcripts in human brain. *Neuron* **1**:669–677.

O'Connor, M., Peifer, M. and Bender, W. (1989). Construction of large DNA fragments in *Escherichia coli*. *Science* **244**:1307–1312.

O'Hara, B. F., Fisher, S., Oster-Granite, M. L., Gearhart, J. D., and Reeves, R. H. (1989).

Developmental expression of the amyloid precursor protein, growth associated protein 43, and somatostatin in normal and trisomy 16 mice. *Dev. Brain Res.* **49**:300–304.

Park, J. P., Wurster-Hill, D. H., Andrews, P. A., Cooley, W. C., and Graham, J. M. (1987). Free proximal trisomy 21 without the Down syndrome. *Clin. Genet.* **32**:342–348.

Quon, D., Wong, Y., Catalano, R., Marian Scardina, J., Murakami, K., and Cordell, B. (1991). Formation of β-amyloid protein deposits in brains of transgenic mice. *Nature* **352**, 239–241.

Rahmani, Z., Blouin, J. L., Creau-Goldberg, N., Watkins, P. C., Mattei, J. F., Poissonier, M., Prieur, M., Chettouh, Z., Nicole, A., Aurias, A., Sinet, P. M., and Delabar, J. M. (1989). Critical role of the D21S55 region on chromosome 21 in the pathogenesis of Down syndrome. *Proc. Natl. Acad. Sci. U.S.A.* **86**:5958–5962.

Reeves, R. H., Gallahan, D., O'Hara, B. F., Callahan, R., and Gearhart, J. D. (1987). Genetic mapping of *Prm*-1, *Igl*-1, *Smst*, *Mtv*-6, *Sod*-1, and *Ets*-2 and localization of the Down syndrome region on mouse chromosome 16. *Cytogenet. Cell Genet.* **44**:76–81.

Reeves, R. H., O'Hara, B. F., Pavan, W. J., Gearhart, J. D., and Haller, O. (1988). Genetic mapping of Mx within the region of mouse chromosome 16 that is homologous to human chromosome 21. *J. Virol.* **62**:4372–4375.

Reeves, R. H., Crowley, M. R., Lorenzon, N., Pavan, W. J., Smeyne, R. J., and Goldowitz, D. (1989). The mouse neurological mutant weaver maps within the region of chromosome 16 which is homologous to human chromosome 21. *Genomics* **5**:522–526.

Richa, J., and Lo, C. W. (1989). Introduction of human DNA into mouse eggs by injection of dissected chromosome fragments. *Science* **245**:175–177.

Robertson, E. J. (1987). "Teratocarcinomas and Embryonic Stem Cells: A Practical Approach." IRL Press, Oxford.

Searle, A. G., Peters, J., Lyon, M. F., Hall, J. G., Evans, E. P., Edwards, J. H., and Buckle, V. J. (1989). Chromosome maps of mouse and man. IV. *Ann. Hum. Genet.* **53**:89–140.

Singer, H. S., Tiemeyer, H., Hedreen, J. C., Gearhart, J., and Coyle, J. T. (1984). Morphologic and neurochemical studies of embryonic brain development in murine trisomy 16. *Dev. Brain Res.* **15**:155–166.

Stefani, L., Galt, J., Palmer A., Affara, N., Ferguson-Smith, M., and Nevin, N. C. (1988). Expression of chromosome 21 specific sequences in normal and Down's syndrome tissues. *Nucleic Acids Res.* **16**:2885–2896.

Sweeney, J. E., Hohmann, C. F., Oster-Granite, M. L., and Coyle, J. T. (1989). Neurogenesis of the basal forebrain in euploid and trisomy 16 mice: An animal model for developmental disorders in Down syndrome. *Neuroscience* **31**:413–425.

5

Mammalian X Chromosome Inactivation

Stanley M. Gartler
Departments of Medicine and Genetics
University of Washington
Seattle, Washington

Karen A. Dyer
Vivigen, Inc.
Santa Fe, New Mexico

Michael A. Goldman
Department of Biology
San Francisco State University
San Francisco, California

I. INTRODUCTION

Aneuploidy is generally associated with multiple severe phenotypic effects in animals. An exception to this rule occurs in X chromosome aneuploidy in mammals, in which associated phenotypic effects are relatively mild. Avoidance of the aneuploidy effect is a secondary consequence of X chromosome inactivation, a mammalian developmental process that leads to inactivation of all but one X chromosome in somatic cells (Lyon, 1961). X inactivation is a form of dosage compensation, a mechanism found in all species with an XY system of sex determination, which serves to bring about the equivalence in expression of the two X chromosomes in the female and the one X in the male and to maintain similar autosomal:sex chromosomal ratios in the two sexes. As expected, abnormal conditions of excess X chromosomal material leads to severe aneuploidy effects (Kushnick et al., 1987; Takagi and Abe, 1990). Mammalian X inactivation has been well reviewed in the past (Lyon, 1974, 1988; Cattanach, 1975; Gartler and Riggs, 1983; Graves, 1987; Grant and Chapman, 1988); in this

Molecular Genetic Medicine, Vol. 2

work, we focus on major points from early studies, the current status of molecular studies, and future prospects for understanding the molecular basis of mammalian X inactivation. Because most of the work on molecular aspects of X inactivation has been done in humans and mice, our review is strongly biased in that direction.

In the early 1960s Lyon (1961) and Beutler *et al.* (1962) independently proposed that dosage compensation in mammals occurs by X chromosome inactivation. As presented in great detail by Lyon (1961), the basic idea is that early in development, the two X chromosomes in the female embryo differentiated such that one X chromosome in a cell became inactivated and the other remained active. The X inactivation event is random, so that in some cells the paternal X is inactive and the maternal X is active, and in other cells the complementary pattern occurs. Once the cell becomes differentiated in this way, the pattern of inactivation is fixed for that cell and its somatic descendants. This results in mosaicism in the mammalian female, with some cells having a paternal X chromosome active and others with the maternal X chromosome active. In rodents this mosaicism is obvious in individuals heterozygous for an X-linked trait affecting pigmentation, the result of which is variegated coat color pattern. However, in humans it is more difficult to detect such mosaicism because epidermal cells have a different pattern of embryological migration than do pigment cells (Clark *et al.*, 1990). Finally, it was predicted that the Barr body or sex chromatin was the heterochromatic manifestation of the inactive X in interphase (Ohno *et al.*, 1959), and that the two Xs differed in the cell cycle time at which they replicated DNA (Taylor, 1960; Grumbach *et al.*, 1963). This important hypothesis has stood the test of time, though there have been significant additions unforseen in the early 1960s.

Mammalian X inactivation is best described in developmental terms (Figure 5.1). The two X chromosomes in the early female embryo are not initially differentiated, either cytologically or functionally. X inactivation occurs in the early blastocyst (Austin, 1966; DeMars, 1967; Plotnick *et al.*, 1971; Adler *et al.*, 1977; Epstein *et al.*, 1978; Kratzer and Gartler, 1978; Monk and Harper, 1979), occurring first in the trophectoderm and next in the extraembryonic endoderm. X inactivation appears to be initiated as cells differentiate but is not found in pluripotent cells. Inactivation in the early stages of development is confined to extraembryonic cells. It is distinguished by the fact that the paternal X chromosome is preferentially inactivated (Takagi and Sasaki, 1975; West *et al.*, 1977). This distinction may have evolutionary significance because in marsupials X inactivation is largely, though not exclusively, confined to the paternal X at all stages of development (Graves, 1987). Later, random inactivation occurs in the inner cell mass or embryo proper. It appears that all the cells in the embryo, including the germ cells, are subject to X inactivation. However, in contrast to somatic cells, in which the inactivation pattern becomes a fixed part of the cell's

Developmental Stage			X-Inactivation Status
Fertilized Egg			$X_m^a\ X_p^a$
Morula			$X_m^a\ X_p^a$
Early Blastocyst	trophectoderm		$X_m^a\ X_p^i$
	rest of embryo		$X_m^a\ X_p^a$
Mid Blastocyst	extraembryomic endoderm		$X_m^a\ X_p^i$
	inner cell mass		$X_m^a\ X_p^a$
Late Blastocyst	epiblast		$X_m^a\ X_p^i$ $X_m^i\ X_p^a$
		somatic cells	stable inactivation
		germ cells	oogonia inactivated
			oocytes reactivated

Figure 5.1. Ontogeny of X Inactivation. Developmental biology of X chromosome inactivation in the mammalian female embryo as determined in the mouse; X^a, active; X^i, inactive; X_m, maternal; X_p, paternal.

somatic heredity, the inactive X chromosome in the female germ line is reactivated at the onset of meiosis. The inactivation pattern in the female germ line is cyclic, inactive during the oogonial or mitotic phase and active during the oocytic stage. In the male, with a single X chromosome, X inactivation does not occur in somatic cells; however, in the germ line the single X is condensed and inactivated early in meiosis. It appears that in the germ line the female and male exhibit reciprocal patterns of X inactivation (Gartler *et al.*, 1975; Grant and Chapman, 1988).

The active and inactive X chromosomes are distinguished in interphase by the heterochromatic structure of the inactive X, known as the Barr body or sex chromatin. The two X chromosomes also have different replication patterns, the inactive X initiating DNA replication later than the active X. Because these features seemed to involve the entire X chromosome, it was assumed that inactivation involved the complete X chromosome. However, it is now known that genes in the pairing region of the X and Y chromosomes (pseudoautosomal), where crossing-over regularly occurs, escape inactivation (mice and humans) and that genes in other areas of the X (humans) may be active or only partially inactivated (J. A. Brown *et al.*, 1976; Migeon *et al.*, 1982; Goodfellow *et al.*, 1984; Brown and Willard, 1989, 1990; Schneider-Gadicke *et al.*, 1989; Gough *et al.*, 1990). There is also a recent report of a sequence that is only expressed from the inactive X (Brown *et al.*, 1991a,b) (Figure 5.2). However, it appears that for any X, most of the chromosome exhibits either a pattern of activity or inactivity. That is, if one X has the glucose-6-phosphate dehydrogenase A (*GdA*) allele and the phosphoglycerate kinase 1 (*Pgk1*) allele and the homologue has the *GdB* and *Pgk2* alleles, the cell will express either *GdA* and *Pgk1* or *GdB* and *Pgk2*, not *GdA* and *Pgk2* or *GdB* and *Pgk1*. Those and similar results imply that the determination of which X chromosome is active or inactive occurs at a single site or control center. This interpretation is supported by observations of X inactivation patterns in X-autosome translocations. In those cases wherein the rearranged X is inactivated, only one of the X chromosome fragments is inactivated, most likely that part containing the center presumed to be the initiation site for X inactivation (Cattanach, 1975; Gartler and Riggs, 1983).

In 1975 several workers (Holliday and Pugh, 1975; Riggs, 1975; Sager and Kitchin, 1975) proposed that DNA methylation might play a significant role in X activation. The first evidence that a DNA modification, such as methylation, could play a role in X chromosome inactivation came from a study in which it was shown that purified DNA from the inactive X chromosome could not function as a transforming vector for the hypoxanthine phosphoribosyltransferase (*hprt*) gene (Liskay and Evans, 1980). Soon after, it was shown that 5-azacytidine (5AC), a known demethylating agent, induced reactivation of genes on the human inactive X chromosome in rodent–human somatic cell hybrids (Mohandas *et al.*, 1981a). Shortly thereafter, it was shown that reactivated DNA from 5AC-treated cells could function in transfection studies (Lester *et al.*, 1982; Venolia *et al.*, 1982). Further support for a suppressive role of DNA methylation came from molecular analyses of the GC-rich promoter regions of X-linked housekeeping genes that showed hypermethylation on the inactive alleles (Wolf *et al.*, 1984; Yen *et al.*, 1984; Keith *et al.*, 1986; Lock *et al.*, 1986; Toniolo *et al.*, 1988). The GC-rich hypomethylated promoter

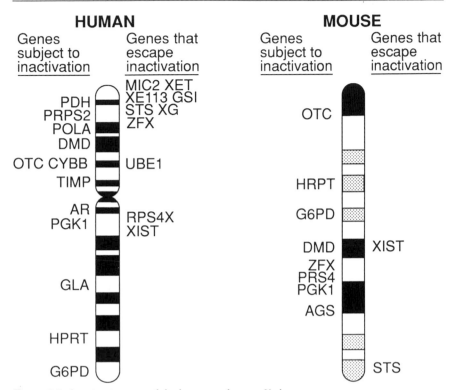

Figure 5.2. Inactivation map of the human and mouse X chromosome.

regions on active genes are hypersensitive to nucleases, in contrast to the nuclease resistance characteristic of the hypermethylated inactive genes (Wolf and Migeon, 1985; Riley *et al.*, 1986; Yang and Caskey, 1987; Hansen *et al.*, 1988). It should be pointed out that the hypomethylation and nuclease sensitivity characteristics of the active X-linked housekeeping genes are also general features of transcribed autosomal housekeeping genes. These transfection and methylation studies were carried out on somatic cells derived from the true embryonic lineage. Similar studies on tissues and cultures derived from extra-embryonic lineages are limited, but their results indicate that inactivation in these cells may not involve DNA methylation (Kratzer *et al.* 1983; Grant and Chapman, 1988). In fact, the latter observation is consistent with the possibility that the hypermethylation characteristic of the 5′ GC-rich promoter regions of inactive X-linked housekeeping genes may be a secondary step in determining their repression (Gartler *et al.*, 1985; Lock *et al.*, 1987).

The key step in any developmental system, including X inactivation, is its *initiation*. If inactivation begins at one site on the X chromosome, such as an inactivation center, and subsequently most of the remainder of the X chromosome becomes inactivated, then the *spreading* of the signal to some 10^8 bp of DNA must occur. An observation critical to the development of the X inactivation hypothesis involved the spreading of the inactivation signal from the X chromosome into an adjacent autosomal insert carrying a coat color marker (Cattanach, 1975). Normally, animals heterozygous for this autosomal coat color marker exhibit a simple dominant phenotype; when the dominant allele is inserted into the inactive X, variegation results. Once the two X chromosomes in a cell become differentiated, this difference must be *maintained* through every somatic cell mitosis.

II. INITIATION OF X INACTIVATION

A. Inactivation in extraembryonic cells

The maternal and paternal X chromosomes are in an active configuration in the early embryo, with no evidence of dosage compensation into the morula stage of development (Adler *et al.*, 1977; Epstein *et al.*, 1978; Kratzer and Gartler, 1978). At the morula–blastocyst transition, sex chromatin, asynchronous replication, and gene expression differences occur, seemingly almost simultaneously (Austin, 1966; DeMars, 1967; Takagi, 1974). This is also the time when the first detectable differentiative event occurs in the developing embryo, that of separation of the inner cell mass and the trophectoderm. The trophectoderm gives rise to extraembryonic tissues only, whereas the inner cell mass gives rise to the embryo proper and to other extraembryonic tissues. X inactivation, which is restricted to the trophectoderm at this stage, is nonrandom, with the paternal X being preferentially inactivated. Takagi (1974) first described this phenomenon in rodent embryos using differential X chromosome replication as a marker. Later, the same phenomenon was demonstrated at the level of gene expression when it was shown that the maternal *Pgk* allele is preferentially active in extraembryonic tissues of the mouse (West *et al.*, 1977). In a recent study using purified cytotrophoblast cells from humans, Harrison (1989) presented convincing evidence that the maternal X-linked *Gd* allele was preferentially expressed in this extraembryonic tissue. Preferential paternal inactivation occurs in all tissues of marsupials and monotremes (Graves, 1987).

The active and inactive X chromosomes in extraembryonic tissues clearly are distinguished from one another, but the manner in which they differ is distinct from that of embryonic cells, even at the molecular level. The transfection studies already discussed support this notion. There is strong evidence that the DNA of extraembryonic cells and tissues is generally undermethylated relative to cells of the embryo (Sanford et al., 1985; Monk et al., 1987). This conclusion is based on observations of both repetitive and low-copy-number sequences without respect to linkage. From the transfection results in extra-embryonic cells, one would have predicted an absence of hypermethylation on the inactive X in the 5' region. However, limited observations of the hprt and Gd genes in human chorionic villus cells do not bear out this expectation (Mohandas et al., 1989). It will be necessary to repeat and extend these studies with homogeneous extraembryonic cells and with a well-characterized methylation analysis.

   Preferential inactivation is a subset of a larger developmental phenomenon known as genomic imprinting. Imprinting is the process by which the genetic material is apparently "marked" as to parental origin or history during passage through the germ line (Solter, 1988). This phenomenon was first described in certain insects, in which the entire paternal genome is marked for heterochromatization and inactivation in males (Crouse, 1960; Chandra and Brown, 1975). In mammals there is a requirement for the functional presence of both the maternal and paternal genomes (Solter, 1988). This requirement appears to be based upon the fact that various parts of the mouse and human genomes are differentially expressed depending on their parental origin (Cattanach and Kirk, 1985; Myers et al., 1985; Spence et al., 1988; Nicholls et al., 1989).

   Because all embryos begin development with both X chromosomes active, there must be some mechanism by which the paternal X is recognized and preferentially inactivated later in development. That the paternal genome is marked in some way in early development is supported by the observation of Odartchenko and Kenklis (1973) that the paternal chromosomal complement appears to have a restricted nuclear location in early blastomeres of the mouse. The preferential inactivation of the paternal X in extraembryonic tissues may be related to the requirement for the presence of the paternal genome for normal extraembryonic development (Solter, 1988). Because the male does not have a paternal X chromosome, X-linked genes critical to extraembryonic development would adversely affect male development. Preferential inactivation of the paternal X in the female may be a selective mechanism that prevents such genes from accumulating on the X chromosome.

B. Late replication and X chromosome inactivation

The inactive X chromosome is said to be allocyclic; it replicates out of phase with its homologue and the autosomes (Taylor, 1960; Grumbach et al., 1963; Lyon, 1972, 1988). Though the inactive X chromosome generally begins replication late (Willard and Latt, 1976), the first sign of replication asynchrony is in the early extraembryonic lineage in which the inactive X replicates earlier than other chromosomes (Takagi *et al.*, 1984). This condition continues through day 6 of development, when the inactive X has become late replicating in extraembryonic cells (Grant and Chapman, 1988). Late replication is used to assay which of the two X chromosomes is inactive, and has been used to analyze the spreading of the inactive state into autosomal DNA segments in X-autosome translocations (Keitges and Palmer, 1986). Although the inactive X chromosome generally replicates later in S phase than the active homologue, some tissue-specific differences in the precise sequence in which the bands of the inactive X replicate have been reported (Epplen *et al.*, 1975; Willard, 1977). Differences in replication timing of bands of the inactive X chromosome have been reported in lymphocytes from a single individual (Schmidt *et al.*, 1982), strongly implying that the precise sequence of replication of inactive X bands is not rigidly controlled.

The spreading of the inactive state into autosomal regions in X-autosome translocations has been extensively studied, and this spreading has been correlated with the late replication of the affected autosomal segments. Allderdice *et al.* (1978) reported on an X;14 translocation in which inactivation of the rearranged X chromosome resulted in suppression of the phenotypic effects of partial chromosome 14 trisomy. Couturier *et al.* (1979) reported a case study in which a patient had an X;21 translocation and would have shown the phenotype of trisomy 21 if the supernumerary segment had not been inactivated by the spread of X inactivation. This segment was observed to be late replicating in the patient. Disteche *et al.* (1979) showed that the mitochondrial malic enzyme locus (*Mod-2*), which is autosomal in mice, was inactivated and late replicating in mice carrying Cattanach's translocation, in which that locus is translocated onto the X chromosome. Mohandas *et al.* (1981b, 1982) reported an X;13 translocation in which the esterase D locus on chromosome 13 was inactivated and late replicating.

Migeon *et al.* (1986) reported that an inactive X chromosome from human chorionic villus cells became spontaneously reactivated and simultaneously early replicating in rodent–human hybrid cells, but this work could not be repeated (Mohandas *et al.*, 1989). 5-Azacytidine treatment of hybrid cells and some nonhybrid transformed cells can lead to reactivation of genes on the inactive X chromosome (Mohandas *et al.*, 1981b; Lester *et al.*, 1982; Beggs *et al.*, 1986; Nadon *et al.*, 1986). Under these conditions, the chromosomal replication pattern may show no apparent change or the entire chromosome may become early replicating (Hors-Cayla *et al.*, 1983). However, when a specific reactivated gene was studied both at a refined cytological level (Schmidt *et al.*, 1985) and at a molecular level (Schmidt and Migeon, 1990), the expected switch to early replication was observed. Several reports have indicated a correlation between 5-azacytidine treatment and a change to early chromosomal replication in short-term studies (Shafer and Priest, 1984; Jablonka et al., 1985; Schmidt et al., 1985). It seems possible that the short-term effects of induced demethylation may be extensive, but that remethylation may reverse some of them, including the replication pattern.

In the short arm of the X chromosome, regions that normally escape X inactivation appear to replicate earlier in S phase than do inactive regions (Schempp and Meer, 1983); this includes the Xp22.13–22.3 region. The corresponding Y chromosomal region, Yp11.2–11.32, is also early replicating. In addition, a part of human chromosome band Xq13.1 replicates early in S phase (Schempp & Meer, 1983), suggesting that a locus in the region might escape inactivation. Band Xq13 is the putative location of the X chromosome inactivation center (Gartler and Riggs, 1983; Mattei et al., 1983), and it is tempting to speculate that X inactivation is a process that requires an active gene at that center. Brown et al. (1991a,b) have recently described a transcript specific to the inactive X and encoded in this region of the chromosome.

McKay et al. (1987) and Riggs (1990) have argued that late replication may be the basis for the establishment of X chromosome inactivation. Although X inactivation is fundamentally different in eutherian mammals and marsupials (inactivation in marsupials is nonrandom and does not involve extensive methylation), the marsupial X is late replicating (McKay et al., 1987). Riggs (1990) states that late replication could provide the sort of memory effect required for inheritance of the inactive state, because early replication appears to be necessary for transcription (Goldman et al., 1984; Goldman, 1988) and because transcription may be required for initiation of replication in certain chromosomal regions (DePamphilis, 1988). Thus, the effects of late replication and transcriptional silence may tend to stabilize each other by a feedback mechanism.

That DNA methylation plays a role in the stabilization of the inactive state seems likely. Riggs (1990) suggests that methylation of replication origins on the inactive X chromosome may be responsible for late replication. Support for this possibility comes from the previously mentioned studies that indicate an advancement in replication timing following 5-azacytidine treatment. Methylation may not cause the late-replicating state initially, but could stabilize that state once established. Significant methylation differences have not been found between X-linked tissue-specific genes on the active and inactive X chromosomes (Cullen et al., 1986). Such genes usually lack a GC-rich promoter region, which is the region of critical methylation differences for active and inactive X-linked housekeeping genes. It seems possible that methylation differences in pertinent replication origins might play a role in the differential expression of X-linked tissue-specific genes.

Although this idea is very attractive, there are contrary data. McBurney and Adamson (1976) have studied a murine teratocarcinoma cell line and found that one X chromosome appears to be inactivated, based on the dosage level of several X-linked gene products. Furthermore, the induced mutation rate at the X-linked *hprt* locus in this line is characteristic of a cell line with a single active X chromosome. However, the two X chromosomes in this cell line do not exhibit replication asynchrony. These results would place dosage compensation before the onset of replication asynchrony. In another related study, Hors-Cayla *et al.* (1983) reported on the reactivation and replication patterns of the inactive human X in five hamster–human hybrid clones following treatment with 5-azacytidine and selection in hypoxanthine/aminopterin/thymidine (HAT) medium. In two lines the human inactive X became early replicating and in the other three lines the human X replicated late. However, the pattern of gene reactivation in these lines was not correlated with replication. These results suggest that replication asynchrony may not play a causative role in X chromosome inactivation. Furthermore, the onset of replication asynchrony shows the inactive X replicating early for a brief period (Takagi *et al.*, 1984), a pattern the house shrew apparently exhibits at all times (Rao *et al.*, 1970). These observations argue against a firm requirement for late replication in achieving transcription repression. Finally, the fact that several genes are known to replicate early and are not transcribed (e.g., α-globin; Goldman *et al.*, 1984) supports the conclusion that early replication is a necessary but not sufficient condition for gene expression (Goldman, 1988).

C. Genetic and molecular characterization of the X inactivation center

As mentioned earlier, the chromosomal nature of inactivation and the pattern of inactivation in X-autosome translocations implies the existence of a single initiation site for X inactivation. At that site the initial differentiation event presumably occurs, followed by spreading of the activation or inactivation message, differential methylation of the 5′ GC-rich regions of housekeeping genes and perhaps other genes, and the development of replication asynchrony. The complexities of the developmental process of inactivation imply that it is a multistage process.

The initial step, which distinguishes the two X chromosomes, is nonrandom in extraembryonic cells and random when it occurs later in embryonic cells. This means that there could be two distinct initiation points, one for each lineage, or there could be a single one with the X chromosomes in the extraembryonic lineage imprinted such that the paternal X is preferentially inactivated. Second and third events in the inactivation process could be the actual heterochromatinization of one X chromosome and the onset of replication asynchrony. These might be the only steps that occur in extraembryonic cells, whereas in the embryonic lineage a further DNA modification step involving methylation in GC-rich promoters may follow at a later stage.

The idea of an X chromosomal control site was first hypothesized following the discovery of X chromosome inactivation (Grumbach et al., 1963). Cattanach and Isaacson (1967) coined the term "X controlling element" (Xce) to identify a locus involved in the chromosomal determination of inactivation. Today, most workers consider that the initiation site for X inactivation, which is sometimes indicated as Xic, is identical to Cattanach's Xce. (We use the terms Xce and Xic interchangeably in this review.) Cattanach assumed that Xce, like any other gene, should be subject to variation and searched for such variants by selecting for changes in the extent of variegation in mice heterozygous at a coat color locus. If variant Xce alleles existed, one should be able to find an allele that inactivated preferentially. Limited evidence for such alleles was found, and they were mapped to the vicinity of the murine Pgk locus. That null alleles were not found could reflect the possibility that such mutants would result in early embryonic death due to an aneuploidy effect. Further studies of mouse X-autosome translocations and deletions (Rastan, 1983; Rastan and Brown, 1990) support and extend the Xce concept of Cattanach. In humans, studies based on replication patterns in abnormal X chromosomes (Therman and Sarto, 1983), on chromosome bending (Flejter et al., 1984), and on X-autosome translocations and deletions (Brown and Willard, 1989; Rocchi et al., 1989) indicate that Xce maps to a region close to Xq13, which is also the region to which the Pgk gene maps. The basic approach in using X-autosome translocations or deletions is that if a single Xce exists, when an X chromosome is rearranged in a translocation, for example, only that part carrying the Xce locus will be subject to inactivation. This observation was first made by Russell (1963). In most X-autosome translocations the intact X is usually inactivated even though initially inactivation is random. When the rearranged X is inactivated, the adjoining autosomal segment may also become inactivated, leading to an aneuploidy effect and a resulting population in which only cells with the normal X inactivated survive. However, in unbalanced X-autosome translocations, the rearranged X is often inactivated, providing some cases for this type of analysis.

As suggested by the Lyon hypothesis, there must be some "counting mechanism" that ensures that only one active X is maintained in any diploid somatic cell. Rastan (1983) suggested that each inactivation center could either be in a free or a blocked state. Blocking of the inactivation center, according to Rastan's hypothesis, occurs by binding of some cellular product that is present in an amount sufficient to block only one inactivation center. Once the inactivation center is blocked, that X chromosome remains active, but any other X chromosomes in the cell are subject to subsequent events initiating the inactivation process at the inactivation center.

Localization of the human X chromosome inactivation center to Xq13 would suggest that a chromosome walk toward *Xce* might lead to molecular cloning and characterization of this important locus. This approach is complicated by the fact that we know nothing about the potential molecular features of *Xce* and therefore we do not know what we are looking for at the DNA level. Furthermore, we do not have any useful mutants at this locus. One approach to identifying a sequence as *Xce* would be to transfect candidate sequences into target cells and look for an inactivation effect in a ligated reporter gene or on sequences adjoining the integration site. A transient expression system would be best and, of course, it would be necessary to carry out such experiments in a cell culture system capable of undergoing inactivation. If *Xce* is relatively small and autonomous, this approach could be successful; however, if the gene is large and site dependent, then these experiments would likely produce only negative results. Rastan and Brown (1990) present an excellent analysis of such a proposal. Transgenic mouse experiments would be another possibility, although costly and possibly difficult to interpret. Integration into an X chromosome might be without effect, and integration into an autosomal site might result in early embryonic lethality.

An alternate approach for identifying and isolating the *Xce* locus would be to try to induce null mutations in it. Such mutations would provide an end point for determining whether a particular sequence obtained in a chromosomal walk was a reasonable candidate. Furthermore, if the mutations were induced by a retroviral insertional system, it might be possible to use such a marker to isolate the gene. If the initial event is one of inactivation, then the absence of a functional *Xce* on one X should lead to preferential inactivation of the other X chromosome. This nonrandom inactivation could be distinguished with careful selection and screening methods. On the other hand, if the initial event is one of marking one X to remain active, then the absence of a functional *Xce* on one X could lead to a cell with two active X chromosomes. Such a condition would not be viable in an intact organism (Takagi and Abe, 1990) but should be compatible with cell division in cell culture and could be detected with selective methods. Such experiments could be carried out in teratocarcinoma cultures that have already been used for other studies of X inactivation *in vitro* (McBurney and Adamson, 1976; Martin *et al.*, 1978; McBurney and Strutt, 1980; Takagi *et al.*, 1983; Okuyama *et al.*, 1986). Molecular isolation of genetically identified sequences would have to be followed up with transfection studies to provide definitive proof that the *Xce* had indeed been cloned.

Other approaches to identifying *Xce* depends on whether it represents a passive or an active site. It could be a binding site for a chromosomal protein with cooperative properties that induces heterochromatin formation in an early step in the inactivation process (Cook, 1974). Abe *et al.* (1988) recently reported a possible protein difference between human male and female chromosomal proteins, and several reports have appeared recently indicating the existence in *Drosophila* of heterochromatin-specific proteins (James and Elgin,

1986; James *et al.*, 1989; Reuter *et al.*, 1990). Candidate proteins could be used in protein–DNA binding studies to try and identify a passive-type *Xce*. On the other hand, if *Xce* represents an active site, then one might look for a gene or genes expressed only from the inactive X. Genes expressed from the inactive X can be detected in rodent–human somatic cell hybrids retaining the human inactive X chromosome, and recently a gene (*XIST*) expressed only from the inactive X has been reported (Brown *et al.*, 1991a,b). The gene maps within the region predicted for *Xce*, which makes it an attractive candidate for this critical component of the inactivation process. Multiple transcripts have been detected at *XIST*, but the existence of multiple stop codons in the transcripts implies that *XIST* may not code for a protein. The authors suggest that the gene may code for a structural RNA, which could differentially modify the Xs by the blocking of the site on the active X chromosome. This interpretation implies that the *XIST* sites are blocked on both Xs in embryonic cells prior to inactivation and that the initial event of the process is one of inactivating a previously active chromosome. We may be close to a molecular understanding of the repression of the inactive X chromosome, but a major problem in mammalian dosage compensation may still remain. It is important to realize that dosage compensation must not only bring about equivalence of X-linked gene expression in males and females, but it must also maintain equivalent autosomal:sex chromosomal ratios in both sexes. The *Drosophila* system meets both requirements in that both the Xs in the female remain active and the single X in the male is transcribed at twice the rate of each X in the female. The mammalian system appears counterproductive in that the autosomal:sex chromosomal ratio is disturbed in both sexes. Lyon (1974) considered this question and proposed an evolutionary explanation involving duplication of the X chromosome. This hypothesis is not well supported, but another possibility relates to the *Drosophila* dosage compensation story. The *mle* gene in *Drosophila* plays an initial role in dosage compensation as shown by the fact that males, mutant at this locus, exhibit depressed levels of X-linked gene expression. Kuroda *et al.* (1991) have shown that the protein coded by *mle* is found on the male X and not on the female X chromosomes. The *mle*-encoded protein, which appears to be a helicase, presumably enhances the general transcription rate of the single X in the male. It seems possible that a similar function could act in mammalian cells on the single active X in both females and males to bring about an autosomal:sex chromosomal balance.

III. SPREADING OF THE X INACTIVATION SIGNAL

After its initiation, the inactivation process must spread through nearly the entire length of the X chromosome. Two important aspects of the spreading problem are that (1) the inactivation process regularly skips over certain regions of the X chromosome and (2) it can penetrate into adjacent autosomal regions in X-autosome translocations. These observations imply that there may be particular DNA sequence characteristics that render certain loci accessible to inactivation and/or other loci immune from this effect.

A number of X-linked loci in humans appear to escape inactivation, including those for the Xg blood group (Race and Sanger, 1975) and the MIC2 surface antigen (Goodfellow *et al.*, 1984), the ZFX locus (Schneider-Gadicke *et al.*, 1989), the A1S9T locus (Brown and Willard, 1989, 1990), and the loci for arylsulfatase-C (Chang *et al.*, 1990), a ribosomal protein gene (Fisher *et al.*, 1990), and an inactive-X-specific transcript that maps to the apparent inactivation center (Brown *et al.*, 1991a,b). In addition, the steroid sulfatase (Sts) locus partially escapes inactivation (Shapiro *et al.*, 1979; Migeon *et al.*, 1982). The map location of these genes extends from the X–Y pairing region to the proximal long arm of the X chromosome (Figure 5.2). It may be that the genes in this region are only partially repressed when on the inactive X chromosome. To determine that a locus is only partially repressed requires careful quantitative work, and such studies have only been carried out for the Sts gene.

The only murine gene known to escape X inactivation is the Sts gene (Keitges *et al.*, 1985; Keitges and Gartler, 1986), although Jones *et al.* (1989) have reported that this escape may only be partial. The murine Sts locus maps in the X–Y pairing region, and there are functional copies of this gene on both the X and Y chromosomes. Goldman *et al.* (1987) have shown that a chicken transferrin gene inserted onto the X chromosome in transgenic mice escapes X chromosome inactivation, although it resides on a part of the X chromosome that is normally inactivated (M. A. Goldman and C. M. Disteche, unpublished data).

These observations raise the question of why most genes naturally found or inserted onto the X chromosome are subject to X chromosome inactivation, whereas some are not. One can imagine that there is a defined border between the segment of the X chromosome that undergoes inactivation and the segment that does not, and that the behavior of a gene is determined by its position with respect to that boundary. Alternatively, DNA sequence characteristics in or near specific genes may protect those loci from inactivation.

In X-autosome translocations, the inactive state may spread into the autosome, may fail to do so, or may "skip" proximal autosomal regions while spreading into more distal ones (Keitges and Palmer, 1986). Mohandas *et al.* (1987) have reported on a patient having a duplication of distal Xq in which the duplicated segment is located in Xp, distal to the Sts locus. Both copies of the Gd gene are inactivated, but the Sts gene remains active. These findings clearly imply regional or local control of the inactivation process as opposed to the existence of a "border" beyond which X inactivation cannot venture (Goldman *et al.*, 1987; Goldman, 1988; Brown and Willard, 1990). The inactivation of a locus is gene dependent rather than position dependent.

If susceptibility to X chromosome inactivation is a characteristic of a gene or chromatin domain [a supercoilable, looped domain as defined in Goldman (1988)], then we might suppose that some genes or domains escape X inactivation because they are not accessible to methylation. For instance, a gene may lack the usual GC-rich promoter associated with housekeeping genes. This latter possibility is clearly not the case for the human MIC2 gene in the pseudoautosomal region; it has a typical GC-rich promoter that is unmethylated on the active X, the inactive X, and the Y chromosomes (Mondello et al., 1988). In addition, the murine Sts gene, which is also pseudoautosomal, is inactivated in cell culture; this inactivation can be reversed by the demethylating agent, 5-azacytidine (Schorderet et al., 1988), implying that it is indeed methylatable. Several autosomal housekeeping genes have also been shown to become inactivated by aberrant methylation in cell culture (Harris, 1982, 1984). Mandel and Chambon (1979) have shown that the transferrin gene in chickens is hypomethylated in expressing but not in nonexpressing tissues. These data imply that the resistance of many of the loci to inactivation is not due to an inherent resistance to methylation.

Based on studies of transgenic mice that have X-linked inserts, we have proposed a model for the spreading of X inactivation in which specific signal sequences are required at segments along the X chromosome in order for those intervals to become inactivated (Goldman et al., 1987; Goldman, 1988). Chromosomal DNA in vertebrates is organized into discrete regions or domains, of the order of 100 kb in length, that are anchored to a protein matrix at a matrix- or scaffold-associated region (MAR or SAR) and form torsionally independent loops (reviewed in Goldman, 1988). These domains appear to be functional units that may take on specific conformational characteristics when the region is capable of transcription (reviewed in Goldman, 1988). We propose that the functional unit for the spread and maintenance of X inactivation is such a chromatin domain (Goldman et al., 1984, 1987; Goldman, 1988). Because this domain is a unit considerably larger than a transcriptional unit, signal sequences required for X inactivation would need to occur only once per domain. Some autosomal genes could be inactivated in X-autosome translocations because they occur in domains that have signal sequences, but others lack these sequences and therefore escape inactivation. The chicken transferrin gene may escape inactivation because the 187-kb expanse in which it is found forms one or more independent domains that lack X inactivation signal sequences (Goldman et al., 1987). A mouse α-fetoprotein gene insert (Krumlauf et al., 1986) is subject to X inactivation because either it has such sequences or its <40-kb span is included in a domain that has these sequences. Consistent with this model are recent studies on two other transgenes, a metallothionein–vasopression fusion gene with a total insert size of approximately 30 kb (R. Behringer, R. Brinster, J. Habener, J. Peschon, and R. Palmiter, unpublished; M. Goldman, E. Parker, C. Wirth, and W. Zupko, unpublished) and a protamine–SV40 large T antigen fusion gene having a total insert size of <40 kb (R. Behringer, R. Brinster, J. Peschon, and R. Palmiter, unpublished). Both transgenes are subject to X chromosome inactivation.

One possible characteristic of a chromatin domain would be the presence of a nuclear MAR. Such sites have been found in and near the genes encoding Hprt, factor IX, and ornithine transcarbamylase (Sykes *et al.*, 1988; Beggs and Migeon, 1989). The presence or absence of a MAR in an X-linked transgene might be expected to correlate with the pattern of inactivation of the transgene.

The ZFX locus escapes inactivation in humans, but its homologue in mice does not (Adler *et al.*, 1991). The human ZFX gene is near the pseudoautosomal region whereas the murine ZFX locus maps to region D, a chromosomal segment containing genes known to be inactivated. The different inactivation patterns of the murine and human ZFX genes may be related to their different map positions on the X chromosomes.

The spread of the inactive state may occur in a processive manner along the length of the X chromosome. Riggs (1990) has proposed a model for the spreading of X inactivation in which proteins similar to prokaryotic type I restriction endonucleases (which cleave at a considerable distance from the recognition sequence) bind specific sites and reel DNA in so that chromosomal loops might be connected at their bases by such proteins. The protein involved in *Drosophila* position-effect variegation, which contains several zinc finger regions (Reuter *et al.*, 1990), or other proteins implicated in *Drosophila* heterochromatin formation (James and Elgin, 1986; James *et al.*, 1989) might be prospects for such reeling activity. It is not clear, however, how specific regions of the chromosome might be skipped. Perhaps these regions lack binding sites for the proposed protein and bind instead an alternative protein that maintains the active state.

It is not necessary that the spreading of the X inactivation signal be processive. An alternative view is that the effect of the initial signal is to dump the inactive X into a compartment where susceptible domains are heterochromatinized. Genes on the inactive X that escape inactivation would presumably reside in domains that hinder heterochromatin formation. However, the conditions of these domains are not etched in stone: inactive genes can be reactivated and genes that escape inactivation, such as the Sts gene, can be inactivated in transformed cell cultures. Thus, genes such as MIC2 and Sts are protected from methylation under normal conditions, but become targets for inactivating methylation in transformed cell culture. It appears that hypermethylation of usually methylation-free promoter regions may be a frequent occurrence for both autosomal and X-linked genes in transformed cell culture (Dobrovic *et al.*, 1988; Schorderet *et al.*, 1988; Wise and Harris, 1988; Antequera *et al.*, 1990; Jones *et al.*, 1990).

IV. MAINTENANCE OF X INACTIVATION

A. Methylation patterns in somatic cells

In 1975 the idea that DNA methylation might play a role in differentiation of the X chromosomes, as well as other differentiative events, was put forward by three groups (Holliday and Pugh, 1975; Riggs, 1975; Sager and Kitchin, 1975). The idea was based on two points: (1) DNA methylation was known to affect the binding of proteins to DNA and thus affect transcriptional potential, and (2) methylases tend to be very ineffective in *de novo* methylation, but very efficient at methylating half-methylated sites. The significance of the latter is that two undifferentiated X chromosomes could be marked differentially by the slow *de novo* methylase action, but once a chromosome is methylated, the efficient maintenance function of the methylase would perpetuate its methylated state. This idea was proposed as an explanation for the initial distinction between the two undifferentiated X chromosomes in a female cell, the target being a control point on the X chromosome from which the methylation signal would spread to individual genes. Because we now have the first molecular candidate for *Xce* (Brown *et al.*, 1991a), we may soon know something about its methylation characteristics. For the present we do know that methylation differences do characterize active and inactive X-linked housekeeping genes, and they clearly play a role in maintaining the repressed state of many genes on the inactive X chromosome.

The human gene encoding phosphoglycerate kinase is the most thoroughly studied X-linked gene with respect to methylation. There are 120 CpG sites in the *Pgk* GC-rich promoter region, and all the sites have been analyzed in normal cells (leukocytes) and hamster–human hybrids containing either the active or inactive human X chromosome with and without 5AC treatment (Keith *et al.*, 1986; Hansen *et al.*, 1988; Hansen and Gartler, 1990; Pfeifer *et al.*, 1990a). This region is about 500 bp long and extends about 100 bp downstream of the transcription start site. The *Pgk* gene on the active X chromosome in leukocytes and in cultured cells is unmethylated at all 120 CpG sites in the promoter region. In contrast, the *Pgk* gene on the inactive X chromosome in hamster–human hybrid cells is methylated at all but one of these sites, but may exhibit some mosaicism in leukocytes. Analysis of cell clones from 5AC-treated hamster–human hybrid cells containing the inactive X chromosome has led to further definition of the role of methylation in this region. Most 5AC-reactivated clones exhibit complete demethylation of the promoter region; however, some are methylated at specific positions, indicating that methylation at these sites does not have a major effect on expression. This noncritical region, which is hypomethylated on the active X, may extend 1 kb or more downstream of the start site. Most nonreactivated clones appear to be completely methylated, but some exhibit mosaic patterns with interspersed methylated and nonmethylated regions and sites. These clones are not completely stable as there is a tendency for remethylation of demethylated sites. Remethylation is not rapid, suggesting that cooperativity does not play a major role in the remethylation process in these cells. A detailed analysis of a small number of these clones has led to the suggestion that a region close to the transcription start site may play a determinative role in the methylation pattern of the *Pgk* promoter. If this region remains methylated after 5AC exposure, but other regions in the promoter are demethylated, the gene probably remains inactivated and gradually remethylation occurs. If demethylation of this region occurs, transcription probably begins and further methylation, both *de novo* and maintenance, is inhibited; this leads to rapid and complete demethylation of the promoter.

The evidence is strong that methylation of the promoter regions of X-linked housekeeping genes is necessary to keep them stably inactivated in somatic cells. However, it is most likely not the only factor involved. *In vitro* methylated herpes thymidine kinase DNA microinjected into rodent cells is transcribed for approximately 8 hours before it is shut down (Buschhausen *et al.*, 1987). This result suggests that transcription factors can bind to methylated DNA and that some further modification of chromatin structure is required for inactivation. The transcription factors Sp1 and CTF bind to their recognition sites irrespective of methylation (Harrington *et al.*, 1988; Höller *et al.*, 1988; Ben-Hattar *et al.*, 1989). Recently, Meehan *et al.* (1989) have isolated a protein that binds preferentially to heavily methylated DNA (15 or more methylated sites), a factor that could prevent binding of transcription factors to methylated DNA.

Multiple factors and steps are involved in eukaryotic transcription systems, and methylation, complex in itself, is only one of the factors maintaining the inactive state of housekeeping genes on the inactive X. For at least one tissue-specific gene, the κ immunoglobulin gene (Kelley *et al.*, 1988), it has been shown that an enhancer can override the repressive effect of methylation. Although the methylation in this instance does not involve 5′ GC-rich hypermethylation, this case illustrates the complexities of regulatory mechanisms and indicates the possibility of overriding the system even for a 5′ GC-rich promoter region.

If all 120 CpGs of the *Pgk* promoter need to be demethylated for reactivation to occur at the *Pgk* locus, it is not likely that it would ever occur accidentally or perhaps even with 5AC treatment. In normal cells the inactivation system is extremely stable. However, in transformed cells and especially in somatic cell hybrids, reactivation occurs spontaneously at some loci with a frequency of up to 1×10^{-5} per cell division and with a frequency of several percent following 5AC treatment. This observation is in keeping with our analysis that a more restricted region of methylated sites must be demethylated for reactivation and subsequent general demethylation to occur.

If inactivation required simultaneous methylation of all 120 CpGs, such an event would probably never occur, but if only a single site had to be methylated for inactivation then inactivation would be a common event. Neither extreme appears to be the case; in transformed cells inactivation occasionally occurs both in autosomal housekeeping genes and in at least one X-linked gene that normally escapes X inactivation (Harris, 1982, 1984; Schorderet et al., 1988). Two recent studies report extensive methylation of the 5' regions of several tissue-specific genes in transformed cell cultures (Antequera et al., 1990; Jones et al., 1990).

How do the observed 5' methylation differences between the active and inactive X chromosomes come about? Szyf et al. (1990) have described a 214-bp fragment in the 5' GC-rich promoter of the Thy-1 gene that appears to protect the region from methylation in an embryonic stem cell. They propose that such a mechanism could explain the repression of methylation at the 5' end of X-linked housekeeping genes on the active X. If so, there would have to be a mechanism by which the very same sequence on the inactive X permitted methylation. A simpler model is that the promoter binding of transcription factors may act as protection against methylation as long as transcription continues; the GC-rich region of all active housekeeping genes would be resistant to methylation. If transcription is shut down, then it may be that a resulting change in chromatin conformation allows the region to become methylated. The key to establishing the methylation difference would be the initial cessation of transcription on one of them.

The work of Lock et al. (1987) is often cited as evidence that methylation of the promoter region is a late step in the repression of housekeeping genes on the inactive X chromosome. Lock et al. studied the onset of methylation at a methylation-sensitive restriction site in the first intron of the mouse hprt gene. They reported that methylation does not occur until about 10 days of embryonic development, which is several days after the onset of X inactivation. As has been shown for the human Pgk gene (Hansen and Gartler, 1990), the methylation status of flanking CpGs may not have a significant effect on gene expression. Such sites may normally be methylated on the inactive X and unmethylated on the active X, but changes in their methylation pattern may be without effect. It is not known for the murine hprt gene whether the methylation status of the site analyzed by Lock et al. (1987) in the first intron is critical to gene expression. Methylation of a critical region of the hprt gene may occur at an earlier time. Evidence that methylation plays an important role in the repression of genes on the inactive X follows from the kinetics of 5AC reactivation, in which reactivants occur in a time pattern suggesting that only methylation is involved in their repression (Ellis et al., 1987). Further support for a primary role for methylation in gene repression comes from studies in which it can be shown that demethylation precedes the appearance of mRNA when an inactive gene is turned on or is reactivated (Paroush *et al.*, 1990; T. Sasaki and S. M. Gartler, unpublished observations).

Although methylation plays a significant role in the differentiation of X-linked housekeeping genes, its role with respect to tissue-specific X-linked genes is not yet clear. Most of these genes do not have GC-rich promoters; however, in the case of murine ornithine carbamoyl transferase (OCT), an interesting methylation difference among the Xs has been found 10 kb upstream of the first exon. One site is unmethylated on the active X in expressing tissue, but is methylated on the inactive X. In nonexpressing tissue, both the active and inactive Xs are methylated at this site (Ryall *et al.*, 1986; Mullins *et al.*, 1987). Another X-linked tissue-specific gene, for human factor IX, has been analyzed with methylation-sensitive enzymes but with no evidence of a significant difference among the Xs (Cullen *et al.*, 1986). Because only about 4 kb of upstream region was examined, the possibility remains of a significant methylation difference further upstream.

Indirect evidence for the role of methylation as part of the system of repression of genes on the inactive X comes from a study of the human *MIC2* gene, which is located in the X–Y pairing region. It is an active housekeeping gene with a typical GC-rich 5' promoter region and functional X- and Y-linked alleles. As predicted, both GC-rich promoter regions are unmethylated (Mondello *et al.*, 1988). It is likely that the murine *Sts* gene, which is also active on the inactive X, is unmethylated (Schorderet *et al.*, 1988).

There are a number of CpGs that are methylated on the active X and unmethylated on the inactive X. These sites occur in the body of housekeeping genes and in noncoding regions. Although the density of CpGs is relatively high in promoter regions, the bulk of CpGs (90% or more) are in nonpromoter regions. If this methylation pattern holds for all of the X chromosome nonpromoter regions, then the active X overall would be considerably more methylated than the inactive X. Several sites in the X-linked *hprt* (Yen *et al.*, 1984; Lock *et al.*, 1986) and *Pgk* genes exhibit hypomethylation on the inactive X and hypermethylation on the active X, but a number of sites in the *Gd* (Toniolo *et al.*, 1988) and factor IX (Cullen *et al.*, 1986) genes exhibit similar methylation patterns on the active and inactive X chromosomes. Too few sites have been analyzed to warrant any firm conclusion. Several *in situ* cytological studies of methylation have been reported, with conflicting results. Anti-5-methylcytosine antibodies failed to show any difference between the active and inactive X chromosomes (Miller *et al.*, 1982), whereas in a study of *Hha*I-sensitive sites, most *Hha*I sites appeared to be methylated on the active X and unmethylated on the inactive X (Viegas-Pequignot *et al.*, 1988). However, a study using *Hpa*II digestion followed by *in situ* nick translation indicated somewhat more methylation of *Hpa*II sites on the inactive X than on the active X (Prantera and

Ferraro, 1990). The *in situ* studies are complicated by accessibility of nucleases and may not be the most accurate way to assay the general methylation level of the active and inactive X chromosomes. The significance of these methylation patterns (methylated on active and unmethylated on inactive) is unknown.

B. Chromatin structure and X inactivation

1. Sex chromatin structure

The maintenance of X inactivation throughout the cell cycle and from one cell generation to the next, as well as the relationship of active domains to inactive domains on the inactive X, must have a visible structural basis. A consistent form that is unique to the inactive X is a necessity for this concept. Inactive X chromosomes are cytogenetically different from their active counterpart, the distinction recognizable as a sex chromatin body (Barr body) in an interphase nucleus and as a "bend" (Flejter *et al.*, 1984) in the proximal long arm of the inactive X at metaphase. The appearance of sex chromatin is one of the earliest visible indications of the onset of X chromosome inactivation. DeMars (1967) reported that sex chromatin in cultured mouse embryos was detectable at about the 20-cell stage, prior to blastocyst formation.

We examined the structure of the sex chromatin in intact cells at interphase using the high-voltage electron microscope (HVEM) and also attempted to determine its orientation to the nuclear envelope by visualization of a pericentromeric probe for the X chromosome. HVEM observations indicate that the sex chromatin body (SCB) in intact human fibroblasts has the morphology of a metaphase chromosome (Figure 5.3). Structures that we identified as SCBs were not found in male cells, but occurred in the expected numbers in multiple X cells. The condensed SCB appears to be formed of two "arms," one shorter than the other, which are juxtaposed so that the telomeres are in close association. The arms consist of loops that are in turn composed of strands. The dense chromatin is surrounded by less compact loops that appear to define the nuclear space of the SCB (Figure 5.3). The contour of these more loosely wound loops is similar to that which we observed in tetrachrome-stained whole mounts and is coincident with a "ribbon" of nick-translatable chromatin *in situ* (Dyer *et al.*, 1985). This finding suggests that this part of the interphase structure is accessible to large enzymes that cannot penetrate the SCB. Replication, which occurs asynchronously in the inactive X, and transcription of active genes on the inactive X may occur in this looped-out region. "Genome exposure" is a concept proposed by Krystosek and Puck (1990) in which they postulate that genes specific to the extant developmental stage are located in the nuclear rim, where they are exposed to regulatory factors, whereas inactive genes are

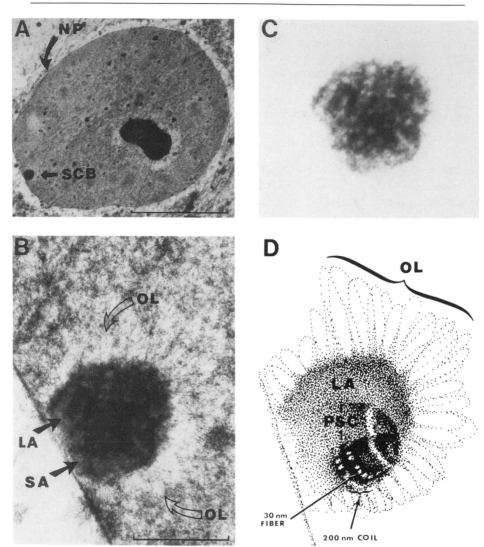

Figure 5.3. High-voltage electron microscopy of the sex chromatin body (SCB). (A) Nucleus with a single SCB; NP, nuclear periphery; bar = 10 μm. (B) Enlargement of A to show two distinct arms, long (LA) and short (SA), surrounded by loosely coiled outer loops (OL) of chromatin; bar = 1 μm. (C) Computer-processed image of the SCB in B to show internal coils and fibers. (D) Artist's interpretation of the same SCB; PSC, putative sister chromatids. This preparation was from a whole-mounted fibroblast that was grown directly on the electron microscope grid, fixed in glutaraldehyde, critical-point dried, and lightly coated with carbon.

internally sequestered. This presumably is a dynamic condition in normal cells that becomes static in cells that have been transformed. Added support for a regulatory function imposed by nuclear structure comes from work of others. For example, Paddy *et al.* (1990) describe the interaction of chromatin and a discontinuous network of nuclear envelope lamins. Also, channels of DNase sensitivity (and, therefore, accessibility) have been described in interphase nuclei (Hutchison and Weintraub, 1985). The ability of the inactive X in interphase to respond structurally to changes in physiology was shown by Borden and Manuelidis (1988); nuclear migration of the X chromosomes occurs differentially in response to changes in cell physiology in normal and epileptic neuronal foci in humans. The recent findings of a number of active genes on the inactive X encourage experiments in which specific nuclear localization of sequences dependent upon activity state and coincident with a defined structure can be determined. *In situ* fluorescence hybridization technology combined with confocal microscopy may give clear demonstration of differential nuclear organization.

We suspected that specific nuclear proteins may be a component of a structure that isolates the SCB from the rest of the nuclear genome. A candidate for such a protein is topoisomerase II, a bifunctional nuclear enzyme that creates negative supercoils in DNA and is also a structural component of the chromosome scaffold, where it appears to anchor loops of chromatin (Earnshaw and Heck, 1985). It is not present in detectable quantities in G_1, but is found in all other stages of the cell cycle (Heck and Earnshaw, 1986). Using an antibody (kindly provided by L. Liu) to localize topoisomerase II in interphase cells, we found preferential immunocytochemical staining of the SCB in some nuclei (unpublished observations). Although the cells in these cultures were not synchronized, the cell cycle effect was apparent in that cells that were lightly 4', 6-diamidino-2-phenylindole dihydrochloride (DAPI) staining (therefore, likely in G_1) did not react with topoisomerase II antibody. Many of these lightly DAPI-staining cells did have visible SCBs, and, according to our hypothesis, they should have been positive for topoisomerase II. Except for the possibility that cells at this stage of the cell cycle may be impermeable to the detection system, it would appear that topoisomerase II does not play a causative role in sex chromatin structure. The protein perichromin appears to be highly concentrated in the sex chromatin structure in interphase nuclei (Figure 5.4). Antibodies to this protein specifically recognize condensed chromosomes (McKeon *et al.*, 1984); the affinity of this antibody for sex chromatin supports the concept that this structure is in metaphase conformation.

Specific attachment to the nuclear envelope has been postulated as a mechanism for perpetuating the inactive X (Gartler *et al.*, 1985), and that view is supported by topographical studies of interphase chromatin that indicate that

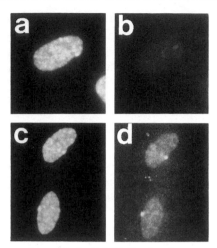

Figure 5.4. Antibodies to perichromin (gift of M. W. Kirschner) recognize the sex chromatin body (SCB). (a) DAPI-stained nucleus; SCB is evident at 2 o'clock; (b) same nucleus with no perichromin antibody in the incubation mix; (c) DAPI-stained nuclei; SCB in each nucleus—upper at 4 o'clock and lower at 9 o'clock; (d) perichromin detected by fluorescent IgG.

the sex chromatin has a nonrandom intranuclear position (Rappold *et al.*, 1984; Bourgeois *et al.*, 1985; Belmont *et al.*, 1986). In rodent–human hybrid cells that retain an inactive human X chromosome, the favored edge position of sex chromatin found in human fibroblasts is lost (Dyer *et al.*, 1989). Because the hybrid cell has a complete rodent genome and only a limited number of human chromosomes, it seems possible that this effect may be due to the nuclear structure being specified in large part by the rodent (host) genome rather than the imported human inactive X chromosome. It has been postulated that the instability of the human inactive X chromosome in such hybrids may be due to a disturbance of the normal nuclear membrane attachment site of the sex chromatin (Gartler *et al.* 1985).

2. Nuclease sensitivity studies

Active chromatin is generally more sensitive to DNase I digestion than is inactive chromatin (Weintraub and Groudine, 1976; Weisbrod, 1982; Garrard *et al.*, 1988; Reeves, 1988; Siegfried and Elgin, 1990). In certain regions of active genes, usually the promoter, stretches of DNA about 200 bp in length are found that are highly sensitive to DNase I digestion, although the corresponding region in a cell type in which the gene is not active does not show this sensitivity. These regions are referred to as DNase I-hypersensitive sites (Gross and

Garrard, 1988; Siegfried and Elgin, 1990). A slight nuclease sensitivity encompasses a broad region around active or potentially active genes, often about 100 kb in length (Lawson *et al.*, 1982; Groudine *et al.*, 1983). These regions are flanked by sequences that are extremely sensitive to nuclease digestion, and are known as superhypersensitive sites or locus activator regions (Tuan and London, 1984; Forrester *et al.*, 1987).

Specific proteins bind to DNA at or near promoters or other regulatory sites in chromatin, displacing or preventing formation of the normal nucleosome configuration. The presence of these proteins is required for active transcription. DNA devoid of nucleosomes is relatively open to attack by nucleases. Although binding of regulatory nonhistone proteins protects DNA from degradation to some extent, the borders between regions of DNA covered by such proteins and those not covered often create zones that are hypersensitive to nuclease digestion.

DNase I-sensitive sites in active X chromatin were first demonstrated at the 3' (Riley *et al.*, 1984, 1986) and 5' (Riley *et al.*, 1986) ends of the human *Pgk* gene. The 5' site is more sensitive than is the 3' site, and is markedly more sensitive to nuclease digestion on the active X chromosome than on the inactive X. Nuclease sensitivity differences were also demonstrated in the X-linked human *hprt* (Wolf and Migeon, 1985; Lin and Chinault, 1988) and *Gd* promoters (Wolf and Migeon, 1985) and the mouse *hprt* promoter (Yang and Caskey, 1987).

In addition to DNase I sensitivity, the active X chromosome exhibits increased sensitivity to restriction enzymes, including *Msp*I (Wolf and Migeon, 1985; Hansen *et al.*, 1988), and S1 nuclease (Wolf and Migeon, 1985; Yang and Caskey, 1987; Lin and Chinault, 1988). We have shown that the DNase I site at the 3' end of the human *Pgk* gene corresponds precisely to a series of sites that are sensitive to *Msp*I cleavage in chromatin. A generalized sensitivity to restriction endonucleases is expected in active chromatin because of the lack of protection afforded by nucleosomes. On the other hand, nontranscribed sequences, such as pseudogenes, exhibit little or no nuclease sensitivity regardless of whether they are on the active or inactive X chromosome (Riley *et al.*, 1986; Lin and Chinault, 1988).

Many active genes are imbedded in a stretch of chromatin that is slightly more sensitive to DNase I digestion than is the surrounding, inactive chromatin. Riley *et al.* (1986) reported more generalized nuclease sensitivity around the *Pgk* gene, and found that the active allele was more sensitive to digestion than its inactive homologue. The pseudogene on the inactive X, however, displayed no difference, with respect to DNase I sensitivity, between the active and inactive X chromosomes. Lin and Chinault (1988), studying the human *hprt* locus, found that the gene (excluding the promoter region) on the active X was approximately twofold more sensitive to nuclease digestion than were the genes on the inactive X. However, they pointed out that inactive autosomal pseudogenes show approximately the same nuclease resistance as does the inactive gene on the X chromosome, suggesting that the degree of chromatin condensation is similar between the inactive X chromosome and inactive autosomal DNA.

The differences between the active and inactive X chromosomes that are reflected in nuclease sensitivity studies seem to be correlated with gene expression. These differences, however, are the ones that are associated with gene expression and gene repression generally, rather than any special kind of nuclease insensitivity that is restricted to the inactive X chromosome. Moreover, the bulk, inactive chromatin on the active X seems to be no more sensitive to nuclease digestion than is the bulk, inactive chromatin on the inactive X, nor does it seem to differ from the inactive chromatin of the autosomes.

3. *In situ* nick translation experiments

Differences in chromatin conformation have been demonstrated at the cytological level using an *in situ* nick translation assay (Kerem *et al.*, 1983, 1988; Kuo and Plunkett, 1985), in which chromosomes fixed to a microscope slide are labeled with ^{3}H-labeled nucleotides in the presence of DNase I and DNA polymerase I. Nick translation of the inactive X chromosome occurs much more slowly than that of the remaining active chromosomes. It has been hypothesized that nick translation of the inactive X is reduced because of a decreased accessibility to the nuclease and/or polymerase, apparently reflecting a more condensed state of the chromatin. The same type of difference was observed in interphase cells, wherein nick translation of the sex chromatin body was markedly reduced, leaving a gap in the relatively uniform labeling of the interphase nucleus (Dyer *et al.*, 1985, 1989).

A number of investigators have studied the influence of 5-azacytidine on *in situ* nick translation. Jablonka *et al.* (1985) found an increase in *in situ* nick translation of the inactive X following 5AC treatment of *Gerbillus* cells. The change in *in situ* nick translation occurred in approximately 80% of the chromosomes that had become early replicating following 5-azacytidine treatment. These findings are consistent with a model in which susceptibility to *in situ* nick translation reflects active chromatin conformation. Kerem *et al.* (1988) studied mouse–*Microtus agrestis* hybrid cells having either the active *Microtus* X, the inactive X, or an inactive X that had been 5AC reactivated as assayed by selection for the HPRT$^+$ phenotype. The inactive X was resistant to nick translation and the active X was readily susceptible, but the reactivated X was resistant to nick translation. They concluded that reactivation in this case was probably a localized phenomenon, encompassing a region of the chromosome too small to be observed cytologically. They also noted that the noninactivated segment of the X chromosome appeared to be subject to nick translation.

Chandley and McBeath (1987) studied the human X–Y bivalent at meiosis. They found that the pairing segment and band Xq13, in which the inactivation center is believed to reside, showed increased susceptibility to *in situ* nick translation, and noted that Separovic and Chandley (1987) did not find increased susceptibility to *in situ* nick translation in the pairing segment of the mouse X–Y bivalent, but did show that the band D, containing the putative inactivation enter (*Xce* locus), was susceptible to nick translation. These observations are consistent with the notion that the inactivation center lies in a region of the X chromosome that is in an active chromatin configuration even in male meiosis.

4. DNA-binding proteins

Preferential binding of factors to the active X chromosome as opposed to the inactive one has been demonstrated. Yang *et al.* (1988) described protected regions (footprints) in the promoter region of the phosphoglycerate kinase 1 (*Pgk 1*) gene in HeLa cell extracts. Additional sites were demonstrated *in vivo* by Pfeifer *et al.* (1990b), using a highly sensitive ligation-mediated polymerase chain reaction (LMPCR) technique (Pfeifer *et al.*, 1989). Eight footprints were identified within the CpG island and were shown to be unique to the active X chromosome. Several of the sites footprinted in human cells bear homology to the mouse *Pgk* promoter region (Adra *et al.*, Pfeifer *et al.*, 1987; 1990b).

None of the proteins identified appear to be unique to X-linked genes (Yang *et al.* 1988). This is consistent with the failure to find promoter sequences that are exclusive to the X chromosome. The observation of preferential binding of protein factors to the active X chromosome is consistent with these proteins being transcription factors and with their role in preventing the normal assembly of nucleosomes, characteristic of inactive promoters. However, these results do not imply a complete absence of proteins binding to the inactive X. Proteins binding preferentially to methylated DNA have been observed (Meehan *et al.*, 1989), and one would expect that such proteins would be present on the highly-methylated promoter regions of the inactive X-linked genes. However, since the spreading of X inactivation is likely to be controlled on a regional basis (Cullen *et al.*, 1986; Goldman, 1988), it is possible that only a restricted part of each such control domain is involved in binding of specific repressor factors.

Recent studies on position-effect variegation in *Drosophila* have demonstrated the existence of a specific DNA-binding protein, the zinc finger protein encoded by the *Suvar(3)7* locus, that may be involved in heterochromatin condensation (Alberts and Sternglanz, 1990; Reuter *et al.*, 1990). Other *Dros-*

ophila proteins influencing heterochromatin formation have also been identified (James and Elgin, 1986; James *et al.*, 1989). It is tempting to speculate that binding sites for similar proteins will be found on the DNA of the X chromosome, and that such proteins may be encoded or regulated by the X inactivation center.

C. Methylation patterns and X inactivation in germ cells

Because the female transmits an undifferentiated X chromosome to her daughters and germ cell precursors are subject to inactivation in the early embryo, it must be that the inactive X in the female germ line is subject to reactivation. Several lines of evidence indicate that reactivation in the germ line occurs around the time of entry to meiosis (Gartler *et al.*, 1975, 1980; Johnston, 1981; Kratzer and Chapman, 1981; McMahon *et al.*, 1981; Monk and McLaren, 1981). In marsupials reactivation of the inactive X in the female germ line apparently occurs much later. Assuming that germ cell inactivation involves the same steps as in somatic cells, reversal of the process should involve several events, including demethylation.

Several studies indicate that methylation patterns in germ cells are different from those found in somatic cells (see below). Except for one recent report (Driscoll and Migeon, 1990), repeated sequences, which are not unique to the X chromosome, were analyzed. Strum and Taylor (1981) first showed that a repeated sequence in bovine DNA is unmethylated in sperm but methylated in somatic cells. This same pattern was reported later for a minor satellite in murine sperm and somatic cell DNA. Ponzetto-Zimmerman and Wolgemuth (1984) and Sanford *et al.* (1984) showed that the major murine satellite DNA is hypomethylated in sperm relative to somatic tissues and that this hypomethylation is evident in cells prior to entry into meiosis. Sanford *et al.* (1984) also showed that the mouse minor satellite is hypomethylated in sperm and in oocytes. In addition, a dispersed repetitive sequence (LI) was found to be unmethylated in oocytes but methylated in sperm. More recently, Sanford *et al.* (1987) have shown that two low-copy sequences (intercisternal A particle and major urinary protein) are methylated at all stages of spermatogenesis and hypomethylated in oocytes. The LI dispersed repetitive sequences appear to be unmethylated in the female germ line before the onset of meiosis (Monk *et al.*, 1987). The methylation pattern of a number of single-copy autosomal sequences have been examined in sperm, and the general result is that there is little if any difference between somatic and sperm cell methylation patterns (reviewed in Groudine and Conkin, 1985).

The results of a methylation study of single-copy X-linked genes in human oocytes are compatible with the data derived from studies of repetitive sequences (Driscoll and Migeon, 1990). Four different X-linked housekeeping genes (*hprt Pgk, Gd*, and P_3) were studied, and there was no evidence of methylation either at the 5′ ends or in the body of the genes at any oocyte stage. The same results were obtained for two tissue-specific genes, one X-linked (*F9*) and one autosomal (*EPO*). Limited evidence suggests that these patterns may be present in premeiotic female germ cells. In contrast, X-linked and autosomal genes of male germ cells were methylated in the body of the different genes studied, just as they are on the active X and autosomes in somatic cells (Driscoll and Migeon, 1990). Driscoll and Migeon (1990) conclude that the female germ line may be completely unmethylated throughout its history, which implies that reactivation would not involve demethylation. However, recent studies on the fragile X site lead to a different conclusion. Laird (1987) hypothesized that the fragile X syndrome might result from an imprinting mutation, involving methylation, which prevents reactivation of the region upon passage through the female germ line. Bell *et al.* (1991) and Vincent *et al.* (1991) have both shown that fragile X patients have a methylated CpG island on their active X whereas normal and transmitting males do not. These results indicate that a methylation/demethylation cycle accompanies the inactivation/reactivation cycle in female germ cell ontogeny.

Although there may be more than one reason for the methylation patterns found in germ cells, we believe that a major purpose for demethylation of repeated sequences is to facilitate the pairing requirement in meiosis. Differential methylation of homologues would affect structure in a differential way and make homologous pairing difficult. The absence of methylation in autosomal genes may reflect the shutdown of the methylase for the purpose of avoiding differential methylation of the Xs. In the male germ line, homologues are similarly methylated, and the scattered methylation in the body of genes may pose no structural pairing problem. However, the methylated, heterochromatic centromeric satellites, of both X chromosomes and autosomes, may pose a pairing problem and, therefore, we find that even in sperm these sequences are not methylated. It is difficult to recognize sex chromatin in murine cells because of the presence of centromeric heterochromatin. However, in early embryonic mouse cells, such as those of the amnion, sex chromatin is readily detectable, apparently because the centromeric satellite has not become methylated and condensed.

V. PERSPECTIVES

The basic question of X inactivation is the nature of the switch that leads to the differentiation of the two X chromosomes in female cells of the early mammalian embryo. The idea of a unique site in the X chromosome functioning as this switch was proposed early in the history of X inactivation studies. Models of how such a switch could work varied from episomal factors to heterochromatinization proteins perpetuating a pattern of cellular heredity. None of the ideas discussed here are mutually exclusive, but until the Xce is identified, progress in answering this important question will be difficult. Mapping data appear to localize Xce to a region amenable to molecular cloning, and a candidate gene has been identified. The answer to the complete operation of Xce may be more complex than we imagine at present, especially if we consider that there probably has to be some kind of communication between the two Xce genes at the time of the initial inactivation event. The Xce will probably also play some role in explaining preferential paternal X inactivation in extraembryonic cells. We favor the possibility that the initial major effects of Xce will be isolation of the inactive X into a compartment that tends to inhibit transcription. The remaining regulatory phenomena that distinguish inactive and active X-linked alleles may not be significantly different from the regulatory events controlling active and inactive autosomal genes. We imagine the next step in inactivation to be the binding of heterochromatinizing protein(s) to the segregated X chromosome, with the exception of those domains escaping inactivation (e.g., the X–Y pairing region). The compartmentalization and the nature of the inactivating proteins may act to stabilize the differentiated state and may be the only events taking place in the extraembryonic lineage. Later in the embryonic lineage, methylation of the promoter region of the housekeeping genes of the inactive X will occur, this event being facilitated by the already inactive and condensed domains on the chromosome. Perhaps a final event may be the binding of a methylation-specific protein to these regions, which would more or less make permanent their active state.

We do not rule out that differential methylation may play an important switching role in some of the earlier events in X inactivation. Methylation still remains one of the most attractive molecular mechanisms for distinguishing two identical chromosomes in the same cell.

Acknowledgments

We are grateful to Dr. L. Goldstein for his critical reading of this work and to Terry Canfield for her editorial help. Research in our laboratories is supported by grants from the National Institutes of Health (HD16659) and the National Science Foundation (DCB8509523) to S.M.G. and a Bristol Myers Company Grant of Research Corporation and an NIH–San Francisco State University Biomedical Research Support Grant to M.A.G. S.M.G. is a recipient of a National Institutes of Health Career Award.

References

Abe, K., Takagi, N., and Sasaki, M. (1988). Nonhistone nuclear proteins specific to certain mouse embryonal carcinoma clones having an inactive X chromosome. *Exp. Cell Res.* **179:**590–594.

Adler, D. A., West, J. D., and Chapman, V. M. (1977). Expression of alpha-galactosidase in preimplantation mouse embryos. *Nature (London)* **267:**838–839.

Adler, D. A., Bressler, S. L., Chapman, V. M., Page, D. C., and Disteche, C. M. (1991). Inactivation of the *Zfx* gene on the mouse X chromosome. *Proc. Natl. Acad. Sci. U.S.A.* **88:**4592–4595.

Adra, C. N., Boer, P. H., and McBurney, M. W. (1987). Cloning and expression of the mouse *pgk*-1 gene and the nucleotide sequence of its promoter. *Gene* **60:**65–74.

Alberts, B., and Sternglanz, R. (1990). Chromatin contract to silence. *Nature (London)* **344:**193–194.

Allderdice, P. W., Miller, O. J., Miller, D. A., and Klinger, H. P. (1978). Spreading of inactivation in an (X;14) translocation. *Am. J. Med. Genet.* **2:**233–240.

Antequera, F., Boyes, J., and Bird, A. (1990). High levels of *de novo* methylation and altered chromatin structure at CpG islands in cell lines. *Cell (Cambridge, Mass.)* **62:**503–514.

Austin, C. R. (1966). Sex chromatin in embryonic and fetal tissues. *In* "The Sex Chromatin" (K. L. Moore, ed.), pp. 241–254. Saunders, Philadelphia; Pennsylvania.

Beggs, A. H., and Migeon, B. R. (1989). Chromatin loop structure of the human X chromosome: Relevance to X inactivation and CpG clusters. *Mol. Cell Biol.* **9:**2322–2331.

Beggs, A. H., Axelman, J., and Migeon, B. R. (1986). Reactivation of X-linked genes in human fibroblasts transformed by origin-defective SV40. *Somatic Cell Mol. Genet.* **12:**585–594.

Bell, M. V., Hirst, M. C., Nakahori, Y., MacKinon, R. N., Roche, A., Flint, T. J., Jacobs, P. A., Tommerup, N., Tranebjaerg, L., Froster-Iskevins, V., Ken, B., Turner, G., Lindenbaum, R. H., Winter, R., Penilrey M., Thilodeau, S., and Davies, K. E. (1991). Physical mapping across the fragile X: Hypermethylation and clinical expression of the fragile X syndrome. *Cell (Cambridge, Mass.)* **64:**861–866.

Belmont, A. S., Bignone, F., and Ts'o, P. O. P. (1986). The relative intranuclear positions of Barr bodies in XXX non-transformed human fibroblasts. *Exp. Cell Res.* **165:**165–179.

Ben-Hattar, J., Beard, P., and Jiricny, J. (1989). Cytosine methylation in CTF and SP1 recognition sites of an HSV tk promoter: Effects on transcription *in vivo* and on factor binding *in vitro*. *Nucleic Acids Res.* **17:**10179–10190.

Beutler, E., Yeh, M., and Fairbanks, V. F. (1962). The normal human female as a mosaic of X-chromosome activity: Studies using the gene for G-6-PD deficiency as a marker. *Proc. Natl. Acad. Sci. U.S.A.* **48:**9–16.

Borden, J., and Manuelidis, L. (1988). Movement of the X chromosome in epilepsy. *Science* **242:**1687–1691.

Bourgeois, C. A., Laquerriere, F., Hemon, D., Hubert, J., and Bouteille, M. (1985). New data on the *in situ* position of the inactive X chromosome in the interphase nucleus of human fibroblasts. *Hum. Genet.* **69:**122–129.

Brown, C. J., and Willard, H. F. (1989). Noninactivation of a selectable human X-linked gene that complements a murine temperature-sensitive cell cycle defect. *Am. J. Hum. Genet.* **45:**592–598.

Brown, C. J., and Willard, H. F. (1990). Localization of a gene that escapes inactivation to the X chromosomal proximal short arm: Implications for X inactivation. *Am. J. Hum. Genet.* **46:**273–279.

Brown, C. J., Ballabio, A., Rupert, J. L., Lafreniere, R. G., Grompe, M., Tonlorenzi, R., and Willard, H. F. (1991a). A gene from the region of the human X inactivation centre is expressed exclusively from the inactive X chromosome. *Nature (London)* **349:**38–44.

Brown, C. J., Lafreniere, R. G., Powers, V. E., Sebastio, G., Ballabio, A., Pettigrew, A. L., Ledbetter, D. H., and Levy, E. (1991b). Localization of the X inactivation centre on the human X chromosome in Xq13. *Nature (London)* **349:**82–84.

Brown, J. A., Goss, S., Klinger, H. P., Miller, O. J., Ohno, S., and Siniscalco, M. (1976). Report of the committee on the genetic constitution of the X and Y chromosomes. *Cytogenet. Cell Genet.* **16:**54–59.

Buschhausen, G., Wittig, B., Graessmann, M., and Graessmann, A. (1987). Chromatin structure is required to block transcription of the methylated herpes simplex virus thymidine kinase gene. *Proc. Natl. Acad. Sci. U.S.A.* **84**:1177–1181.

Cattanach, B. M. (1975). Control of chromosome inactivation. *Annu. Rev. Genet.* **9**:1–18.

Cattanach, B. M., and Isaacson, J. H. (1967). Controlling elements in the mouse X chromosome. *Genetics* **57**:331–346.

Cattanach, B. M., and Kirk, M. (1985). Differential activity of maternally and paternally derived chromosome regions in mice. *Nature (London)* **315**:496–498.

Chandley, A. C., and McBeath, S. (1987). DNase I hypersensitive sites along the XY bivalent at meiosis in man include the XpYp pairing region. *Cytogenet. Cell Genet.* **44**:22–31.

Chandra, H. S., and Brown, S. W. (1975). Chromosome imprinting and the mammalian X chromosome. *Nature (London)* **253**:165–168.

Chang, P. L., Müller, O. T., Lafrenic, R. M., Varey, P. A., Rosa, N. E., Davidson, R. G., Henry, W. M., and Shows, T. B. (1990). The human arylsulfatase-C isoenzymes: Two distinct genes that escape from X inactivation. *Am. J. Hum. Genet.* **46**:729–737.

Clark, R. P., Goff, M. R., and MacDermot, K. D. (1990). Identification of functioning sweat pores and visualization of skin temperature patterns in X-linked hypohidrotic ectodermal dysplasia by whole body thermography. *Hum. Genet.* **86**:7–13.

Cook, P. R. (1974). On the inheritance of differentiated traits. *Biol. Rev. Cambridge Philos. Soc.* **49**:51–84.

Couturier, J., Dutrillaux, B., Garber, P., Raoul, O., Croquette, M., Fourlinnie, J. C., and Maillard, E. (1979). Evidence for a correlation between late replication and autosomal gene inactivation in a familial translocation t(X;21). *Hum. Genet.* **49**:319–326.

Crouse, H. V. (1960). The controlling element in sex chromosome behavior in sciara. *Genetics* **45**:1429–1445.

Cullen, C. R., Hubberman, P., Kaslow, D. C., and Migeon, B. R. (1986). Comparison of factor IX methylation on human active and inactive X chromosomes: Implications for X inactivation and transcription of tissue-specific genes. *EMBO J.* **5**:2223–2229.

DeMars, R. (1967). The single-active-X: Functional differentiation at the chromosome level. *Natl. Cancer Inst. Monogr.* **26**:327–351.

DePamphilis, M. L. (1988). Transcriptional elements as components of eukaryotic origins of DNA replication. *Cell (Cambridge, Mass.)* **52**:635–638.

Disteche, C. M., Eicher, E. M., and Latt, S. A. (1979). Late replication in an X-autosome translocation in the mouse: Correlation with genetic inactivation and evidence for selective effects during embryogenesis. *Proc. Natl. Acad. Sci. U.S.A.* **76**:5234–5238.

Dobrovic, A., Gareau, J. L. P., Ouellette, G., and Bradley, W. E. C. (1988). DNA methylation and genetic inactivation at thymidine kinase locus: Two different mechanisms for silencing autosomal genes. *Somatic Cell Mol. Genet.* **14**:55–68.

Driscoll, D. J., and Migeon, B. R. (1990). Sex differences in methylation of single-copy genes in human meiotic germ cells: Implications for X chromosome inactivation, parental imprinting, and origin of CpG mutations. *Somatic Cell Mol. Genet.* **16**:267–282.

Dyer, K. A., Riley, D., and Gartler, S. M. (1985). Analysis of inactive X chromosome structure by *in situ* nick translation. *Chromosoma* **92**:209–213.

Dyer, K. A., Canfield, T. K., and Gartler, S. M. (1989). Molecular cytological differentiation of active from inactive X domains in interphase: Implications for X chromosome inactivation. *Cytogenet. Cell Genet.* **50**:116–120.

Earnshaw, W. C., and Heck, M. M. S. (1985). Localization of topoisomerase II in mitotic chromosomes. *J. Cell Biol.* **100**:1716–1725.

Ellis, N., Keitges, E., Gartler, S. M., and Rocchi, M. (1987). High-frequency reactivation of X-linked genes in Chinese hamster × human hybrid cells. *Somatic Cell Mol. Genet.* **13**:191–204.

Epplen, J. T., Siebers, J. W., and Vogel, W. (1975). DNA replication patterns of human chromosomes from fibroblasts and amniotic fluid cells revealed by Giemsa staining technique. *Cytogenet. Cell Genet.* **15**:177–185.

Epstein, C. J., Smith, S., Travis, B., and Tucker, G. (1978). Both X chromosomes function before visible X-chromosome inactivation in female mouse embryos. *Nature (London)* **274**:500–503.

Fisher, E. M. C., Bear-Romero, P., Brown, L. G., Ridley, A., McNeil, J. A., Lawrence, J. B., Willard, H. F., Bieber, F. R., and Page, D. C. (1990). Homologous ribosomal protein genes on the human X and Y chromosomes: Escape from X inactivation and possible implications for Turner syndrome. *Cell (Cambridge, Mass.)* **63**:1205–1218.

Flejter, W. L., Van Dyke, D. L., and Weiss, L. (1984). Bends in human mitotic metaphase chromosomes, including a bend marking the X-inactivation center. *Am. J. Hum. Genet.* **36**:218–226.

Forrester, W. C., Takegawa, S., Papayannopoulous, T., Stamatoyannopoulos, G., and Groudine, M. (1987). Evidence for a locus activation region: The formation of developmentally stable hypersensitive sites in globin-expressing hybrids. *Nucleic Acids Res.* **15**:10159–10177.

Garrard, W. T., Cockerill, P. N., Aunting, D. W., McDaniel-Gerwig, D., Szent-Györgyi, C., Xu, M., and Gross, D. S. (1988). Active and inactive chromatin. *In* "Chromosomes and Chromatin" (K. W. Adolph, ed.), Vol. 1, pp. 133–178. CRC Press, Boca Raton, Florida.

Gartler, S. M., and Riggs, A. D. (1983). Mammalian X-chromosome inactivation. *Annu. Rev. Genet.* **17**:155–190.

Gartler, S. M., Andina, R., and Gant, N. (1975). Ontogeny of X-chromosome inactivation in the female germ line. *Exp. Cell Res.* **91**:454–457.

Gartler, S. M., Rivest, M., and Cole, R. E. (1980). Cytological evidence for an inactive X chromosome in murine oogonia. *Cytogenet. Cell Genet.* **28**:203–207.

Gartler, S. M., Dyer, K. A., Graves, J. A. M., and Rocchi, M. (1985). A two-step model for mammalian X-chromosome inactivation. *Prog. Clin. Biol. Res.* **198**:223–235.

Goldman, M. A. (1988). The chromatin domain as a unit of gene regulation. *BioEssays* **9**:50–55.

Goldman, M. A., Holmquist, G. P., Gray, M. C., Caston, L. A., and Nag, A. (1984). Replication timing of genes and middle repetitive sequences. *Science* **224**:686–692.

Goldman, M. A., Stokes, K. R., Idzerda, R. I., McKnight, G. S., Hammer, R. E., Brinster, R. L., and Gartler, S. M. (1987). A chicken transferrin gene in transgenic mice escapes X-chromosome inactivation. *Science* **236**:593–595.

Goodfellow, P., Pym, B., Mohandas, T., and Shapiro, L. J. (1984). The cell surface antigen locus, MIC2X, escapes X-inactivation. *Am. J. Hum. Genet.* **36**:777–782.

Gough, N. M., Gearing, D. P., Nicola, N. A., Baker, E., Pritchard, M., Collen, D. F., and Sutherland, G. R. (1990). Localization of the human GM-CSF receptor gene to the X–Y pseudoautosomal region. *Nature (London)* **345**:734–736.

Grant, S. G., and Chapman, V. M. (1988). Mechanisms of X-chromosome regulation. *Annu. Rev. Genet.* **22**:199–233.

Graves, J. A. M. (1987). The evolution of mammalian sex chromosomes and dosage compensation: Clues from marsupials and monotremes. *Trends Genet.* **3**:252–256.

Gross, D. S., and Garrard, W. T. (1988). Nuclease hypersensitive sites in chromatin. *Annu. Rev. Biochem.* **57**:159–197.

Groudine, M., and Conkin, K. F. (1985). Chromatin structure and *de novo* methylation of sperm DNA: Implications for activation of the paternal genome. *Science* **228**:1061–1068.

Groudine, M., Kohwi-Shigematsu, T., Gelinas, R., Stamatoyannopoulos, G., and Papayannopoulou, T. (1983). Human fetal to adult hemoglobin switching: Changes in chromatin structure of the β-globin gene locus. *Proc. Natl. Acad. Sci. U.S.A.* **80**:7551–7555.

Grumbach, M. M., Morishima, A., and Taylor, J. H. (1963). Human sex chromosome abnormalitites in relation to DNA replication and heterochromatinization. *Proc. Natl. Acad. Sci. U.S.A.* **49**:581–589.

Hansen, R. S., and Gartler, S. M. (1990). 5-Azacytidine-induced reactivation of the human X chromosome-linked *PGK1* gene is associated with a large region of cytosine demethylation in the 5' CpG island. *Proc. Natl. Acad. Sci. U.S.A.* **87:**4174–4178.

Hansen, R. S., Ellis, N. A., and Gartler, S. M. (1988). Demethylation of specific sites in the 5' region of the inactive X-linked human phosphoglycerate kinase gene correlates with the appearance of nuclease sensitivity and gene expression. *Mol. Cell Biol.* **8:**4692–4699.

Harrington, M. A., Jones, P. A., Imagawa, M., and Karin, M. (1988). Cytosine methylation does not affect binding of transcription factor Sp1. *Proc. Natl. Acad. Sci. U.S.A.* **85:**2066–2070.

Harris, M. (1982). Induction of thymidine kinase in enzyme-deficient Chinese-hamster cells. *Cell (Cambridge, Mass.)* **29:**483–492.

Harris, M. (1984). Variants inducible for glutamine synthetase in V79-56 cells. *Somatic Cell Mol. Genet.* **10:**275–281.

Harrison, K. B. (1989). X-chromosome inactivation in the human cytotrophoblast. *Cytogenet. Cell Genet.* **52:**37–41.

Heck, M. M. S., and Earnshaw, W. C. (1986). Topoisomerase II: A specific marker for cell proliferation. *J. Cell Biol.* **103:**2569–2581.

Höller, M., Westin, G., Jiricny, J., and Schaffner, W. (1988). Sp1 transcription factor binds DNA and activates transcription even when the binding site is CpG methylated. *Genes Dev.* **2:**1127–1135.

Holliday, R., and Pugh, J. E. (1975). DNA modification mechanisms and gene activity during development. *Science* **187:**226–232.

Hors-Cayla, M. C., Heuertz, S., and Frezal, J. (1983). Coreactivation of four inactive X genes in a hamster × human hybrid and persistence of late replication of reactivated X chromosome. *Somatic Cell Genet.* **9:**645–657.

Hutchison, N., and Weintraub, H. (1985). Localization of DNase I-sensitive sequences to specific regions of interphase nuclei. *Cell (Cambridge, Mass.)* **43:**471–482.

Jablonka, E., Gointein, R., Marcus, M., and Cedar, H. (1985). DNA hypomethyation causes an increase in DNase I sensitivity and an advance in the time of replication of the entire inactive X chromosome. *Chromosoma* **93:**152–156.

James, T. C., and Elgin, S. C. R. (1986). Identification of a nonhistone chromosomal protein associated with heterochromatin in *Drosophila melanogaster* and its gene. *Mol. Cell. Biol.* **6:**3862–3872.

James, T. C., Eissenberg, J. C., Craig, C., Dietrich, V., Hobson, A., and Elgin, S. C. R. (1989). Distribution patterns of HP1, a heterochromatin-associated nonhistone chromosomal protein of *Drosophila. Eur. J. Cell Biol.* **50:**170–180.

Johnston, P. G. (1981). X chromosome activity in female germ cells of mice heterozygous for Searle's translocation T(X;16)16H. *Genet. Res.* **37:**317–322.

Jones, J., Peters, J., Rasberg, C., and Cattenach, B. M. (1989). X-inactivation of the *Sts* locus in the mouse: An anomaly of the dosage compensation mechanism. *Genet. Res.* **55:**193–199.

Jones, P. A., Wolkowicz, M. J., Rideout, W. M., III, Gonzales, F. A., Marzias, C. M., Coctzee, G. A., and Tapscotl, S. J. (1990). *De novo* methylation of the Myo D1 CpG island during the establishment of immortal cell lines. *Proc. Natl. Acad. Sci. U.S.A.* **87:**6117–6121.

Keitges, E. A., and Gartler, S. M. (1986). Dosage of the *Sts* gene in the mouse. *Am. J. Hum. Genet.* **39:**470–476.

Keitges, E. A., and Palmer, C. G. (1986). Analysis of spreading of inactivation in eight X autosome tranlocations utilizing the high resolution RBG technique. *Hum. Genet.* **72:**231–236.

Keitges, E. A., Rivest, M., Siniscalco, M., and Gartler, S. M. (1985). X-linkage of steroid sulphatase in the mouse is evidence for a functional Y-linked allele. *Nature (London)* **315:**226–227.

Keith, D. H., Singer Sam, J., and Riggs, A. D. (1986). Active X chromosome DNA is unmethylated at eight CCGG sites clustered in a guanine-plus-cytosine-rich island at the 5' end of the gene for phosphoglycerate kinase. *Mol. Cell. Biol.* **6:**4122–4125.

Kelley, D. E., Pollok, B. A., Atchison, M. L., and Perry, R. P. (1988). The coupling between enhancer activity and hypomethylation of K immunoglobulin genes is developmentally regulated. *Mol. Cell. Biol.* **8:**930–937.

Kerem, B. S., Goitein, R., Richler, C., Marcus, M., and Cedar, H. (1983). *In situ* nick-translation distinguishes between active and inactive X chromosomes. *Nature (London)* **304:**88–90.

Kerem, B. S., Kottusch-Geiseler, V., Kalscheuer, V., Goitein, R., Sperling, K., and Marcus, M. (1988). DNase I sensitivity of *Microtus agrestis* active, inactive and reactived X chromosomes in mouse–*Microtus* cell hybrids. *Chromosoma* **96:**227–230.

Kratzer, P. G., and Chapman, V. M. (1981). X chromosome reactivation in oocytes of *Mus caroli*. *Proc. Natl. Acad. Sci. U.S.A.* **78:**3093–3097.

Kratzer, P. G., and Gartler, S. M. (1978). HGPRT activity changes in preimplantation mouse embryos. *Nature (London)* **274:**503–504.

Kratzer, P. G., Chapman, V. M., Lambert, H., Evans, R. E., and Liskay, R. M. (1983). Differences in the DNA of the inactive X chromosome of fetal and extraembryonic tissues of mice. *Cell (Cambridge, Mass.)* **33:**37–42.

Krumlauf, R., Chapman, V. M., Hammer, R. E., Brinster, R., and Tilghman, S. M. (1986). Differential expression of alpha-fetoprotein genes on the inactive X chromosome in extra-embryonic and somatic tissues of a transgenic mouse line. *Nature (London)* **319:**224–226.

Krystosek, A., and Puck, T. T. (1990). The spatial distribution of exposed nuclear DNA in normal, cancer, and reverse-transformed cells. *Proc. Natl. Acad. Sci. U.S.A.* **87:**6560–6564.

Kuo, M. T., and Plunkett, W. (1985). Nick-translation of metaphase chromosomes: *In vitro* labeling of nuclease-hypersensitive regions in chromosomes. *Proc. Natl. Acad. Sci. U.S.A.* **82:**854–858.

Kuroda, M. J., Kernan, M. J., Kreber, R., Ganetzky, B., and Baker, B. S. (1991). The maleless protein associates with the X chromosome to regulate dosage compensation in *Drosophila*. *Cell* **66:**935–948.

Kushnick, T., Irons, T. G., Wiley, J.-E., Gettig, E. A., Rao, K. W., and Bowyer, S. (1987). 45X/46X, r(x) with syndactyly and severe mental retardation. *Am. J. Med. Genet.* **28:**567–574.

Laird, C. D. (1987). Proposed mechanism of inheritance and expression of the human fragile-X syndrome of mental retardation. *Genetics* **117:**587–599.

Lawson, G. M., Knoll, B. J., March, C. J., Woo, S. L. C., Tsai, M., and O'Malley, B. W. (1982). Definition of 5' and 3' structural boundaries of the chromatin domain containing the ovalbumin multigene family. *J. Biol. Chem.* **257:**1501–1507.

Lester, S. C., Korn, N. J., and DeMars, R. (1982). Derepression of genes on the human inactive X chromosome: Evidence for differences in locus-specific rates of derepression and rates of transfer of active and inactive genes after DNA-mediated transformation. *Somatic Cell Genet.* **8:**265–284.

Lin, D., and Chinault, A. C. (1988). Comparative study of DNase I sensitivity at the X-linked human HPRT locus. *Somatic Cell Mol. Genet.* **14:**261–272.

Liskay, R. M., and Evans, R. J. (1980). Inactive X chromosome DNA does not function in DNA-mediated cell transformation for the hypoxanthine phosphoribosyltransferase gene. *Proc. Natl. Acad. Sci. U.S.A.* **77:**4895–4898.

Lock, L. F., Melton, D. W., Caskey, C. T., and Martin, G. R. (1986). Methylation of the mouse *hprt* gene differs on the active and inactive X chromosomes. *Mol. Cell. Biol.* **6:**914–924.

Lock, L. F., Takagi, N., and Martin, G. R. (1987). Methylation of the *Hprt* gene on the inactive X occurs after chromosome inactivation. *Cell (Cambridge, Mass.)* **48:**39–46.

Lyon, M. F. (1961). Gene action in the X-chromosome of the mouse (*Mus musculus* L.). *Nature (London)* **190:**372–373.

Lyon, M. F. (1972). X-chromosome inactivation and developmental patterns in mammals. *Biol. Rev. (Cambridge, Philos. Soc.* **47:**1–35.

Lyon, M. F. (1974). Mechanisms and evolutionary origins of variable X-chromosome activity in mammals. *Proc. R. Soc. London, Ser. B* **187:**243–268.

Lyon, M. F. (1988). The William Allan Memorial Award Address: X-chromosome inactivation and the location and expression of X-linked genes. *Am. J. Hum. Genet.* **42:**8–16.

Mandel, J. L., and Chambon, P. (1979). DNA methylation: Organ specific variation in the methylation within and around ovalbumin and other chicken genes. *Nucleic Acids Res.* 7:2081–2103.

Martin, G. R., Epstein, C. J., Travis, B., Tucker, G., Yatziv, S., Martin, D. W., Jr., Clift, S., and Cohen, S. (1978). X-Chromosome inactivation during differentiation of female teratocarcinoma stem cellls. *Nature (London)* 271:329–333.

Mattei, M. G., Mattei, J. F., and Giraud, F. (1983). Some aspects of the inactivation centers on the X chromosome. *In* "Cytogenetics of the Mammalian X Chromosome" (A. Sandberg, ed.), Part A, pp. 327–339. Alan R. Liss, New York.

McBurney, M. W., and Adamson, E. D. (1976). Studies on the activity of the X chromosomes in female teratocarcinoma cells in culture. *Cell (Cambridge, Mass.)* 9:57–70.

McBurney, M. W., and Strutt, B. J. (1980). Genetic activity of X chromosomes in pluripotent female teratocarcinoma cells and their differentiated progeny. *Cell (Cambridge, Mass.)* 21:357–364.

McKay, L. M., Wrigley, J. M., and Graves, J. A. M. (1987). Evolution of mammalian X-chromosome inactivation: Sex chromatin in monotremes and marsupials. *Aust. J. Biol. Sci.* 40:397–404.

McKeon, F. D., Tuffanelli, D. L., Kobayashi, S., and Kirschner, M. W. (1984). The redistribution of a conserved nuclear envelope protein during the cell cycle suggests a pathway for chromosome condensation. *Cell (Cambridge, Mass.)* 36:83–92.

McMahon, A., Fosten, M., and Monk, M. (1981). Random X-chromosome inactivation in female primordial germ cells in the mouse. *J. Embryol. Exp. Morphol.* 64:251–258.

Meehan, R. R., Lewis, J. D., McKay, S., Kleiner, E. L., and Bird, A. P. (1989). Identification of a mammalian protein that binds specifically to DNA containing methylated CpGs. *Cell (Cambridge, Mass.)* 58:499–507.

Migeon, B. R., Shapiro, L. J., Norum, R. A., Mohandas, T., Axelman, J., and Dabora, R. L. (1982). Differential expression of steroid sulphatase locus on active and inactive human X chromosome. *Nature (London)* 299:838–840.

Migeon, B. R., Schmidt, M., Axelman, J., and Cullen, C. R. (1986). Complete reactivation of X chromosomes from human chorionic villi with a switch to early DNA replication. *Proc. Natl. Acad. Sci. U.S.A.* 83:2182–2186.

Miller, D. A., Okamoto, E., Erlanger, B. F., and Miller, O. J. (1982). Is DNA methylation responsible for mammalian X chromosome inactivation? *Cytogenet. Cell Genet.* 33:345–349.

Mohandas, T., Sparkes, R. S., and Shapiro, L. J. (1981a). Reactivation or an inactive human X chromosome: Evidence for inactivation by DNA methylation. *Science* 211:393–396.

Mohandas, T., Crandall, B. F., Sparkes, R. S., Passage, M. B., and Sparkes, M. C. (1981b). Late replication studies in a human X/13 translocation: Correlation with autosomal gene expression. *Cytogenet. Cell Genet.* 29:215–220.

Mohandas, T., Sparkes, R. S., and Shapiro, L. J. (1982). Genetic evidence for the inactivation of a human autosomal locus attached to an inactive X chromosome. *Am. J. Hum. Genet.* 34:811–817.

Mohandas, T., Geller, R. L., Yen, P. H., Rosendorff, J., Bernstein, R., Yoshida, A., and Shapiro, L. J. (1987). Cytogenetic and molecular studies on a recombinant human X chromosome: Implications for the spreading of X chromosome inactivation. *Proc. Natl. Acad. Sci. U.S.A.* 84:4954–4958.

Mohandas, T., Passage, M. B., Williams III, J. W., Sparkes, R. S., Yen, P. A., and Shapiro, L. J. (1989). X-Chromosome inactivation in cultured cells from human chorionic villi. *Somatic Cell Mol. Genet.* 15:131–136.

Mondello, C., Goodfellow, P. J., and Goodfellow, P. N. (1988). Analysis of methylation of a human X located gene which escapes X inactivation. *Nucleic Acids Res.* 16:6813–6824.

Monk, M., and Harper, M. I. (1979). Sequential X chromosome inactivation coupled with cellular differentiation in early mouse embryos. *Nature (London)* 281:311–313.

Monk, M., and McLaren, A. (1981). X-chromosome activity in foetal germ cells of the mouse. *J. Embryol. Exp. Morphol.* **63:**75–84.

Monk, M., Boubelik, M., and Lehnert, S. (1987). Temporal and regional changes in DNA methylation in the embryonic, extraembryonic and germ cell lines during mouse embryo development. *Development (Cambridge, UK)* **99:**371–382.

Mullins, L. J., Veres, G., Caskey, T., and Chapman, V. (1987). Differential methylation of the ornithine carbamoyl transferase gene on active and inactive mouse X chromosomes. *Mol. Cell. Biol.* **7:**3916–3922.

Myers, R. H., Cupples, L. A., Schoenfeld, M., D'Agostino, R. B., Tenin, N. C., Goldmakher, N., and Wold, P. A. (1985). Maternal factors in onset of Huntington disease. *Am. J. Hum. Genet.* **37:**511–523.

Nadon, N., Sekhon, G., Brown, L. J., Korn, N., Petersen, J. W., Strandtmann, J., Chang, C., and DeMars, R. (1986). Derepression of *HPRT* locus on inactive X chromosome of human lymphoblastoid cell line. *Somatic Cell Mol. Genet.* **12:**541–554.

Nicholls, R. D., Knoll, J. H. M., Butler, M. G., Karam, S., and Lalande, M. (1989). Genetic imprinting suggested by maternal heterodisomy in non-deletion Prader–Willi Syndrome. *Nature (London)* **342:**281–285.

Odartchenko, N., and Kenklis, T. P. (1973). Localization of paternal DNA in interphase nuclei of mouse eggs during early cleavage. *Nature (London)* **241:**528–529.

Ohno, S., Kaplan, W. D., and Kinosita, R. (1959). Formation of the sex chromatin by a single X-chromosome in liver cells of *Rattus norvegicus. Exp. Cell Res.* **18:**415–418.

Okuyama, K., Takagi, N., and Sasaki, M. (1986). Sequential X-chromosome reactivation and inactivation in cell hybrids between murine embryonal carcinoma cells and female rat thymocytes. *Exp. Cell Res.* **164:**323–334.

Paddy, M. R., Belmont, A. S., Saumweber, H., Agard, D. A., and Sedat, J. W. (1990). Interphase nuclear envelope lamins form a discontinuous network that interacts with only a fraction of the chromatin in the nuclear periphery. *Cell (Cambridge, Mass.)* **62:**89–106.

Paroush, Z., Keshet, I., Yisraeli, J., and Galan, H. (1990). Dynamics of demethylation and activation of the α-actin gene in myoblasts. *Cell (Cambridge, Mass.)* **63:**1229–1237.

Pfeifer, G. P., Steigerwald, S. D., Mueller, P. R., Wold, B., and Riggs, A. D. (1989). Genomic sequencing and methylation analysis by ligation mediated PCR. *Science* **246:**810–813.

Pfeifer, G. P., Steigerwald, S. D., Hansen, R. S., Gartler, S. M., and Riggs, A. D. (1990a). Polymerase chain reaction-aided genomic sequencing of an X chromosome-linked CpG island: Methylation patterns suggest clonal inheritance, CpG site autonomy, and an explanation of activity state stability. *Proc. Natl. Acad. Sci. U.S.A.* **87:**8252–8256.

Pfeifer, G. P., Tanguay, R. L., Steigerwald, S. D., and Riggs, A. D. (1990b). *In vivo* footprint and methylation analysis by PCR-aided genomic sequencing: Comparison of active and inactive X chromosomal DNA at the CpG island and promoter of human PGK-1. *Genes Dev.* **4:**1277–1287.

Plotnick, F., Klinger, H. P., and Kosseff, A. L. (1971). Sex-chromatin formation in pre-implantation rabbit embryos. *Cytogenetics* **10:**244–253.

Ponzetto-Zimmerman, C., and Wolgemuth, D. J. (1984). Methylation of satellite sequences in mouse spermatogenic and somatic DNAs. *Nucleic Acids Res.* **12:**2807–2822.

Prantera, G., and Ferraro, M. (1990). Analysis of methylation and distribution of CpG sequences on human active and inactive X chromosomes by *in situ* nick translation. *Chromosoma* **99:**18–23.

Race, R. R., and Sanger, R. (1975). "Blood Group in Man," 6th ed. Blackwell, Oxford.

Rao, S. R. V., Sharma, V. K., and Shah, V. C. (1970). DNA synthesis in duplicate-type sex chromosomes of the Indian house shrew, *Suncus murinus* (Insectivora). *Cytogenetics* **9:**384–395.

Rappold, G. A., Cremer, T., Hager, H. D., Davies, K. E., Müller, C. R., and Yang, T. (1984). Sex chromosome positions in human interphase nuclei as studied by *in situ* hybridization with chromosome specific DNA probes. *Hum. Genet.* **67:**317–325.

Rastan, S. (1983). Non-random X-chromosome inactivation in mouse X-autosome translocation embryos—Location of the inactivation centre. *J. Embryol. Exp. Morphol.* **78:**1–22.

Rastan, S., and Brown, S. D. M. (1990). The search for the mouse X-chromosome inactivation centre. *Genet. Res.* **56:**99–106.

Reeves, R. (1988). Active chromatin structure. *In* "Chromosomes and Chromatin" (K. W. Adolph, ed.) Vol. 1, pp. 109–131. CRC Press, Boca Raton, Florida.

Reuter, G., Giarre, M., Farah, J., Gausz, J., Spierer, A., and Spierer, P. (1990). Dependence of position-effect variegation in *Drosophila* on dose of a gene encoding an unusual zinc-finger protein. *Nature (London)* **344:**219–223.

Riggs, A. D. (1975). X inactivation, differentiation and DNA methylation. *Cytogenet. Cell Genet.* **14:**9–25.

Riggs, A. D. (1990). DNA methylation and late replication probably aid cell memory, and type I DNA reeling could aid chromosome folding and enhancer function. *Philos. Trans. R. Soc. London, Ser. B* **326:**285–297.

Riley, D. E., Canfield, T. K., and Gartler, S. M. (1984). Chromatin structure of active and inactive human X chromosomes. *Nucleic Acids Res.* **12:**1829–1845.

Riley, D. E., Goldman, M. A., and Gartler, S. M. (1986). Chromatin structure of active and inactive human X-linked phosphoglycerate kinase gene. *Somatic Cell Mol. Genet.* **12:**73–80.

Rocchi, M., Archidiacono, N., Bertorello, M., Neri, C., and Forabosco, A. (1989). X inactivation center is located in the region Xcen-q12.2. *Cytogenet. Cell Genet.* **51:**1066–1067.

Russell, L. B. (1963). Mammalian X-chromosome action: Inactivation limited in spread and region of origin. *Science* **140:**976–978.

Ryall, J. C., Quantz, J. A., and Shore, G. C. (1986). Rat liver and intestinal mucosa differ in the developmental pattern and hormonal regulation of carbamoyl-phosphate synthetase I and ornithine carbamoyl transferase gene expression. *Eur. J. Biochem.* **156:**453–458.

Sager, R., and Kitchin, R. (1975). Selective silencing of eukaryotic DNA. *Science* **189:**426–433.

Sanford, J. P., Forrester, L., and Chapman, V. M. (1984). Methylation patterns of repetitive DNA sequences in germ cells of *Mus musculus. Nucleic Acids Res.* **12:**2823–2836.

Sanford, J. P., Chapman, V. M., and Rossant, J. (1985). DNA methylation in extraembryonic lineages of mammals. *Trends Genet.* **1:**89–93.

Sanford, J. P., Clark, H. J., Chapman, V. M., and Rossant, J. (1987). Differences in DNA methylation during oogenesis and spermatogenesis and their persistence during early embryogenesis in the mouse. *Genes Dev.* **1:**1039–1046.

Schempp, W., and Meer, B. (1983). Cytologic evidence for three human X-chromosomal segments escaping inactivation. *Hum. Genet.* **63:**171–174.

Schmidt, M., and Migeon, B. R. (1990). Asyncrhonous replication of homologous loci on human active and inactive X chromosomes. *Proc. Natl. Acad. Sci. U.S.A.* **87:**3685–3689.

Schmidt, M., Stolzmann, W. M., and Baranovskaya, L. I. (1982). Replication variants of the human inactive X chromosome. I. Variability within lymphocytes of single individuals. *Chromosoma* **85:**405–412.

Schmidt, M., Wolf, S. F., and Migeon, B. R. (1985). Evidence for a relationship between DNA methylation and DNA replication from studies of the 5-azacytidine-reactivated allocyclic X chromosome. *Exp. Cell Res.* **158:**301–310.

Schneide-Gadicke, A., Beer-Romero, P., Brown, L. G., Nussbaum, R., and Page, D. C. (1989). ZFX has a gene structure similar to ZFY, the putative human sex determinant, and escapes X inactivation. *Cell (Cambridge, Mass.)* **57:**1247–1258.

Schorderet, D. F., Keitges, E. A., Dubois, P. M., and Gartler, S. M. (1988). Inactivation and reactivation of the sex-linked steroid sulfatase gene in murine cell culture. *Somatic Cell Mol. Genet.* **14:**113–121.

Separovic, E. R., and Chandley, A. C. (1987). Lack of evidence that the XqYq pairing tips at meiosis in the mouse show hypersensitivity to DNase I. *Chromosoma* **95**:290–294.

Shafer, D. A., and Priest, J. H. (1984). Reversal of DNA methylation with 5-azacytidine alters chromosome replication patterns in human lymphocyte and fibroblast cultures. *Am. J. Hum. Genet.* **36**:534–545.

Shapiro, L. J., Mohandas, T., Weiss, R., and Romeo, G. (1979). Non-inactivation of an X-chromosome locus in man. *Science* **204**:1224–1226.

Siegfried, E., and Elgin, S. C. R. (1990). Chromatin structure of active genes. In "Eukaryotic Nucleus" (P. R. Strauss and S. H. Wilson, eds.), Vol. 2, pp. 713–736. Telford Press, Caldwell, New Jersey.

Solter, D. (1988). Differential imprinting and expression of maternal and paternal genomes. *Annu. Rev. Genet.* **22**:127–146.

Spence, J. E., Perciaccante, R. G., Greig, G. M., Willard, H. F., Ledbetter, D. H., Hejtmancik, J. F., Pollack, M. S., O'Brien, W. E., and Beaudet, A. L. (1988). Uniparental disomy as a mechanism for human genetic disease. *Am. J. Hum. Genet.* **42**:217–226.

Strum, K. S., and Taylor, J. H. (1981). Distribution of 5-methylcytosine in the DNA of somatic and germline cells from bovine tissues. *Nucleic Acids Res.* **9**:4537–4546.

Sykes, R. C., Lin, D., and Huang, S. J. (1988). Yeast ARS function and nuclear matrix association coincide in a short sequence from the human *Hprt* locus. *Mol. Gen. Genet.* **212**:301–309.

Szyf, M., Tanigawa, G., and McCarthy, P. L., Jr. (1990). A DNA signal from the *Thy*-1 gene defines *de novo* methylation patterns in embryonic stem cells. *Mol. Cell. Biol.* **10**:4396–4400.

Takagi, N. (1974). Differentiation of X chromosomes in early female mouse embryos. *Exp. Cell Res.* **86**:127–135.

Takagi, N., and Abe, K. (1990). Detrimental effects of two active X chromosomes on early mouse development. *Development (Cambridge, UK)* **109**:189–201.

Takagi, N., and Sasaki, M. (1975). Preferential inactivation of the paternally derived X chromosome in the extraembryonic membranes of the mouse. *Nature (London)* **256**:640–642.

Takagi, N., Yoshida, M. A., Sugawara, O., and Sasaki, M. (1983). Reversal of X-inactivation in female mouse somatic cells hybridized with murine teratocarcinoma stem cells *in vitro*. *Cell (Cambridge, Mass.)* **34**:1053–1062.

Takagi, N., Endo, S., and Sugawara, O. (1984). X chromosome inactivation in bone marrow cells of adult mice carrying Searle's X-autosome translocation: Occurrence of the early-replicating inactive X chromosome. *Cytogenet. Cell Genet.* **38**:62–69.

Taylor, J. H. (1960). Asynchronous duplication of chromosomes in cultured cells of Chinese hamster. *J. Biophys. Biochem. Cytol.* **7**:455–464.

Therman, E., and Sarto, G. E. (1983). Inactivation center on the human X chromosome. In "Cytogenetics of the Mammalian X Chromosome" (A. Sandberg, ed.), Part A, pp. 315–325.

Toniolo, D., Martini, G., Migeon, B. R., and Dono, R. (1988). Expression of the G6PD locus on the human X chromosome is associated with demethylation of three CpG islands within 100 kb of DNA. *EMBO J.* **7**:401–406.

Tuan, D., and London, I. M. (1984). Mapping of DNase I-hypersensitive sites in the upstream DNA of human embryonic β-globin gene in K562 leukemia cells. *Proc. Natl. Acad. Sci. U.S.A.* **81**:2718–2722.

Venolia, L., Gartler, S. M., Wassman, E. R., Yen, P., Mohandas, T., and Shapiro, L. J. (1982). Transformation with DNA from 5-azacytidine-reactivated X chromosomes. *Proc. Natl. Acad. Sci. U.S.A.* **79**:2352–2354.

Viegas-Pequignot, E., Dutrillaux, B., and Thomas, G. (1988). Inactive X chromosome has the highest concentration of unmethylated *Hha*I sites. *Proc. Natl. Acad. Sci. U.S.A.* **85**:7657–7660.

Vincent, A., Heitz, D., Petit, C., Kretz, C., Oberle, I., and Mandel, J. L. (1991). Abnormal pattern detected in fragile-X patients by pulsed field gel electrophoresis. *Nature (London)* **349:**624–626.

Weintraub, H., and Groudine, M. (1976). Chromosomal subunits in active genes have an altered conformation. *Science* **193:**848–856.

Weisbrod, S. (1982). Active chromatin. *Nature (London)* **297:**289–295.

West, J. D., Frels, W. I., Chapman, V. M., and Papaioannou, V. E. (1977). Preferential expression of the maternally derived X chromosome in the mouse yolk sac. *Cell (Cambridge, Mass.)* **12:**873–882.

Willard, H. F. (1977). Tissue-specific heterogeneity in DNA replication patterns of human X chromosomes. *Chromosoma* **61:**61–73.

Willard, H. F., and Latt, S. A. (1976). Analysis of deoxyribonucleic acid replication in human X chromosomes by fluorescence microscopy. *Am. J. Hum. Genet.* **28:**213–227.

Wise, T. L., and Harris, M. (1988). Deletion and hypermethylation of thymidine kinase gene in V79 Chinese hamster cells resistant to bromodeoxyuridine. *Somatic Cell Mol. Genet.* **14:**567–581.

Wolf, S. F., and Migeon, B. R. (1985). Clusters of CpG dinucleotides implicated by nuclease hypersensitivity as control elements of housekeeping genes. *Nature (London)* **314:**467–469.

Wolf, S. F., Jolly, D. J., Lunnen, K. D., Friedmann, T., and Migeon, B. R. (1984). Methylation of the hypoxanthine phosphoribosyltransferase locus on the human X chromosome: Implications for X-chromosome inactivation. *Proc. Natl. Acad. Sci. U.S.A.* **81:**2806–2810.

Yang, T. P., and Caskey, C. T. (1987). Nuclease sensitivity of the mouse *HPRT* gene promoter region: Differential sensitivity on the active and inactive X chromosomes. *Mol. Cell. Biol.* **7:**2994–2998.

Yang, T. P., Singer-Sam, J., Flores, J. C., and Riggs, A. D. (1988). DNA binding factors for the CpG-rich island containing the promoter of the human X-linked PGK gene. *Somatic Cell Mol. Genet.* **14:**461–472.

Yen, P. H., Patel, P., Chinault, A. C., Mohandas, T., and Shapiro, L. J. (1984). Differential methylation of hypoxanthine phosphoribosyltransferase genes on active and inactive human X chromosomes. *Proc. Natl. Acad. Sci. U.S.A.* **81:**1759–1763.

6 Molecular Analysis of Mutation in the Human Gene for Hypoxanthine Phosphoribosyltransferase

B. Lambert, B. Andersson, S.-M. He, S. Marcus, and A.-M. Steen
Department of Clinical Genetics
Karolinska Institute
Stockholm, Sweden

I. INTRODUCTION

For more than 20 years it has been known that certain "DNA-reactive" chemicals can induce gene mutation in mammalian cells in culture. This effect was first demonstrated by Chu and Malling (1968), who made use of specific antimetabolites to select for cells with functional loss of the gene for the purine salvage enzyme hypoxanthine phosphoribosyltransferase (HPRT). Since then, the *hprt* system has been a favorite target for mutation analysis in animal and human cells, because it offers possibilities to study both forward and reverse mutation by efficient metabolic selection procedures. Some important landmarks in the development of the *hprt* system are given in Table 6.1.

The *hprt* locus became of great interest to medical geneticists when it was discovered that inherited deficiency of HPRT activity in humans is associated with two X-linked conditions, Lesch–Nyhan syndrome (LNS) and HPRT-related gout (Seegmiller *et al.*, 1967). Early attempts to characterize the germline mutations responsible for these conditions focused on protein chemistry and characterization of the abnormal HPRT enzyme in HPRT-deficient patients. This research eventually led to the elucidaton of the amino acid sequence of the HPRT protein and the identification of several human germ-line mutations (Wilson *et al.*, 1982, 1983). At about the same time, somatic *hprt* mutations in humans became available for detailed molecular study by the development of the T cell cloning technique, which allows the isolation and enumeration of HPRT-deficient T lymphocytes from the peripheral blood of humans (Albertini *et al.*, 1982; Morley *et al.*, 1983).

Molecular Genetic Medicine, Vol. 2

Table 6.1. Research on the Structure and Function of the *hprt* Gene

Study	References
Chemical induction of *hprt* mutation in cell culture	Chu and Malling (1968)
HPRT deficiency identified as the cause of the Lesch– Nyhan syndrome	Seegmiller *et al.* (1967)
Cloning of the *hprt* gene	
Mouse	Melton *et al.* (1981)
Hamster	Konecki *et al.* (1982)
Human	Brennand *et al.* (1982), Jolly *et al.* (1982)
Isolation of somatic *hprt* mutants in humans by T cell cloning	Albertini *et al.* (1982) Morley *et al.* (1983)
Amino acid sequence of the HPRT protein	Wilson *et al.* (1982)
Nucleotide sequence of the *hprt* coding region	Jolly *et al.* (1982), Patel *et al.* (1984)
Promoter region of the *hprt* gene sequenced	Kim *et al.* (1986), Patel *et al.* (1986)
Complete nucleotide sequence of the human *hprt* gene	Edwards *et al.* (1990)

The advent of recombinant DNA technology and its application to human genetics has opened a window on the molecular nature of mutation, and offered an insight into the function of normal and mutated genes. The *hprt* gene from several species has been cloned, and the entire human *hprt* gene of more than 44 kb has recently been sequenced (Table 6.1). The extensive information about *hprt* gene structure and function derived from this work, in combination with T cell cloning and mutant selection procedures, now makes it possible to analyze a variety of mutational changes at the molecular level in the *hprt* gene in human somatic and germ-line cells.

In this article we will focus on the use of the human *hprt* locus as a model system for analysis of mutation in human cells *in vivo*. Several comprehensive reviews have described the clinical features and biochemical basis of LNS (Kelley and Wyngaarden, 1983; Melton, 1987; Stout and Caskey, 1985, 1988). These aspects will therefore be dealt with only briefly, to provide the necessary background information. First, we will give a short account of the strucural features and normal function of the human HPRT protein and its gene to facilitate the subsequent discussion on mutational change.

II. THE HPRT ENZYME AND CLINICAL FEATURES OF HPRT DEFICIENCY

HPRT catalyzes the phosphoribosylation of hypoxanthine and guanine to form the corresponding mononucleotides IMP and GMP, respectively, using phosphoribosyl pyrophosphate (PRPP) as a cosubstrate (Figure 6.1). This "salvage"

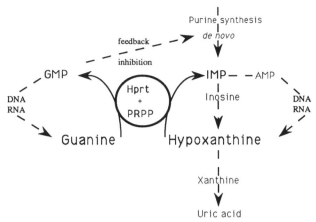

Figure 6.1. The role of the HPRT enzyme in purine metabolism. HPRT catalyzes the "salvage" of the free purines, guanine and hypoxanthine, by converting them into their corresponding mononucleotides, guanosine and inosine monophosphate (GMP and IMP), using phosphoribosyl pyrophosphate (PRPP) as a cosubstrate. GMP exerts important feedback control of *de novo* purine synthesis. Decreased intracellular concentration of GMP due to HPRT deficiency accelerates the *de novo* synthesis. This eventually results in excessive concentrations of purines, which are converted to xanthine and further to uric acid by xanthine oxidase.

pathway of purine mononucleotide biosynthesis in mammalian cells was initially considered to be relatively unimportant (as opposed to the *de novo* synthesis of purines from smaller precursors), until it was discovered that excessive purine synthesis and uric acid secretion are associated with HPRT deficiency in patients with LNS (Seegmiller *et al.*, 1967), an X-linked familial disorder that had been described a few years earlier by Lesch and Nyhan (1964). Later, a group of patients with less severe HPRT deficiency and an incomplete form of the syndrome, familial gout, was identified. It was soon realized that HPRT, in addition to its purine salvage function, plays an important role in the regulation of purine metabolism in human cells.

The complete amino acid sequence of HPRT in human erythrocytes has been established (Wilson *et al.*, 1982). The enzyme is composed of four identical subunits, each containing 217 amino acids (see later, Figure 6.9). There are multiple electrophoretic variants of the normal enzyme, probably due to posttranslational modifications of the primary subunit structure.

The clinical symptoms in HPRT deficiency can be divided into two groups (Kelley and Wyngaarden, 1983). Gouty arthritis and renal stones are symptoms caused by hyperuricemia. Neurological and central nervous system (CNS) symptoms including choreoathetosis, dystonia, mental retardation, and compulsive self-mutilation probably have another biochemical background and are poorly understood. There is a certain degree of correlation between the severity of the clinical symptoms and the degree of HPRT deficiency. Patients with a moderate decrease in HPRT activity show symptoms associated with hyperuricemia, whereas patients with virtually no HPRT activity also develop neurological and CNS manifestations. A third group of patients with intermediary HPRT activity, who, in addition to hyperuricemic symptoms, show mild neurological disturbances (ataxia, slight mental retardation, and speech disturbances but no self-mutilation) has also been described (Page *et al.*, 1981).

The age of onset of the disease varies (Kelley and Wyngaarden, 1983). Most patients with LNS develop hematuria and renal symptoms during the first year of life, followed by the successive manifestations and development of the neurological and CNS symptoms. Severe mental retardation is commonly considered to be a feature of the LNS, but the mental capacity has probably been underestimated in many patients. In HPRT-related gout there is a progression toward chronic gouty arthritis and renal failure in middle age. The degree of deficiency together with other factors affecting urate metabolism define the clinical course.

HPRT is a cytoplasmic protein that is present in many different cells and tissues, and it is often referred to as a "housekeeping" enzyme. Studies of several tissues have demonstrated high HPRT activities in fetal cells, erythrocytes, and lymphocytes, but invariably, the highest HPRT activity in humans and other mammals is found in the brain, particularly the basal ganglia. There are certain similarities in the symptoms of LNS patients and patients suffering from lesions in the basal ganglia (choreoathetosis and dystonia) or animals with experimentally induced lesions in the dopamine pathways in the brain stem (self-mutilation and rigidity). However, there is as yet no morphological or biochemical evidence associating HPRT deficiency with developmental defects of the basal ganglia or dopamine neurons in the CNS.

III. LOCALIZATION, STRUCTURE, AND EXPRESSION OF THE *hprt* GENE

HPRT is coded for by an X-linked gene in humans and in other mammals studied. Linkage analysis and chromosomal breakpoint mapping in somatic cell hybrids have localized the human *hprt* gene to Xq26. This region in the distal segment of the X chromosome has been extensively mapped and shown to harbor several disease-causing genes (Figure 6.2).

The isolation and characterization of human HPRT cDNA were accomplished at about the same time in two separate laboratories, whose workers subsequently described the structural organization of the gene, including its promoter region (Table 6.1). As shown in Figure 6.3, the gene contains nine

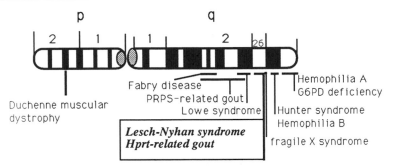

Figure 6.2. The *hprt* locus in the human X chromosome.

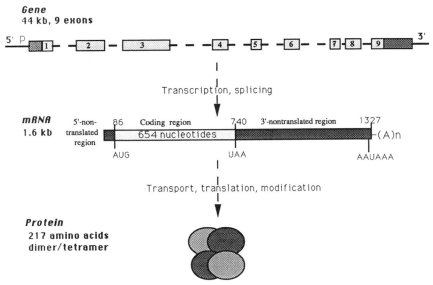

Figure 6.3 The human *hprt* gene and its transcription and translation products. Schematic illustration showing the *hprt* gene (top) with its promoter region (P) and exons (boxes numbered 1–9) separated by introns. The intron line is broken to indicate that the drawing is not to scale, e.g., introns 1 and 3 are about 13 kb, intron 7 is only 170 bp, and the other introns range from about 1.6 to 4 kb. The coding and noncoding regions of the mRNA (middle) are indicated. AUG and UAA are the translation initiation and termination codons, respectively, AAUAAA is the polyadenylation signal, and (A)n is the poly(A) tail. The nucleotide lengths of the various parts of the mRNA are given by the numbers above the regions. The bottom drawing illustrates only the di- or tetrameric nature of the protein; its true conformational structure is unknown.

exons within a region of more than 44 kb. The primary transcript is spliced into a mRNA with a coding region of 654 nucleotides and a total size of about 1600 nucleotides.

The promoter region of the *hprt* gene has several features typical of the so-called housekeeping genes, which code for enzymes involved in essential metabolic functions in many types of cells. These genes are generally expressed at relatively low levels with little tissue specificity. Housekeeping promoters contain several GC-rich sequence motifs that are likely to be involved in the regulation of gene expression, whereas the TATA-box sequences, which direct transcription initiation in tissue-specific genes, are missing (review in Dynan, 1986).

Deletion mapping of the *hprt* promoter demonstrated that only a limited region, including the most proximal GC-rich sequence motif, is necessary for expression. The exact location of the transcription initiation in the *hprt* promoter is not known, and multiple transcription start sites have been demonstrated (review in Melton, 1987). Other evidence suggests that the *hprt* promoter has a limited bidirectional activity and is able to direct the initiation of several transcripts in the 5′ end of the *hprt* gene (Johnson and Friedmann, 1990; Melton, 1987). Moreover, some still unidentified regulatory regions in the first and second intron of the human *hprt* gene seem to be required for effective expression of the gene in embryonic stem cells, whereas other somatic cell lines do not show these reqirements (Reid *et al.*, 1990). Hence, the identification and phenotypic characterization of mutation in the regulatory regions of the *hprt* gene may pose considerable problems, and in fact, no such mutations have yet been described.

Studies of *hprt* expression in terms of enzyme activity and mRNA contents in various tissues have shown the highest levels in the basal ganglia of the brain, where the *de novo* synthesis of purines is low. In general, low enzyme activity correllates with low mRNA levels in several other tissues (Melton, 1987). In peripheral human T lymphocytes, HPRT expression is greatly influenced by the growth state of the cells (Steen *et al.*, 1991). Resting lymphocytes show very low levels of HPRT mRNA (less than one molecule per cell), and the relatively high enzyme activity in these cells seems to depend on a stable HPRT protein with a half-life of more than 48 hours. In proliferating lymphocytes the levels of both HPRT mRNA and enzyme activity increase considerably, probably due to transcriptional activation, and the maintenance of steady-state levels depend on continuous growth stimulation. The half-life of HPRT mRNA is about 5 hours, whereas the turnover time of the protein seems to be at least 24 hours.

Thus, in human lymphocytes, the *hprt* gene seems to be regulated at several levels, including transcriptional activation as well as posttranscriptional control of mRNA stability, and posttranslational modifications of the protein

(Steen *et al.*, 1991). The level of expression appears to depend on the rate of cell proliferation, which could reflect the increasing demand for purine precursors during DNA replication. This notion is supported by the generally high-level HPRT activity in rapidly proliferating cells, for example, in fetal tissues. However, because brain tissue shows the highest degree of HPRT activity in spite of its low proliferation rate, and resting lymphocytes show a relatively high activity level, HPRT may also have other important functions in the cell in addition to its role in DNA precursor metabolism. In this context, it is interesting that in Lesch–Nyhan heterozygotes, there is a selection *in vivo* against HPRT-deficient lymphocytes (Albertini and DeMars, 1974), but apparently not against fibroblasts, which may be a reflection of this tentative demand for a high basal HPRT activity in resting lymphocytes.

IV. GERM-LINE MUTATIONS IN HPRT-DEFICIENT PATIENTS

The first analysis of a germ-line *hprt* mutation at the molecular level was based on amino acid sequencing of an aberrant HPRT protein in erythrocytes from a patient with HPRT-related gout (Wilson *et al.*, 1983). A serine-to-leucine substitution at position 109 was identified (see later, Figure 6.9), and as a result of this change, this protein variant (HPRT$_{London}$) showed an increased K_m for hypoxanthine and a decreased intracellular concentration of HPRT protein, which would explain the partial enzyme deficiency *in vivo*. A change of aspartic acid to asparagine at position 193 (HPRT$_{Kinston}$) was identified in a patient with LNS. This substitution caused a markedly elevated K_m for both hypoxanthine and PRPP, resulting in an essentially nonfunctional HPRT protein *in vivo*. This pioneering work (Wilson *et al.*, 1983) had obvious limitations in that protein purification and sequencing are very laborious, and only those patients who produced HPRT protein in amounts sufficient for amino acid sequencing could be studied.

The cloning of HPRT cDNA (Brennand *et al.*, 1982; Jolly *et al.*, 1982) had made DNA probes available, and alterations in HPRT DNA and HPRT mRNA could be studied by Southern and Northern blot analyses. Using these approaches, Yang *et al.* (1984) studied 28 unrelated LNS patients. Southern blot analysis revealed HPRT DNA alterations in five of the patients (18%), and all of the alterations were different as expected for independent mutational events. Three patients showed total or partial deletions of the gene, while the changes in two other patients suggested rearrangements of HPRT DNA. In one additional patient with a normal Southern blot pattern, no HPRT mRNA could be detected by Northern blot analysis, suggesting that the mutation in this case affected gene transcription or the stability of the mRNA. An important additional result in this study (Yang *et al.* 1984) was that the *hprt* mutation in the large majority of LNS patients (23 of 28, or 82%) is too small (<100 bp) to be detected by Southern blot analysis.

Consequently, the polymerase chain reaction (PCR) applied to genomic HPRT DNA or HPRT cDNA became the method of choice for the analysis of point mutations, in combination with sequencing of the amplified PCR product (Davidson et al., 1988a,b, 1989; Gibbs et al., 1989, 1990). These and other procedures have now been used to study more than 50 HPRT-deficient patients. A variety of mutations have been described; these will be considered separately to appreciate the different levels of resolution of the methods used to detect them, possible differences in the mechanisms of mutagenesis, as well as their different phenotypic effects (Table 6.2).

A. Chromosomal mutations

Deletion or translocation of the X chromosome, with a breakpoint affecting the *hprt* locus, could lead to inactivation of the gene. Thus, theoretically, chromosomal mutation could be one mutagenic mechanism at this locus. However, LNS patients show a normal karyotype, and to the best of our knowledge, there have been no reports of karyotypic abnormality involving the X chromosome in patients with inherited HPRT deficiency. This suggests that X chromosomal rearrangement is a rare cause of mutation at this locus. On the other hand, cytogenetic karyotyping is limited by the resolution of the light microscope, and

Table 6.2. Mutations at the *hprt* Locus

Type of mutation	Method used for detection	Comment
Chromosomal mutation	Cytogenetic karyotyping	Includes deletions and translocations of the X chromosome affecting the *hprt* locus
Gross structural alterations	Southern blot analysis	In general, only deletions larger than about 100 bp will be detected unless a restriction site is affected
Point mutations	Sequencing of PCR-amplified cDNA or genomic DNA	
Missense mutations		Coding error giving rise to a single amino acid substitution
Nonsense mutations		Coding error producing a stop codon
Frameshift mutations		Small deletion/insertion affecting the reading frame
Splice mutations		Change affecting sequence involved in splicing functions

molecular techniques have resolved deletions and rearrangements of the *hprt* gene that are too small to be detected using the microscope and yet are large enough to delete the entire *hprt* gene of more than 50 kb.

B. Gross structural alterations

Using Southern blot analysis, loss of or size alterations of HPRT DNA restriction fragments have been described in 15–20% of all HPRT-deficient patients studied (Table 6.2). Some representative examples, including total gene deletion, internal deletion, and terminal deletion, are shown schematically in Figure 6.4. In addition, some patients have shown more complex rearrangements, e.g., a duplication of exons 2 and 3, and as yet undetermined alterations, including a possible inversion. The number of cases is still too small to allow

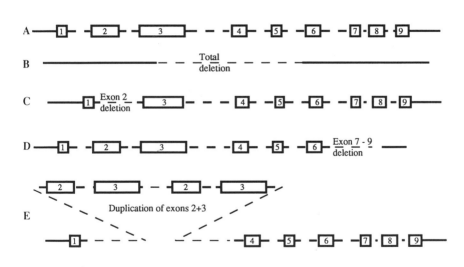

Figure 6.4. Some examples of gross structural alterations in the *hprt* gene. The normal *hprt* gene is shown schematically in A, with exons in the numbered boxes. The solid lines indicate flanking regions and the broken lines indicate intron regions. Examples of mutations include (B) total gene deletion, (C) internal deletion of exon 2, (D) terminal deletion of exons 7–9 extending into the 3′ flanking region, and (E) duplication of exons 2 and 3. The thin broken lines illustrate the fact that neither the the exact position nor the sequence arrangement of the deletion breakpoints is known.

conclusions about the distribution of these alterations along the gene. The identification and sequencing of DNA at the breakpoints for these alterations will shed further light on the mechanisms involved.

C. Missense and nonsense mutations

Point mutations are due to alterations that are too small to be detected by Southern blot analysis, and are identified by DNA sequencing of cDNA or genomic PCR products. As indicated in Table 6.2, four different subtypes of point mutations can be distinguished: missense mutations, nonsense mutations, deletion/insertion mutations causing frame shifts, and splice mutations.

Missense mutations are mostly due to single base substitutions, which cause a coding error and the exchange of one amino acid for another in the HPRT protein. Thus, gene transcription and message translation are not thought to be affected by this type of mutation, and its effect on protein function will depend on the type and position of the substituted amino acid relative to critical catalytic or substrate-binding sites in the protein. Nonsense mutations are single base substitutions giving rise to translational stop codons, resulting in a truncated and nonfunctional protein.

As shown in Figure 6.5, missense mutations appear to be rather evenly distributed along the coding region of the *hprt* gene. Possible exceptions are exons 1 and 2, which seem to be underrepresented so far, and the tendency of a clustering of mutations in the small exon 5. Out of the 23 missense mutations known in patients, 10 are due to transitions and 13 are due to transversions. Nonsense mutations have been found at three sites (Figure 6.5). Interestingly, the mutation altering the CGA codon for arginine, at position 169, to TGA, a translational stop codon, has been described in several unrelated patients, which suggests that this is a mutational "hot spot" (R. A. Gibbs, personal communication).

D. Frameshift mutations

Frameshift mutations are a heterogeneous group, including deletions or insertions of single bases or longer nucleotide sequences. Some of these mutations are compound, i.e., they contain both insertions and deletions. Common to all of these mutations is that they either displace the reading frame, causing frameshift mutations, or delete large regions of the coding sequence. Deletion/insertion mutations also seem to be rather evenly spaced along the HPRT cDNA.

E. Splice mutations

Splice mutations are due to alterations in the splice sequences that are located at the intron/exon borders. These sequences are needed for a correct processing of

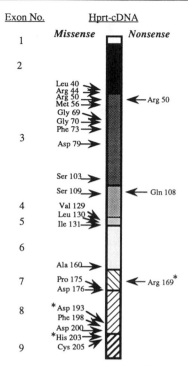

Figure 6.5. Sites of missense and nonsense mutations in HPRT cDNA of HPRT-deficient patients. Arrows indicate the codons at which mutations have been identified (counting the first Ala of exon 1 as no. 1). The asterisks indicate two or more mutations at the same site. Data compiled from Davidson *et al.* (1989), Gibbs *et al.* (1989, 1990), Wilson *et al.* (1983), Skopek *et al.* (1990), and Fujimori *et al.* (1990).

the primary transcript to the final messenger. Splice errors may give rise to truncated messenger RNA, or to the inclusion of intron sequences in the coding frame, which will result in a nonfunctional protein (Figure 6.6). Only five splice mutations have been described so far (Davidson *et al.*, 1989; Gibbs *et al.*, 1990). Two of these were found to have lost exon 8, and two lost exons 7 and 2, respectively, due to base substitutions affecting splice sequences in the flanking introns. The fifth splice mutation showed a partial loss of exon 9 due to a base substitution in the splice acceptor site in intron 8, and the activation of a cryptic splice site within exon 9.

V. SOMATIC *hprt* MUTATIONS

The development of efficient plating techniques for clonal growth of mammalian cells *in vitro* and the exploration of suitable purine analogs for the selection and

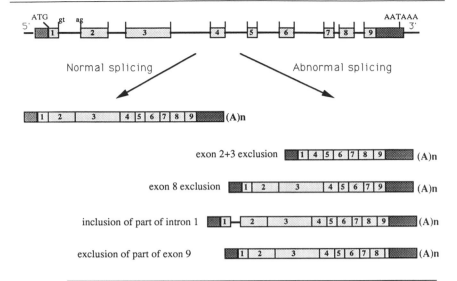

Figure 6.6. Splice mutations. Schematic illustration of some types of splice errors identified in HPRT cDNA. The top drawing shows the *hprt* gene with its nine exons, the ATG start codon, and the AATAAA polyadenylation signal. The splice donor and splice acceptor sites for intron 1 are indicated by gt and ag, the first and last two bases of the corresponding consensus splice sequences, respectively, and by vertical bars in the other introns. The correctly spliced mRNA is shown on the left, and some examples of aberrant splicing products are shown on the right. Exon "skipping" resulting in the exclusion of exons 2 and 3 and exon 8 from the mRNA, for example, may be caused by base substitutions or small deletions in the splice sequences on either side of the skipped exon. Inclusion of intron 1 sequences is due to a mutation affecting the normal splice donor site of intron 1, resulting in the utilization of a cryptic splice site 49 bp into intron 1. Deletion of part of exon 9 is due to an altered splice acceptor site at the 3' end of intron 8, and the activation of a cryptic splice sequence 17 bp into exon 9.

enumeration of *hprt* mutants provided the basis for the first experimental demonstration of mutation induction in hamster cells by chemical agents (Chu and Malling, 1968) and in human fibroblasts by X rays (Albertini and DeMars, 1970).

The existence of two alternative pathways for purine biosynthsis (cf. Figure 6.1), and the availability of efficient inhibitors of each of these, allow selection of mutant cells with deficient HPRT activity, as well as wild-type cells with normal HPRT activity. Purine biosynthesis *de novo* is inhibited by aminopterin, but normal cells will survive the block if they are provided with thymidine (to overcome the effect of aminopterin on thymidine biosynthesis) and hypoxanthine (to supply the cells with purine nucleotides via HPRT). Thus, cells grown in a medium containing hypoxanthine, aminopterin, and thymidine

(HAT medium) will survive only if they have a functional HPRT enzyme. The property of HPRT to use 6-thioguanine (6-TG) and some other toxic purine derivatives with the same affinity as the normal substrates permits efficient selection of HPRT-deficient mammalian cell mutants. Mutant cells lacking HPRT activity are virtually resistant to 6-TG, for example, whereas normal cells will suffer reproductive death due to the HPRT-catalyzed conversion of 6-TG to the corresponding mononucleotide, which, following incorporation into DNA, blocks further DNA replication. Because these efficient selection procedures are applicable to a variety of mammalian cells, the HPRT system has been widely used in experimental mutation research to accomplish various goals:

1. To screen for environmental mutagens with potential harmful effects in man.
2. To determine mammalian and human somatic mutation rates.
3. To investigate the kinds of spontaneous and chemically induced mutations occurring in human and animal cells *in vivo* and *in vitro*.
4. To gain further insight into the mechanisms of mutagenesis.

The most recent development of this system is the human T cell cloning assay (Albertini *et al.*, 1982; Morley *et al.*, 1983), which, in combination with molecular analyses of *hprt* mutation, has opened up an array of applications relating to somatic mutagenesis in humans.

A. Human T cell cloning

Human T lymphocytes, when provided with suitable growth medium, feeder cells, and the appropriate T cell growth factors, will grow and multiply for many weeks *in vitro*. Under these conditions, T cell clones can be derived from single normal or mutant T lymphocytes by limiting dilution in 96-well microtiter plates. The cloning efficiency (CE; the fraction of cells showing clonal growth under the cultivation conditions used) is determined by seeding cells at low density in a nonselective medium. Mutant (HPRT-deficient) cell clones are obtained by seeding cells at high density in a medium containing 6-thioguanine (Figure 6.7). The frequency of mutant cells (MF) is derived from the frequency of TG-resistant cells in the TG plates, divided by the CE.

The same assay can be used for selection and enumeration of mutants induced by chemical treatment or irradiation of cells *in vitro* (Figure 6.7). In this case, however, it is essential that the cells are allowed to grow for a number of cell generations before selection takes place. During this "expression time," the mutation is fixed by DNA replication and preexisting HPRT enzyme is diluted out. HPRT is a relatively stable protein, and the expression time in human T

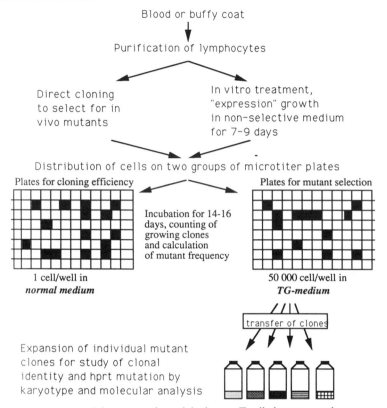

Figure 6.7. Schematic outline of the human T cell cloning procedure.

cells has to be as long as 7–9 days (O'Neill *et al.*, 1990). The rate of spontaneous mutation at the *hprt* locus in human T lymphocytes *in vitro* is low, and has been estimated to be in the range of $(5.5–24.6) \times 10^{-8}$ mutation/cell/generation (Seshadri *et al.*, 1987).

Growing normal or mutant clones can be further expanded by transfer to fresh medium in successively larger vials, until cell numbers allowing cytogenetic and molecular analyses are obtained (Figure 6.7). During recent years, the method has been used to study various parameters:

1. Frequencies of *hprt* mutant T cells *in vivo* in groups of "exposed individuals" in comparison with the background frequency in corresponding "control individuals" (e.g., Dempsey *et al.*, 1985).
2. Frequencies and dose–response relationships for chemically and radiation-

induced *hprt* mutations in human T cells *in vitro* (e.g., O'Neill *et al.*, 1990).
3. Karyotype abnormalities in T cell clones *in vivo* and *in vitro* (e.g., He *et al.*, 1989).
4. Molecular alterations at the *hprt* locus in T cell clones derived from *in vivo* mutants and *in vitro*-induced mutants (e.g., Nicklas *et al.*, 1990).
5. Possible differences between somatic and germ-line mutations by comparative analysis of mutational spectra in Lesch–Nyhan patients and T cell mutants *in vivo* (Rossi *et al.*, 1990).

B. The frequency of *hprt* mutant T cells *in vivo*

The frequency of TG-resistant T lymphocytes *in vivo* in healthy subjects has been determined for many individuals in several laboratories. The mutant frequency has been found to be relatively stable at different sampling times for an individual. In adults it varies considerably in the range of $(0.4–27.8) \times 10^{-6}$ (Albertini *et al.*, 1988), whereas newborns show 10-fold lower values (McGinniss *et al.*, 1990).

Some conditions and exposures associated with an increase in mutant T cells are listed in Table 6.3. In 15- to 79-year-old adults, the frequency of mutant T cells increases 1.3–1.8% per year, and smoking is associated with an increased mutant frequency in several studies. Individual differences in DNA repair capacity could be an additional factor of importance, because patients suffering from the inherited DNA repair disorders xeroderma pigmentosum and ataxia

Table 6.3. Conditions Associated with an Increased Frequency of *hprt* Mutant T Lymphocytes *in Vivo*[a]

Increasing age in healthy subjects
Tobacco smoking in healthy subjects
Individuals with the autosomal recessive conditions
    Xeroderma pigmentosum
    Ataxia telangiectasia
Medical exposure
    Radiotherapy in breast cancer patients
    Radioimmunoglobin therapy in hepatoma patients
    Radio- and chemotherapy in solid tumor and lymphoma patients
Occupational exposure
    Radiotherapy technicians
A-bomb survivors

[a]Details and references are given in the text.

telangiectasia have been found to have markedly elevated frequencies of *hprt* mutant T lymphocytes in their peripheral blood. No difference in the mutant T cell frequency has been found between men and women (Cole *et al.* , 1988; Tates *et al.*, 1989).

Several early studies report a threefold to fivefold increased frequency of *hprt* mutant T cells in individuals receiving radiochemotherapy for various malignant disorders, including breast cancer and other solid tumors, and lymphoma (Dempsey *et al.*, 1985; Messing and Bradley, 1985). In a recent and carefully controlled study of hepatoma patients receiving radioimmunoglobin therapy, a treatment-related 10-fold increase in the mutant T cell frequency was demonstrated (Nicklas *et al.*, 1990).

In contrast to therapeutic treatments with high doses of cytostatics and radiation, diagnostic radiation and occupational exposure to radiation at much lower doses are less convincingly associated with an increase in the mutant T cell frequency (Bachand *et al.*, 1991). Apart from the difficulties in detecting low-dose, as compared to high-dose, exposure, factors related to the fixation and expression of the mutation may be of importance in this context. Because the HPRT protein appears to be very stable in T cells *in vivo* (Steen *et al.*, 1991), the mutant phenotype may not be expressed until many weeks or months after the exposure. Moreover, most T cells are in a "resting" G_0 stage *in vivo,* and repair of treatment-induced DNA damage may occur before the mutation is fixed by replication.

Another consideration concerns the viability of mutant as compared to nonmutant T cells *in vivo.* Several studies have reported lower than expected frequencies of *hprt* mutant T lymphocytes in females who are heterozyguous carries for the Lesch–Nyhan mutation (Albertini and DeMars, 1974). If such a selection against T cells *in vivo* also occurs after sporadic somatic mutation, the frequency of newly induced mutant T lymphocytes would tend to decrease with time after exposure. On the other hand, a significant (50%) increase of the *hprt* mutant T cell frequency has been found among atomic bomb survivors in Hiroshima and Nagasaki who were exposed to an estimated dose of 34–445 rad (Hakoda *et al.*, 1988). The fact that this difference was detected 40 years after exposure implies that *hprt* mutant T lymphocytes do survive for very long times, and therefore should be suitable target cells for estimations of *in vivo* exposure to mutagenic agents.

C. The spectrum of *hprt* mutations in T lymphocytes

Karyotype analyses of more than 100 6-thioguanine-resistant T cell clones have failed to detect chromosomal deletion or rearrangement involving the distal part of the X chromosome, to which the *hprt* gene has been mapped (He *et al.*, 1989; Muir *et al.* 1988). Thus, very few if any *hprt* mutations are due to stable chromosomal alterations that are resolved by conventional karyotyping using the light microscope.

The approaches used to map and identify HPRT DNA alterations in mutant T lymphocyte clones are similar to those described above for Lesch–Nyhan patients. Two major categories of mutational change have been detected; gross structural alterations by use of Southern blot analysis, and point mutations by DNA sequencing of HPRT cDNA PCR products.

Gross structural alterations of HPRT DNA have been identified in 10–15% of mutant T cell clones from human adults. The largest alterations remove the entire *hprt* gene, and the smaller ones delete DNA segments containing single exons within the gene (cf. Figure 6.4). The deletion breakpoints seem to be randomly distributed in the gene. Thus, most breakpoints are in the flanking sequences on either side of the gene and in the large introns 1 and 3 (Nicklas *et al.*, 1989). In contrast, T cell mutants from newborns show a strikingly dissimilar pattern of deletions, with a predominance of breakpoints in the 5' end of the gene. Moreover, these large deletions account for about 80% of all T cell mutants in cord blood (McGinniss *et al.*, 1989). These findings are discussed further below.

A variety of point mutations have been identified in HPRT cDNA, including coding errors giving rise to missense and nonsense mutations, single nucleotide deletions and insertions causing frameshift mutations, and multiple base deletions. In addition, various splicing mutations that give rise to HPRT cDNA of altered size due to exon skipping or inclusion of flanking intron sequences (cf. Figure 6.6) have been detected (Recio *et al.*, 1990; Rossi *et al.*, 1990). DNA alterations causing such splicing errors have been identified in a few of the mutants and have been shown to be due to various types of point mutations in splice sequences flanking the exon involved. Further studies are needed to establish the spectrum of DNA alterations in the intron sequences that are responsible for these splice mutations.

Some of the T cell mutants seem to be unable to produce HPRT mRNA in amounts sufficient for cDNA synthesis and PCR. Although the mutations in these clones are unknown, they may be due to changes in the promoter region of the *hprt* gene, or to changes affecting processing, transport, and stability of the mRNA. Attempts to identify these mutations by sequencing genomic PCR products from noncoding regions of the gene are in progress.

Table 6.4 and Figure 6.8 show the type and location of the point mutations so far identified in human T cell clones *in vivo*. The vast majority of these mutations are unique, which is in accordance with the expected diversity of mutational change at the *hprt* locus. Missense mutations and splice errors of the exon-skipping type predominate among the mutations and account for about one-third each. The mutations appear to be rather evenly spread out along the gene, and so far there are no obvious mutational hot spots.

Table 6.4. Point Mutations in Human T Cell Clones *in Vivo* Studied by HPRT cDNA Analysis

Type of mutation	No. of mutants	Molecular change and its position[a]
Missense and nonsense mutations	26	See Figure 6.8
Frameshift mutations		
Single-base insertions	2	C (482) → GC
		T (609) → TT
Single-base deletion	4	C (8, 9, or 10)
		C (15, 16, or 17)
		C (15, 16, or 17)
		G (46 or 47)
Multiple-base deletions	5	9 bp (41–49) of exon 2
		15 bp (89–94) of exon 2
		11 bp (106/107–116/117) of exon 2
		12 bp (452–456) of exon 6
		2 bp (within 583–586) of exon 9
Splice mutations		
Intron inclusions in HPRT cDNA	2	14 bp of intron 8 between exons 8 and 9
		65 bp of intron 5 between exons 5 and 6
		(T → G change at second base pair of intron 5)
5′ exon deletions in HPRT cDNA	3	5 bp of exon 2
		30 bp of exon 6
		17 bp of exon 9
Exon skipping in HPRT cDNA	19	Exons 2 + 3 in three mutants
		Exon 4 in three mutants
		Exon 5 in two mutants
		Exon 7 in three mutants
		Exon 8 in eight mutants
Total (December 1990)	61	

[a]Numbers in parentheses refer to base position starting from A in the ATG start codon of exon 1. Data from Rossi *et al.* (1990), Recio *et al.* (1990), and S. He (unpublished observations).

VI. CONSIDERATIONS ABOUT THE SOMATIC AND GERM-LINE MUTATIONAL SPECTRA IN THE HUMAN *hprt* GENE

The *hprt* gene is unique among human genes studied so far in the sense that it offers the possibility to compare the spectra for germ-line and somatic mutations at the molecular level. Even before molecular techniques allowed a detailed analysis of the nature of germ-line mutation, it was expected that a high degree of mutational diversity would be found at the *hprt* locus. The phenotypic differences between LNS and HPRT-deficient gout patients with regard to enzyme activity and symptoms could obviously be related to different HPRT mutations

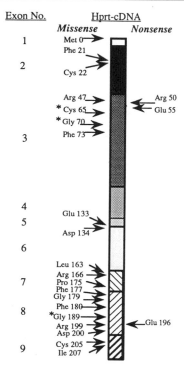

Figure 6.8. Sites of missense and nonsense mutations in the HPRT cDNA of human T cell clones. Arrows indicate the codon at which mutations have been identified (counting the first Ala of exon 1 as no. 1). The asterisks indicate two mutations at the same site. Data compiled from Recio *et al.* (1990), Rossi *et al.* (1990), and S. He (unpublished observations).

in these individuals. Because the patients seldom reproduce, the frequency of disease genes in the population is maintained by recurrent new mutations, including all kinds of DNA alterations that give rise to HPRT deficiency. Consequently, a wide variety of germ-line mutations are expected to occur at the human *hprt* locus, most of which should be of relatively recent origin. In fact, very few mutations have been observed more than once in unrelated families. Only one mutational "hot spot" has been identified, by the discovery of the same base substitution in five unrelated patients (R. A. Gibbs, personal communication). In two other apparently unrelated patients, the same mutation was identified, and in some other cases the mutation has not been defined to the extent that identity with other mutations can be excluded. But the vast majority of the mutations identified so far are different.

The *hprt* mutant T lymphocytes are likely to be true somatic *in vivo* mutants, because they are cloned directly in 6-thioguanine medium, which should be toxic to all cells with even low levels of residual HPRT activity. Moreover, it has been shown by analysis of T cell receptor rearrangements that the vast majority of these *in vivo*-derived clones are indeed unique postthymic mutants (Nicklas *et al.*, 1989). On the other hand, the stringent selection condition used for obtaining T cell mutants limits the collection of mutants to those having severe or complete loss of HPRT activity. The selection procedures will have to be modified to broaden the spectrum of somatic mutations to include mutants with residual HPRT activity.

The frequency distribution of various kinds of *hprt* mutations is remarkably similar in patients and T cells (Table 6.5), which indicates that the predominant mechanisms of somatic and germ-line mutagenesis are similar. There are, however, a few observations with regard to these mutational spectra that deserve further comments.

A. Deletion mutations in newborns and adults

The types and frequencies of *hprt* gene deletions detectable by Southern blot analysis differ considerably between newborn and adult T cell clones *in vivo* (McGinniss *et al.*, 1989). The frequency of such gross structural alterations is 10–15% in adult T cell mutants, whereas it is 85% in cord blood T cell mutants. Moreover, more than half of the newborn T cell mutants show deletions of exons 2 and 3, whereas deletion breakpoints in adults are evenly distributed along the *hprt* gene. Analyses of T cell receptor rearrangements in the mutant clones indicate that the *in vivo* mutations in newborns mainly occur before T cell

Table 6.5. Frequency Distribution of *hprt* Mutations in Germ-Line and Somatic Cells

Type of mutation	Mutations (%)	
	Germ line	T lymphocytes
Chromosomal	0	0
mutation	10–20	10–20 (adults)
Large deletions and re-		(85% in newborns)
arrangements		
Point mutations	80–90	80–90
Missense mutations	52[a]	38[a]
Nonsense mutations	9[a]	5[a]
Frameshift mutations	30[a]	18[a]
Splice mutations	10[a]	39[a]

[a]Refers to percentage of point mutations.

differentiation in the thymus, but adult T cell mutations almost exclusively occur in postthymic cells. To explain this striking difference between the *in vivo* spectrum of large deletion mutations in newborns and adults, it has been suggested that the adult spectrum reflects the accumulation of induced mutations due to exposure to genotoxic chemicals, whereas the newborn spectrum reflects spontaneous mutations occurring in association with the massive recombinase-mediated somatic gene rearrangements that take place during thymic differentiation of T lymphocytes (McGinniss *et al.*, 1989).

B. The types and frequencies of splicing mutations

Mutations affecting splicing functions appear to be more frequent in the somatic as compared to the germ-line mutational spectrum (Table 6.5). In 30% of the mutations detected by sequencing of the HPRT cDNA PCR product from adult T cell mutants, one or two exons were missing in the cDNA (Table 6.4). In contrast, exon skipping has been observed in only 10% of the patients. It is not known if this striking difference is due to the obvious differences in phenotypic selection between patients and T cell mutants (Rossi *et al.*, 1990), or if it indicates that certain mutational events are unique to somatic cells (Recio *et al.*, 1990). Some of the T cell mutants contain a mixed population of normal and mutant HPRT cDNA, indicating that certain mutations affecting the splice function are "leaky." It has been suggested (Rossi *et al.*, 1990) that T cell clones with this type of mutation could display a mutant phenotype under the stringent 6-thioguanine selection conditions, because of the low number of HPRT mRNA molecules in each cell. Moreover, based on analogy with the phenotypic effects of splice mutations at the β-globin locus, it was proposed that leaky *hprt* mutations in the germ line may not give rise to the Lesch–Nyhan phenotype, because normal HPRT would be synthesised in a sufficiently large proportion of the somatic cells *in vivo*. One would then expect leaky splice mutations to be more common among HPRT-related gout patients than among totally HPRT-deficient Lesch-Nyhan patients. The answers to these interesting questions must await the detailed molecular identification of the intron DNA alterations associated with splicing mutations in both T cell mutants and in patients.

There is a predominance of T cell mutants in which exon 8 is missing in the HPRT cDNA (Table 6.4), and two of the five splice mutations in patients are also of this type. This suggests that splice sequences in the regions flanking exon 8 are particularly prone to undergo mutation, or that exon 8 boundaries may be sensitive to a broader range of DNA alterations than is the case for other splice regions. In one of the Lesch–Nyhan patients, a G–A transition in the fifth position of the splice donor site of intron 8 was found to abolish the correct splicing of the preceding exon (Gibbs *et al.*, 1990). Loss of exon 8 in a T cell mutant with a 3-bp deletion in the splice acceptor site at the 5' side of exon 8 was recently identified (B. Andersson, unpublished data). However, many more mutations have to be identified to decide if there is a true mutational "hot spot" or just a wide range of different mutations in the exon 8 splice sequences.

The exclusion of both exons 2 and 3 has been observed in three independent T cell mutants. Although the precise nature of the mutations resulting in multiple exon skipping is not known, their appearance may reflect the order by which splicing occurs in the RNA transcript. Thus, in analogy with the gene encoding thymidine kinase (TK), wherein intron removal occurs in a preferred order in the nascent TK transcript (Gudas *et al.*, 1990), one may speculate that intron 2 would be removed prior to introns 1 and 3 in the HPRT transcript. If so, a single mutation, in the splice acceptor site in intron 1, for example, could result in the exclusion of both exons 2 and 3 simultaneously. However, a germinal Lesch–Nyhan mutation lacking only exon 2 in the HPRT cDNA due to an A–T transversion in the splice acceptor site of intron 1 was recently reported (Gibbs *et al.*, 1990), which indicates that even if early excision of intron 2 is preferred, it may not be the obligatory order for splicing of the HPRT transcript.

C. Mutations at CpG sites

Several reports have suggested that CpG sites in exons are "hot spots" for mutation because cytosine in this position is often methylated and 5-methylcytosine is able to undergo deamination to thymine (Cooper and Krawczak, 1990). Among the 25 base substitution mutations that have been identified in the *hprt* coding sequence in T lymphocytes, only two mutations of the predicted types (C → T and G → A) occur at a CpG site. Based on these limited data, CpG sites do not seem to be particularly prone to undergo somatic mutation in the *hprt* gene. Alternatively, few if any of the nine CpG sites in the coding sequence of the *hprt* gene in T cells are methylated. In Lesch–Nyhan patients, 3 out of 25 base substitution mutations are C → T transitions in CpG sites, and one of these sites is the previously mentioned "hot spot" for a nonsense mutation at codon 169 (cf. Figure 6.5). Accordingly, this "hot spot" is a candidate site for *hprt* mutation via methylation-mediated CpG deamination in the human germ line.

D. Distribution of missense mutations in evolutionarily conserved amino acids

Mammalian HPRT proteins are very similar; the amino acid sequences differ in only 7 out of 217 residues in human and mouse HPRT, and in only 9 residues in human and hamster HPRT. Also, in the more distantly related species, the bilharzia parasite *Schistosoma mansoni* and the malaria parasite *Plasmodium falciparum*, the amino acid sequence for HPRT shows considerable homology to the human enzyme (Craig *et al.*, 1988; King and Melton, 1987). After alignment of the sequences to obtain the best fit, more than 30% of the amino acids are identical in the three species (Figure 6.9). Because evolutionarily conserved regions of same or functionally related proteins may indicate critical sites for the substrate-binding functions or catalytic functions of the enzyme, efforts have been made to combine sequence and structural analyses of several prokaryotic and mammalian phosphoribosyltransferases to define regions with putative functional significance (Argos *et al.*, 1983; Craig *et al.*, 1988; Dush *et al.*, 1985; Hershey and Taylor, 1986). Three such regions have been suggested, as indicated in Figure 6.9.

About half of the *hprt* mutations in patients and T cells are missense mutations giving rise to single amino acid substitutions. Such mutations would be expected to cause severe loss of enzyme activity when the substitution affects amino acids at critical sites. Substitutions at other sites may result in reduced but not total loss of enzyme activity. Somatic T cell mutants of this latter kind are less likely to survive the stringent selection conditions, whereas germ-line mutants may give rise to a less severe clinical phenotype such as gout.

Data for LNS and gout patients include a total of 21 different amino acid substitutions, and 14 of these, or 67%, affect conserved amino acids (Figure 6.9), which is significantly more than expected from a random distribution. The predominance of missense mutations in codons for conserved amino acids becomes even more clear when only LNS patients are considered. With regard to the clinical diagnosis, information is available for 19 patients. Of these, 10 have been reported to have classical LNS, and 9 are described as HPRT-deficient gout patients or as HPRT-deficient variants. Eight of the LNS patients (80%) but only four (44%) of the gout or variant patients have a conserved amino acid substitution (Figure 6.9). In the HPRT mutant human T cell clones a total of 19 sites have been shown to be affected by missense mutations, and 13 of these, or 68%, occur in conserved amino acids, which again is significantly more than expected.

Although these data show that missense mutations are overrepresented among the evolutionary conserved amino acids in the HPRT protein, it is not clear whether this is due to a disproportionate selection, or to a preferential occurrence of point mutations in the codons for these amino acids. However, nonsense mutations (immediate stop codons) due to nucleotide substitutions, and frameshift mutations due to small deletions or insertions of one or two base pairs in the coding region, would be expected to result in a loss of HPRT activity regardless of their position in the coding region. Out of a total of 16 point mutations of these types, 11 (69%) have been found in codons for nonconserved amino acids and 5 (31%) have been found in conserved amino acids, which is very close to the expected frequencies assuming a random distribution. It is therefore likely that the observed distribution of missense mutations in LNS

$$\text{Ala}^M \quad \text{Thr} \quad \text{Arg} \quad \text{Ser} \quad \text{Pro} \quad \text{Gly}^M \quad \text{Val} \quad \overset{I1/I2}{\textbf{Val}} / \text{Ile} \quad \text{Ser} \quad \text{Asp} \quad \text{Asp}_{12}$$

$$\text{Glu} \quad \text{Pro} \quad \textbf{Gly} \quad \text{Tyr} \quad \text{Asp} \quad \text{Leu} \quad \text{Asp} \quad \text{Leu} \quad \overset{\blacksquare}{\textbf{Phe}} \quad \overset{\blacksquare}{\text{Cys}} \quad \text{Ile} \quad \text{Pro}_{24}$$

$$\text{Asn} \quad \text{His} \quad \textbf{Tyr} \quad \text{Ala}^H \quad \text{Glu} \quad \text{Asp} \quad \textbf{Leu} \quad \text{Glu} \quad \text{Arg}^M \quad \textbf{Val} \quad \text{Phe} \quad \text{Ile}_{36}$$

$$\textbf{Pro} \quad \text{His} \quad \textbf{Gly} \quad \overset{\bullet}{\text{Leu}^H} \quad \textbf{Ile} \quad \text{Met} \quad \text{Asp} \quad \overset{\varnothing\ I2/I3}{\text{Arg}} / \text{Thr} \quad \text{Glu} \quad \text{Arg} \quad \overset{\blacksquare}{\text{Leu}}_{48}$$

$$\text{Ala} \quad \overset{\circ}{\text{Arg}} \quad \textbf{Asp} \quad \text{Val} \quad \text{Met} \quad \text{Lys} \quad \text{Glu} \quad \overset{\circ}{\text{Met}} \quad \text{Gly} \quad \text{Gly} \quad \text{His} \quad \text{His}_{60}$$

$$\text{Ile} \quad \text{Val} \quad \text{Ala} \quad \text{Leu} \quad \overset{\blacksquare\blacksquare}{\textbf{Cys}} \quad \text{Val} \quad \textbf{Leu} \quad \textbf{Lys} \quad \overset{\bullet}{\text{Gly}} \quad \overset{\blacksquare\blacksquare\bullet}{\text{Gly}} \quad \text{Tyr} \quad \text{Lys}_{72}$$

$$\overset{\blacksquare\bullet}{\textbf{Phe}} \quad \text{Phe} \quad \text{Ala} \quad \text{Asp} \quad \textbf{Leu} \quad \text{Leu} \quad \overset{\circ}{\text{Asp}} \quad \text{Tyr} \quad \text{Ile} \quad \text{Lys} \quad \text{Ala} \quad \text{Leu}_{84}$$

$$\text{Asn} \quad \text{Arg} \quad \text{Asn} \quad \text{Ser} \quad \text{Asp} \quad \text{Arg} \quad \text{Ser} \quad \text{Ile} \quad \text{Pro} \quad \text{Met} \quad \text{Thr} \quad \text{Val}_{96}$$

$$\text{Asp} \quad \text{Phe} \quad \text{Ile} \quad \textbf{Arg} \quad \text{Leu} \quad \textbf{Lys} \quad \overset{\circ}{\textbf{Ser}} \quad \textbf{Tyr} \quad \text{Cys} \overset{I3/I4}{/ \text{Asn}} \quad \text{Asp} \quad \text{Gln}_{108}$$

$$\overset{\circ}{\textbf{Ser}} \quad \text{Thr} \quad \text{Gly} \quad \text{Asp} \quad \text{Ile} \quad \text{Lys} \quad \text{Val} \quad \text{Ile} \quad \text{Gly} \quad \text{Gly} \quad \text{Asp} \quad \textbf{Asp}_{120}$$

$$\text{Leu} \quad \textbf{Ser} \quad \text{Thr} \quad \text{Leu} \quad \text{Thr} \quad \text{Gly} \quad \overset{I4/I5}{\textbf{Lys}} / \text{Asn} \quad \overset{\bullet}{\textbf{Val}} \quad \overset{\bullet}{\textbf{Leu}} \quad \overset{\circ}{\text{Ile}} \quad \textbf{Val}_{132}$$

$$\overset{\blacksquare\ I5/I6\ \blacksquare}{\textbf{Glu}} / \textbf{Asp} \quad \textbf{Ile} \quad \textbf{Ile} \quad \textbf{Asp} \quad \textbf{Thr} \quad \textbf{Gly} \quad \textbf{Lys} \quad \textbf{Thr} \quad \text{Met} \quad \text{Gln} \quad \text{Thr}_{144}$$

$$\text{Leu} \quad \text{Leu} \quad \text{Ser} \quad \text{Leu} \quad \text{Val} \quad \text{Arg}^M \quad \text{Gln}^H \quad \text{Tyr} \quad \text{Asn}^M \quad \text{Pro} \quad \textbf{Lys} \quad \text{Met}_{156}$$

$$\textbf{Val} \quad \text{Lys} \quad \text{Val} \quad \overset{\circ}{\textbf{Ala}} \quad \overset{I6/I7}{\text{Ser} / \textbf{Leu}} \quad \overset{\blacksquare}{\text{Leu}} \quad \text{Val} \quad \textbf{Lys} \quad \overset{\blacksquare}{\textbf{Arg}} \quad \text{Thr} \quad \text{Pro}^M_{168}$$

$$\text{Arg} \quad \text{Ser} \quad \text{Val} \quad \text{Gly} \quad \text{Tyr} \quad \text{Lys}^M \quad \overset{\blacksquare\circ}{\text{Pro}} \quad \overset{\varnothing\ I8/I9}{\textbf{Asp}} / \textbf{Phe} \quad \textbf{Val} \quad \overset{\blacksquare}{\textbf{Gly}} \quad \overset{\blacksquare}{\textbf{Phe}}_{180}$$

$$\text{Glu} \quad \text{Ile} \quad \textbf{Pro} \quad \text{Asp} \quad \text{Lys} \quad \textbf{Phe} \quad \textbf{Val} \quad \textbf{Val} \quad \overset{\blacksquare\blacksquare}{\textbf{Gly}} \quad \text{Tyr} \quad \text{Ala} \quad \text{Leu}_{192}$$

$$\overset{\bullet\varnothing}{\textbf{Asp}} \quad \text{Tyr} \quad \textbf{Asn} \quad \text{Glu} \quad \text{Tyr} \quad \overset{\bullet}{\textbf{Phe}} \quad \overset{\blacksquare}{\textbf{Arg}} \quad \overset{\circ\blacksquare}{\textbf{Asp}} \quad \textbf{Leu} \quad \overset{I8/I9\ \bullet\varnothing}{\text{Asn} / \textbf{His}} \quad \text{Val}^H_{204}$$

$$\overset{\blacksquare\bullet}{\textbf{Cys}} \quad \text{Val} \quad \overset{\blacksquare}{\textbf{Ile}} \quad \text{Ser} \quad \text{Glu} \quad \text{Thr} \quad \textbf{Gly} \quad \text{Lys} \quad \text{Ala} \quad \textbf{Lys} \quad \text{Tyr} \quad \text{Lys}_{216}$$

$$\text{Ala}_{217}$$

Figure 6.9. Amino acid sequence of the human HPRT Protein showing positions for evolutionary conserved amino acids (in bold face) and mutations. The conserved amino acids are based on the alignment of human, *Schistosoma mansoni*, and *Plasmodium falciparum* amino acid sequences according to Craig *et al.* (1988) and King and Melton (1987). The exon/intron boundaries are shown, and the amino acid positions (counting the first alanine as no. 1) are indicated to the right of each line. Superscripts M and H indicate amino acids that are different in the mouse and hamster, respectively. Underlined sequences are regions that have been discussed in the context of structural or functional

patients and T cell mutants is due to phenotype selection, and reflects the functional importance of the conserved amino acids.

As pointed out previously (Craig *et al.*, 1988; King and Melton, 1987), there is an additional, well-conserved region in the human, schistosomal, and malarial HPRT enzymes between positions 175 and 205 (Figure 6.9); this region has not previously been associated with specific structural or functional properties, but this domain, which accounts for only 14% of the HPRT protein, contains 42% (18/43) of the missense mutations, and all but two of the mutations affect conserved amino acids. This domain may therefore have an important role in protein conformation or enzyme activity.

Further extended comparisons of the kinds and distributions of missense mutations in Lesch–Nyhan and HPRT-related gout patients, as well as in T cell mutants with various phenotypic characteristics, may be useful for a better understanding of the structure–activity relationship of the HPRT protein and the clinical features of HPRT deficiency.

References

Albertini, R. J., and DeMars, R. (1970). Diploid azaguanine-resistant mutants of cultured human fibroblasts. *Science* **169:**482–485.

Albertini, R. J., and DeMars, R. (1974). Mosaicism of peripheral blood lymphocyte populations in females heterozygous for the Lesch–Nyhan mutation. *Biochem. Genet.* **11:**397–411.

Albertini, R. J., Castle, K. L., and Borcherding, W. R. (1982). T-cell cloning to detect the mutant 6-thioguanine-resistant lymphocytes present in human peripheral blood. *Proc. Natl. Acad. Sci. U.S.A.* **79:**6617–6621.

Albertini, R. J., Sullivan, L. M., Berman, J. K. Greene, C. J., Stewart, J. A., Silveira, J. M., and O'Neill, J. P. (1988). Mutagenicity monitoring in humans by autoradiographic assay for mutant T-lymphocytes. *Mutat. Res.* **204:**481–492.

Argos, P., Hanei, M., Wilson, J. W., and Kelley, W. N. (1983). A possible nucleotide binding domain in the tertiary fold of phosphoribosyltransferases. *J. Biol. Chem.* **258:**6450–6457.

Bachand, M., Seifert, A. M., and Messing, K. (1991). Nuclear medicine patients do not have higher mutant frequencies after exposure to thallium-201. *Mutat. Res.* **262:**1–6.

Brennand, J., Chinault, A. C., Konecki, D. S., Melton, D. W., and Caskey, C. T. (1982). Cloned cDNA sequences of the hypoxanthine–guanine phosphoribosyltransferase gene from a mouse neuroblastoma cell line found to have amplified genomic sequences. *Proc. Natl. Acad. Sci. U.S.A.* **79:**1950–1954.

Chu, E. H. Y., and Malling, H. V. (1968). Mammalian cell genetics. II. Chemical induction of

properties, as explained in the text. Mutations were compiled from reports by Davidson *et al.* (1989), Gibbs *et al.* (1989, 1990), Wilson *et al.* (1983), Skopek *et al.* (1990), Fujimori *et al.* (1990), Rossi *et al.* (1990), Recio *et al.* (1990), and S. He *et al.* (unpublished data). Mutations mapping to specific codons are indicated by symbols above the corresponding amino acid, or between two adjacent amino acids if the specific site could not be exactly determined. Missense mutations occurred in classical Lesch–Nyhan patients (●), gout patients (○), HPRT-deficient patients in whom the clinical diagnosis was not specified (∅), and T cells (■).

specific locus mutations in Chinese hamster cells *in vitro*. *Proc. Natl. Acad. Sci. U.S.A.* **61**:1306–1312.

Cole, J., Green, M. H. L., James, S. E., Henderson, L., and Cole, H. (1988). A further assessment of factors influencing measurements of thioguanine-resistant mutant frequency in circulating T-lymphocytes. *Mutat. Res.* **204**:493–507.

Cooper, D. N., and Krawczak, M. (1990). The mutational spectrum of single base pair substitutions causing human genetic disease: Patterns and predictions. *Hum. Genet.* **85**:55–74.

Craig, S. P., III, McKerrow, J. H., Newport, G. R., and Wang, C. C. (1988). Analysis of cDNA encoding the hypoxanthine–guanine phosphoribosyltransferase (HGPRTase) of *Schistosoma mansoni*; a putative target for chemotherapy. *Nucleic Acids Res.* **16**:7087–7101.

Davidson, B. L., Pashmforoush, M., Kelley, W. N., and Palella, T. D. (1988a). Genetic basis of hypoxanthine guanine phosphoribosyltransferase deficiency in a patient with the Lesch–Nyhan syndrome (HPRTFlint). *Gene* **63**:331–336.

Davidson, B. L., Palella, T. D., and Kelley, W. N. (1988b). Human hypoxanthine-guanine phosphoribosyltransferase: A single nucleotide substitution in cDNA clones isolated from a patient with Lesch–Nyhan syndrome (HPRTMidland). *Gene* **68**:85–91.

Davidson, B. L., Tarlé, S. A., Palella, T. D., and Kelley, W. N. (1989). Molecular basis of hypoxanthine–guanine phosphoribosyltransferase deficiency in ten subjects determined by direct sequencing of amplified transcripts. *J. Clin. Invest.* **84**:342–346.

Dempsey, J. L., Seshadri, R. S., and Morley, A. A. (1985). Increased mutation frequency following treatment with cancer therapy. *Cancer Res.* **45**:2873–2877.

Dush, M. K., Sikela, J. M., Khan, S. A., Tischfield, J. A., and Stambrook, P. J. (1985). Nucleotide sequence and organization of the mouse adenine phosphoribosyltransferase gene: Presence of a coding region common to animal and bacterial phosphoribosyltransferases, that has a variable intron/exon arrangement. *Proc. Natl. Acad. Sci. U.S.A.* **82**:2731–2735.

Dynan, W. S. (1986). Promoters for housekeeping genes. *Trends Genet.* **2**:196–197.

Edwards, A., Voss, H., Rice, P., Civitello, A., Stegeman, J., Schwager, C., Zimmerman, J., Erfle, H., Caskey, C. T., and Ansorge, W. (1990). Automated DNA sequencing of the human *hprt* locus. *Genomics* **6**:593–608.

Fujimori, S., Kamatani, N., Nishida, Y., Ogasawara, N., and Akaoka, I. (1990). Hypoxanthiune guanine phosphoribosyltransferase deficiency: Nucleotide substitution causing Lesch–Nyhan syndrome identified for the first time among Japanese. *Hum. Genet.* **84**:483–486.

Gibbs, R. A., Nguyen, P., McBride, L. J., Koepf, S. M., and Caskey, C. T. (1989). Identification of mutations leading to the Lesch–Nyhan syndrome by automated direct DNA sequencing of *in vitro* amplified cDNA. *Proc. Natl. Acad. Sci. U.S.A.* **86**:1919–1923.

Gibbs, R. A., Nguyen, P. N., Edwards, A., Civitello, A. B., and Caskey, C. T. (1990). Multiplex DNA deletion detection and exon sequencing of the hypoxanthine phosphoribosyltransferase gene in Lesch–Nyhan families. *Genomics* **7**:235–244.

Gudas, J. M., Knight, G. B., and Pardee, A. G. (1990). Ordered splicing of thymidine kinase pre-mRNA during the S phase of the cell cycle. *Mol. Cell. Biol.* **10**:5591–5595.

Hakoda, M., Akiyama, M., Kyoizumi, S., Awa, A. A., Yamakido, M., and Otake, M. (1988). Increased somatic cell mutant frequency in atomic bomb survivors. *Mutat. Res.* **201**:39–48.

He, S., Holmberg, K., Lambert, B., and Einhorn, N. (1989). Hprt mutations and karyotype abnormalities in T-cell clones from healthy subjects and melphalan-treated ovarian carcinoma. *Mutat. Res.* **210**:353–358.

Hershey, H. V., and Taylor, M. W. (1986). Nucleotide sequence and deduced amino acid sequence of *Echerichia coli* adenine phosphoribosyltransferase and comparison with other analogous enzymes. *Gene* **43**:287–293.

Johnson, P., and Friedmann, T. (1990). Limited bidirectional activity of two housekeeping gene promoters: Human HPRT and PGK. *Gene* **88**:207–213.

Jolly, D. J., Esty, A. C., Bernard, H. U., and Friedmann, T. (1982). Isolation of a genomic clone partially encoding human hypoxanthine phosphoribosyltransferase. _Proc. Natl. Acad. Sci. U.S.A._ **79**:5038–5041.

Kelley, W. N., and Wyngaarden, J. B. (1983). Clinical syndromes associated with hypoxanthine phosphoribosyltransferase deficiency. In "The Metabolic Basis of Inherited Disease" (J. B. Stanbury _et al._, eds.), 5th ed., pp. 1114–1142. McGraw-Hill, New York.

Kim, S. H., Moores, J. C., David, D., Respess, J. G., Jolly, D. J., and Friedmann, T. (1986). The organization of the human HPRT gene. _Nucleic Acids Res._ **14**:3103–3118.

King, A., and Melton, D. W. (1987). Characterisation of cDNA clones for hypoxanthine–guanine phosphoribosyltransferase from the human malarial parasite, _Plasmodium falciparum:_ Comparisons to the mammalian gene and protein. _Nucleic Acids Res._ **15**:10469–10481.

Konecki, D. S., Brennand, J., Fuscoe, J. C., Caskey, C. T., and Chinault, A. C. (1982). Hypoxanthine phosphoribosyltransferase genes of mouse and Chinese hamster: Construction and sequence analysis of cDNA recombinants. _Nucleic Acids Res._ **10**:6763–6775.

Lesch, M., and Nyhan, W. L. (1964). A familial disorder of uric acid metabolism and central nervous system function. _Am. J. Med._ **36**:561–570.

McGinniss, M. J., Nicklas, J. A., and Albertini, R. A. (1989). Molecular analyses of _in vivo hprt_ mutations in human T-lymphocytes. IV. Studies in newborns. _Environ. Mol. Mutagen._ **14**:229–237.

McGinniss, M. J., Falta, M. T., Sullivan, L. M., and Albertini, R. A. (1990). _In vivo hprt_ mutant frequencies in T-cells of normal human newborns. _Mutat. Res._ **240**:117–126.

Melton, D. W. (1987). HPRT gene organization and expression. _Oxford Surv. Eukaryotic Genes_ **4**:34–76.

Melton, D. W., Konecki, D. S., Ledbetter, D. H., and Hejtmancik, F. (1981). In vitro translation of hypoxanthine/guanine phosphoribosyltransferase mRNA: Characterization of a mouse neuroblastoma cell line that has elevated levels of hypoxanthine/guanine phosphoribosyltransferase protein. _Proc. Natl. Acad. Sci. U.S.A._ **78**(11):6977–6980.

Messing, K., and Bradley, W. E. C. (1985). _In vivo_ mutant frequency rises among breast cancer patients after exposure to high doses of γ-radiation. _Mutat. Res._ **152**:107–112.

Morley, A. A., Trainor, K. J., Seshadri, R., and Ryall, R. G. (1983). Measurement of _in vivo_ mutations in human lymphocytes. _Nature (London)_ **302**:155–156.

Muir, P., Osborne, Y., Morley, A. A., and Turner, D. R. (1988). Karyotypic abnormality of the X chromosome is rare in mutant HPRT-lymphocyte clones. _Mutat. Res._ **197**:157–160.

Nicklas, J. A., Hunter, T. C., O'Neill, J. P., and Albertini, R. J. (1989). Molecular analyses of _in vivo hprt_ mutations in human T-lymphocytes. III. Longitudinal study of _hprt_ gene structural alterations and T-cell clonal origins. _Mutat. Res._ **215**:147–160.

Nicklas, J. A., Falta, M. T., Hunter, T. C., O'Neill, J. P., Jacobson-Kram, D., Williams, J. R., and Albertini, R. J. (1990). Molecular analysis of _in vivo hprt_ mutations in human T-lymphocytes. V. Effects of total body irradiation secondary to radioimmunoglobulin therapy (RIT). _Mutagenesis_ **5**:461–468.

O'Neill, J. P., Sullivan, L. M., and Albertini, R. J. (1990). _In vitro_ induction, expression and selection of thioguanine-resistant mutants with human T-lymphocytes. _Mutat. Res._ **240**:135–142.

Page, T., Bakay, B., Nissinen, E., and Nyhan, W. L. (1981). Hypoxanthine–guanine phosphoribosyltransferase variants: Correlation of clinical phenotype with enzyme activity. _J. Inherited Metab. Dis._ **4**:203–206.

Patel, P. I., Nussbaum, R. L., Framson, P. E., Ledbetter, D. H., Caskey, C. T., and Chinault, A. C. (1984). Organization of the HPRT gene and related sequences in the human genome. _Somatic Cell Mol. Genet._ **10**:483–493.

Patel, P. I., Framson, P. E., Caskey, C. T., and Chinault, A. C. (1986). Fine structure of the human hypoxanthine phosphoribosyltransferase gene. _Mol. Cell. Biol._ **6**:393–403.

Recio, L., Cochrane, J., Simpson, D., and Skopek, T. R. (1990). DNA sequence analysis of *in vivo hprt* mutations in human T-lymphocytes. *Mutagenesis* **5**:505–510.

Reid, L. H., Gregg, R. G., Smithies, O., and Koller, B. H. (1990). Regulation elements in the introns of the human *HPRT* gene are necessary for its expression in the embryonic stem cells. *Proc. Natl. Acad. Sci. U.S.A.* **87**:4299–4303.

Rossi, A. M., Thijssen, J. C. P., Tates, A. D., Vrieling H., Natarajan, A. T., Lohman, P. H. M., and van Zeeland, A. A. (1990). Mutations affecting RNA splicing in man are detected more frequently in somatic than in germ cells. *Mutat. Res.* **244**:353–357.

Seegmiller, J. E., Rosenbloom, F. M., and Kelley, W. N. (1967). Enzyme defect associated with a sex-linked human neurological disorder and excessive purine synthesis. *Science* **155**:1682–1684.

Seshadri, R., Kutlaca, R. J., Trainor, K., Matthews, C., and Morley, A. A. (1987). Mutation rate of normal and malignant human lymphocytes. *Cancer Res.* **47**:407–409.

Skopek, T. R., Recio, L., Simpson, D., Dellaire, L., Melancon, S. B., Ogier, H., O'Neill, J. P., Falta, M. T., Nicklas, J. A., and Albertini, R. J. (1990). Molecular analyses of a Lesch–Nyhan syndrome mutation (hprt$_{Montreal}$) by use of T-lymphocyte cultures. *Hum. Genet.* **85**:111–116.

Steen, A., Sahlén, S., and Lambert, Bo (1991). Expression of the hypoxanthine phosphoribosyl transferase gene in resting and growth-stimulated human lymphocytes. *Biochim. Biophys. Acta* **1088**:77–85.

Stout, J. T., and Caskey, C. T. (1985). HPRT: Gene structure, expression, and mutation. *Annu. Rev. Genet.* **19**:127–148.

Stout, J. T., and Caskey, C. T. (1988). The Lesch–Nyhan syndrome: Clinical, molecular and genetic aspects. *Trends Genet.* **4**:175–178.

Tates, A. D., Bernini, L. F., Natarajan, A. T., Ploem, J. S., and Verwoerd, N. P. (1989). Detection of somatic mutants in man: HPRT mutations in lymphocytes and hemoglobin mutations in erythrocytes. *Mutat. Res.* **213**:73–82.

Wilson, J. M., Tarr, G. E., Mahoney, W. C., and Kelley, W. N. (1982). Human hypoxanthine–guanine phosphoribosyltransferase: Complete amino acid sequence of the erythrocyte enzyme. *J. Biol. Chem.* **257**:10978–10985.

Wilson, J. M., Young, A. B., and Kelley, W. N. (1983). Hypoxanthine–guanine phosphoribosyltransferse deficiency. The molecular basis of the clinical syndromes. *N. Engl. J. Med.* **309**:900–910.

Yang, T. P., Patel, P. I., Stout, J. T., Jackson, L. G., Hildebrand, B. M., and Caskey, C. T. (1984). Molecular evidence for new mutations in the HPRT locus in Lesch–Nyhan patients. *Nature (London)* **310**:412–414.

Regulatory Genes of Human Immunodeficiency Viruses

Flossie Wong-Staal
Department of Medicine and Biology
University of California, San Diego
La Jolla, California

William A. Haseltine
Division of Human Retrovirology
Dana-Farber Cancer Institute
Harvard University
Cambridge, Massachusetts

I. INTRODUCTION

The life cycle of the human pathogenic retroviruses, the human immune deficiency viruses types 1 and 2 (HIV-1 and -2) and the human T cell leukemia/lymphoma viruses (HTLV-1 and -2), is unusual. Disease is delayed by years and sometimes decades between the time of infection and appearance of life-threatening symptoms. The majority of people infected with HTLV-1 and -2 and HIV-2 may never develop overt symptoms of disease. Development of antiviral antibodies in response to infection may also be delayed by many months or years.

Corresponding to the indolent course of the disease is the strict regulation of the extent of virus replication in the infected person. Very few, if any, virus particles or virus-specific proteins are detected in people infected with the human T cell leukemia viruses. Indirect evidence of production of such virus proteins is deduced by detection of antibodies to virus structural or regulatory proteins. Replication of the HTLV virus is so well controlled that antibodies to one of the central regulatory proteins necessary for virus growth, the *rex*-encoded protein, have never been detected even in people with fatal virus-induced leukemia. Many of the HIV-1 virus regulatory proteins are only intermittently antigenic in infected people.

The majority of lymphocytes obtained from patients infected with either HTLV-1 or HIV-1 do not produce virus. Production of virus proteins in culture is only obtained upon mitogenic stimulation of the primary lymphocyte population, revealing a state of controlled infection in this critical cell population.

Studies of acute infection of HIV-1 reveal that production of viral proteins occurs in two stages. Early in infection virus regulatory proteins are made in the absence of significant amounts of the proteins that comprise the virus particle. Late in the infection cycle the balance is reversed. Structural proteins are produced in greater amounts than are regulatory proteins. It is evident that the early-to-late gene switching, typical of many DNA viruses, must occur via a highly unusual process, as all gene products of the retroviruses are derived from a single primary transcript. The problem of how temporal regulation of genes, all encoded on the same primary transcript, occurs is of obvious interest.

An understanding of the factors that govern human retrovirus regulation should illuminate the unusual features of natural infection by these pathogens. Here the knowledge of the regulatory genes and factors that govern virus replication of HIV-1 are summarized. The discussion is relevant to an understanding of the HTLV-1-like virus as well. Further study of these regulatory processes should speed efforts to develop effective treatments as well as to discover general, fundamental principles of gene regulation.

II. RETROVIRUS LIFE CYCLE

Persistence of infection of the human retroviruses is one consequence of the intrinsic life cycle of this class of virus. Infection by retroviruses is initiated when cell-free or cell-associated virus binds to a receptor on the target cell via the virus envelope glycoprotein. The receptor for the HIV-1 viruses is CD4, an integral membrane protein found on the surface of a subpopulation of hematopoietic cells, including helper T cells, monocytes, macrophages, dendritic cells, and microglial cells. After fusion of the virus envelope protein with the cell membrane, the virus core enters the cell, and the single-stranded viral RNA, still associated with some capsid proteins, is converted to double-stranded DNA via the DNA polymerase and ribonuclease H activities of an enzyme in the virus particle, the reverse transcriptase. The newly made double-stranded DNA, called the provirus, then migrates to the nucleus, integrates into the host DNA via the action of the viral integrase protein, and thus completes establishment of infection. Infection persists as long as cells carrying proviruses are present.

The proviral DNA serves as template for production of viral RNA, which in turn serves both as messenger for synthesis of viral proteins and as genomic RNA to be packaged into virus particles. Virus assembly occurs at the surface of membranes. The capsid precursor proteins insert into the cell membrane where they aggregate to form the budding particle. Viral RNA is bound to the capsid precursor and enfolded into the particle. The envelope glycoprotein is deposited on the outer surface of the cell membrane. The virus particle is released from the cell surface and the capsid is processed into mature proteins through the viral protease, completing the life cycle. Provirus may persist in cells without being expressed, accounting, in part, for the long period between infection and disease.

III. COUPLING OF VIRUS REPLICATION TO CELL CYCLE AND ACTIVATION

Replication of retroviruses is generally coupled to the state of proliferation and activation of the infected cells. Neither the HIV nor the HTLV viruses replicate in primary resting T cells. For HIV-1, the first level of restriction appears to be at the level of complete provirus synthesis (1). Upon infection of resting cells, the process of conversion of genomic RNA begins but is not completed. The incomplete provirus is unstable, with a half-life of about 1 day. It is not known whether cellular factors required for complete provirus synthesis are lacking in resting cells, or conversely, resting cells contain factors that prematurely arrest proviral synthesis. As very few T cells replicate at any one time, self-limiting infection of this cell type may be the rule rather than the exception. This observation may help to explain why the T cell population in infected people remains relatively free of proviruses for prolonged periods in patients with chronic low-level viremia.

The requirement of cell proliferation for productive infections is not universal. HIV-1 and HIV-2 can infect nonreplicating cultures of monocytes and macrophages. Moreover, the PBj-14 strain of SIV$_{Mangaby}$, which is highly virulent in susceptible macaque monkeys and kills the infected animals within 10 days of infection, can establish productive infection in resting T cells, whereas closely related SIV isolates do not (P. Fultz, personal communication). This altered growth characteristic of the PBj-14 SIV may account for the increased virulence.

A second restriction of virus replication occurs by limiting initiation of RNA transcription of the integrated proviruses. Primary circulating T cells that harbor HIV and HTLV DNA do not express viral RNA until mitogenic stimulation of such cells. A number of cellular transcription factors, some of which are induced by T cell activation, interact specifically with sequences contained in the HIV-1 long terminal repeat (LTR) (Figure 7.1). The TATA element, located between nucleotides -23 and -27 (the site of RNA initiation is designated $+1$), binds the transcription factor TFIID. TFIID positions the cellular RNA polymerase II for correct initiation (2). Three GC-rich sequences bind to the transcription factor Sp1 (2, 3). Binding of Sp1 increases the rate of transcriptional initiation. The enhancer element is located between nucleotides -120 and -57. The enhancer sequence stimulates RNA initiation from heterologous promoters independent of orientation (4). This region contains imperfect repeat sequences (-109 and -79), which are also consensus recognition sequences for NF-KB protein (5), a cellular protein that is activated upon mitogenic stimulation. Purified NF-KB protein binds to the HIV-1 LTR *in vitro* (6).

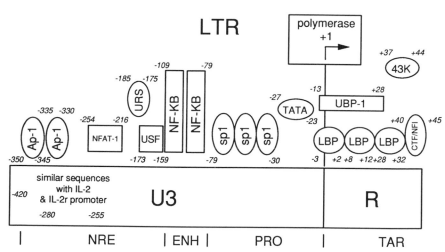

Figure 7.1. Schematic representation of the HIV-1 long terminal repeat (LTR). The 3′ unique (U3) and repeat (R) portions are subregions of the LTR that flank the DNA form of the HIV-1 genetic information. By convention, the site of RNA initiation is shown as $+1$. The LTR sequences extend 420 nucleotides 5′ to the site of initiation. The 5′ nucleotides are designated with negative numbers. The functional regions of the LTR are indicated below the line. These include the negative regulatory element (NRE), the enhancer (ENH), the promoter (PRO), and trans-activator-responsive region (TAR). The approximate location of regions that share consensus sequences with proteins known to bind to DNA and to effect transcription initiation are illustrated above the line. The NFAT-1, USF, NF-KB, Sp-1, LBP, UBP-1, and CTF/NF-1 proteins have all been shown to bind to the positions indicated (see text).

A second potential enhancer is found outside of the LTR in the *gag–pol* coding sequences (between nucleotides 1711 and 6026). These sequences are capable of increasing the rate of RNA synthesis from heterologous promoters independent of orientation (7). The role of these intragenic sequences in the initiation of transcription from the HIV LTR is speculative at present.

The sequences located between nucleotides −410 and −157 have a negative effect on the rate of RNA initiation *in vivo* (4,8–11) and *in vitro* (12). This region of the LTR is called the negative regulatory element (NRE). Deletion of the NRE increases the replication rate of the mutant virus from threefold to fivefold in CD4$^+$ cell lines (11), in fresh peripheral blood lymphocytes, and in fresh monocyte/macrophage cultures (Langhoff, Haseltine, Lu, unpublished observations). Within the NRE are a number of sequences that are recognized by cellular transcription factors. The upstream binding factor (USF), originally identified as a cellular factor that binds to the adenovirus major late promoter (13), also binds to a consensus sequence located between nucleotides −173 and −159 of the HIV-1 LTR (Haseltine, Roeder, Sawadogo and Rosen, unpublished observations). This sequence is similar to a negative regulatory region in the interleukin-2 (IL-2) and IL-2 receptor promoters (14). The binding site for the NFAT-1 protein is also present within the NRE (15). Consensus binding sites for the Ap-1 protein, a transcription factor that increases the rate of transcriptional initiation from proximal promoters, are located at nucleotides −350/−345 and −335/−330 (16). Deletion of several sequences within the NRE, including the Ap-1 and NFAT-1 sites, has no measurable effect on HIV LTR-directed gene expression in transfected cells. In contrast, deletion of the USF sequence results in increased rate of LTR-directed gene expression as well as virus replication in CD4$^+$ T cell lines (17). Evidently, these sequences contain recognition signals for the cellular proteins that repress RNA initiation from the HIV-1 promoter.

Several cellular factors have also been found to bind downstream of the site of RNA initiation, within the R region of the LTR: UBP-1 binds to sites at nucleotides −13/+28 and +37/+44 (18); LBP-1 binds to sites at nucleotides −3/+2, +8/+12, and +28/+32 (19); and CTF/NF-1 bind to a site at nucleotide +40/+45 (19). Recently, a 43-kDa protein distinct from UBP-1 was found to bind to nucleotides +37/+44, a region that overlaps with the transactivation response element (TAR) (Gaynor, personal communication). This protein contains a helix–turn–helix domain that is characteristic of some DNA-binding proteins.

The description of cellular factors that regulate HIV transcription is far from complete even in T cell lines. In addition to proteins that bind to the LTR DNA, additional proteins may participate through protein–protein interactions. The variety and abundance of such transcription factors are likely to vary according to cell type as well as the state of proliferation or activation. The factors that govern HIV RNA expression in monocytes, macrophages, and dendritic cells are poorly defined at present. Unraveling the role of factors that regulate HIV in various cell types remains a challenging problem.

IV. HIV REGULATORY GENES

The genetic organization of the human pathogenic retroviruses is more complex than that of animal viruses previously studied. The genomic structure of HIV-1 and the various spliced mRNA species are shown in Figure 7.2 and are summarized in Table 7.1. At least seven additional genes of HIV-1 and three additional genes of HTLV-1 have been identified. Only two genes of HIV-1, namely, *tat* and *rev,* are known to be essential for virus replication in established T cell lines (20). The others are dispensable for virus replication *in vitro,* but may affect the efficiency of infection and virus production.

Multiple mRNAs often specify each regulatory protein. As an example, a set of mRNAs can serve as templates for the synthesis of active Tat protein. The major form of *tat* mRNA is derived by splicing from the major donor site near the 5′ LTR to an acceptor site 5′ to *tat,* and by a splicing event that joins the first coding exon of *tat* to the second coding exon, which overlaps the *env* gene (Figure 7.2). This *tat* mRNA encodes an 86-amino-acid-long (16-kDa) Tat protein (21, 22). The mRNA that lacks the splicing event encodes a 76-amino-acid (14-kDa) protein derived only from the first coding exon (23). A third form of *tat* mRNA contains an additional exon from the *env* gene and encodes a 28-kDa fusion protein comprising the first 72 amino acids from the *tat*-encoded protein and 38 and 91 amino acids, respectively, from the *env*- and *rev*-encoded proteins. This protein is called either Tnv or Tev (24, 25). There are additional minor forms of *tat* mRNA that may contain noncoding exons in the 5′ untranslated region, or that use an alternative splice acceptor site 5′ to the second coding exon. Similar redundancy is seen with several of the HIV-1 genes, including *rev* and *nef* mRNAs. The significance of these alternative forms of mRNA is not known. A second unusual feature of the HIV-1 mRNA is expression of proteins from polycistronic messages. For example, the 4.2-kb singly spliced *env* mRNA also contains the coding sequences for *rev, nef,* and *vpu.* Two or more of these accessory genes may be expressed from the same mRNA (Cohen & Haseltine, unpublished observations; Pavlakis, personal communication).

V. THE *Tat* TRANS-ACTIVATION PATHWAY

A. The protein

The *tat* gene specifies a trans-activator (Tat) protein that enhances LTR-directed gene expression. Tat function is required for high-level expression of all viral

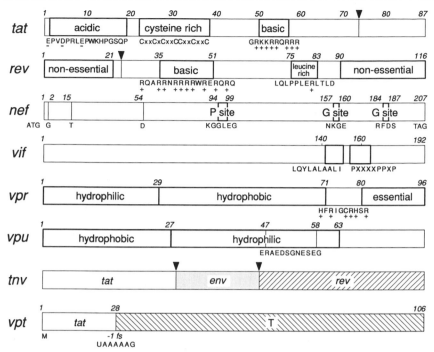

Figure 7.2. Schematic representation of mRNA specified by HIV-1. A schematic diagram of the functional open reading frames of HIV-1 is depicted. The genes are designated by the standard three-letter convention (see Table 7.1 for the related factors and functions). The arrows joining the open boxes at the top of the figure indicate functional genetic regions joined by splicing. Viral mRNAs are divided into two classes, those that accumulate in the absence of Rev activity (the early regulatory mRNAs), and those that accumulate only in the presence of active Rev (the virion and late regulatory protein mRNAs). The mRNAs shown here represent only a subset of all the mRNAs specified by HIV-1. The TAR region at the 5′ end of each mRNA is indicated with a T. The DNA form of the TAR region within the LTR is indicated with the same symbol. The Rev-responsive region present within the *env* gene is indicated by the symbol R. The cis-acting repressive sequences present in *gag*, *pol*, and *env* are indicated by the symbol C. The major splice donor used by all spliced mRNAs is indicated by SD in the *vif* mRNA$_1$. The splice acceptors (SA) preceding *vif*, *vpr*, *tat*, and *vpu* are also indicated. The polyadenylic acid stretch at the 3′ end of the mRNAs is indicated by polyA. The symbol fs in the *gag–pol* mRNA indicates the site at which a −1 frameshift occurs between the *gag* and *pol* open reading frames.

proteins (26, 27). The *tat*-defective mutants do not make virus unless Tat protein is provided in trans (28, 29). The coding sequences of *tat* are located in two exons, the first coding for 76 amino acids and the second coding for 12 amino acids in most strains. Mutational analysis demonstrates that the amino-terminal 58 amino acids of Tat suffice for trans-activation (30). Within this sequence

Table 7.1. HIV Genetic Regulation at a Glance

Factor/element	Gene/region abbreviation	Function
Trans-acting products		
Trans-activator	*tat*	High-level expression of all viral genes
Regulation of virion protein expression	*rev*	Accumulation of full-length and envelope mRNA
Negative factor	*nef*	Proposed to be a negative regulatory factor; also possible regulator for growth in primary lymphocytes and monocytes
Viral protein R	*vpr*	Trans-acting protein present in virus particle
Viral protein U	*vpu*	Cyctoplasmic protein that facilitates virus assembly and export
Virion infectivity factor	*vif*	Increases infectivity of virus particles
Virus protein T	*vpt*	Tat–T open reading frame fusion protein of unknown function
Tat–Env–Rev fusion protein	*tnv*	Hybrid protein of three exons; has Tat and reduced Rev activity
Cis-acting elements		
Trans-activator response region	TAR	Mediates Tat trans-activation
Rev-response element	RRE	Mediates Rev trans-activation
Cis-acting repressive sequences	CRS	Represses expression of RNA in cis; repression relieved by Rev bound to RRE in cis
Negative regulatory element	NRE	Sequences within the LTR that repress HIV-1 gene expression in unstimulated T cells

three functional domains have been identified (Figure 7.3). The amino-terminal domain is composed of an acidic group of amino acids, consisting of two glutamic acids and one aspartic acid arranged with a periodicity of acidic, polar, and hydrophobic residues. This sequence is similar to that of some other trans-acting proteins (31). The acidic residues are critical for function. Substitution of this sequence with amino acids of similar acidity and periodicity results in a Tat protein of reduced activity (32). A cysteine-rich region makes up the second domain. A cluster of seven cysteine residues is conserved among divergent isolates of HIV-1, HIV-2, and SIV Tat proteins. Mutation of all but one (residue 31) of these cysteine residues destroys activity (33–35). It has been proposed that the cysteine residues are involved in metal ion-linked dimerization (36). However, the existence of Tat dimers and the potential role of such dimers in Tat activity have not been established experimentally.

A basic stretch of amino acids is required for concentration of Tat

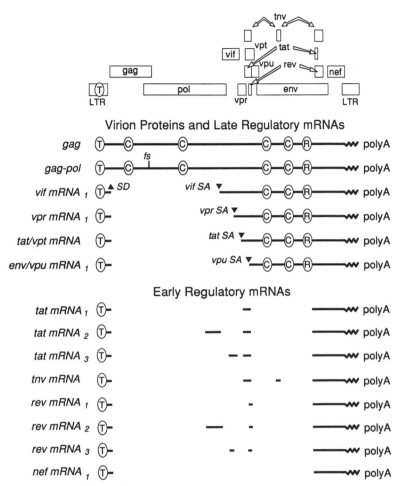

Figure 7.3. Schematic diagram of the HIV-1 regulatory proteins. The length of each protein is indicated above the boxes representing the amino acids of the protein. Functional regions of the protein are indicated within the boxes. The specific amino acid sequences within the functional regions are indicated below the boxes. In certain cases the charge of the amino acid is indicated by a plus or minus sign. For the Tat, Rev, and Tnv proteins, the arrowheads above the boxes and associated lines indicate exon boundaries. The symbol −1 fs below the box for the Vpt protein indicates the −1 frameshift site. The sequence at which the frameshift occurs is shown below the frameshift boundary. The gene names within the boxes of the Tnv protein indicate the regions of the protein specified by *tat*, *env*, and *rev*. For Vpt, the areas representing the portion of the protein encoded by *tat* and the region derived from the T open reading frame are shown.

within the nucleus (37, 38). The nuclear signal motif, GRKKR, can confer nuclear localization upon heterologous proteins (39). A subdomain of this positively charged region is required for concentration of Tat protein within the nucleolus. Mutations in this region that permit Tat to accumulate in the nucleus, but which eliminate Tat concentration in the nucleolus, result in an inactive protein.

B. The Tat-responsive region

The cis-acting Tat-responsive (TAR) sequence was originally mapped at $+1$ to $+80$ (4) and subsequently at $+1$ to $+44$ (39–41). The location of TAR 3' to the site of RNA initiation distinguishes Tat regulation from that of most other viral regulatory proteins. The cis-acting sequences that are responsive to most virus trans-activators are located 5' to the site of RNA initiation. For example, the sequences responsive to the major HTLV trans-activator protein, Tax, are located 5' to the site of initiation (4, 41, 42). The HIV-1 TAR must be located very near the site of RNA initiation and only works on one orientation. TAR comprises the 5' end of all nascent viral RNAs.

TAR contains a long, imperfect palindromic sequence (43). Once transcribed into RNA, this sequence forms a stable stem–loop structure (Figure 7.4) (42, 44). Three unpaired bases form a "bulge" around the 5' base of the loop. Nucleotide substitutions in the loop as well as the bulge dramatically reduce the activity of TAR, whereas mutations in the stem are tolerated as long as compensatory mutations are made to restore stem structure (41, 45–47).

Purified Tat protein binds specifically to TAR RNA and not to TAR DNA (48, 49). A one-to-one high-affinity complex forms between purified Tat protein and purified TAR RNA. Mutations in the bulge region, which disrupt TAR function dramatically, reduce Tat protein binding (50).

Additional experiments argue that Tat binding to 5' RNA sequences is important for function. Fusion proteins have been made that contain the amino-terminal sequences specified by Tat and carboxy-terminal sequences derived from other proteins that bind to RNA. The carboxy-terminal amino acid sequences used were either those of the phage R17 coat protein, a protein that binds to a stem–loop structure in the R17 RNA genome (51), or the basic domain of the HIV-1 Rev protein that binds to an RNA structure in the envelope glycoprotein gene of the HIV-1 genome (52) (see below). Modified LTR sequences were used in which the TAR sequences were replaced with RNA sequences corresponding to the binding sites of the carboxy-terminal peptides of the fusion proteins. The fusion proteins were active in increasing gene expression provided functional recognition sequences were present at the 5' end of the RNAs. Additionally, the Tat–R17 fusion protein is active when the basic region of the Tat protein is deleted (51). Deletions of the acidic or cysteine-rich

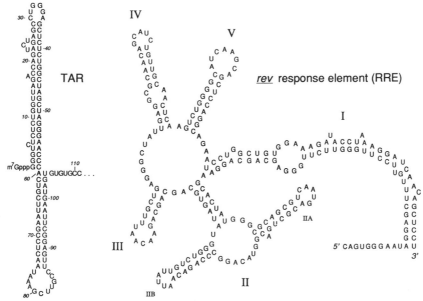

Figure 7.4. Schematic diagram of trans-activator-responsive region (TAR) and RRE sequences of HIV-1. The sequence and secondary structure of TAR is shown; the cap structure at the 5' end of the RNA is shown. The sequence and secondary structure of RRE show the stem–loops; they are designated I to V in a clockwise fashion. The structures proposed predict the relative sensitivity of the sequences to partial digestion with ribonucleases.

regions of the Tat–R17 fusion protein eliminate activity. This observation suggests that the R17 recognition sequences of the Tat–R17 fusion protein substitute for the nucleic acid-binding domain of Tat, which is derived from the basic region. Collectively, the genetic and biochemical experiments described demonstrate that Tat function is mediated by binding of the Tat protein to TAR RNA at the 5' end of the messenger RNA.

C. Host factors required for Tat activity

Host factors may be required for Tat activity. HIV-1 protein expression and HIV-1 LTR-directed heterologous gene expression are greatly reduced in rodent cells as compared to human cells. Experiments using rodent cells that carry subsets of human chromosomes indicate that a gene carried on human chromosome 12 is required for high levels of Tat activity (53).

The TAR sequences have been shown to bind several proteins that are present in HeLa cell nuclei. A 68-kDa protein purified from HeLa cell nuclei binds to TAR sequences (54). Some mutants in TAR that demonstrate decreased response to Tat also show decreased affinity for the 68-kDa protein. Additional proteins of 100 and 46 kDa with TAR-binding activities have also been detected (55, 56).

Cellular proteins that bind to the purified Tat protein have also been identified. Screening of cDNA protein expression libraries for polypeptides that bind to Tat has revealed two proteins that specifically interact with Tat (57). The potential role of the proteins that bind to Tat and to TAR in Tat activation remains to be established.

D. Mode of action of Tat

The effects of Tat on viral protein synthesis and on the synthesis of heterologous proteins directed by the HIV-1 LTR are dramatic. The extraordinarily high level of Tat induction (1000–2000×) is attributed both to the low basal activity of the HIV-1 LTR in the absence of Tat and to a high induced level of protein synthesis in the presence of Tat.

The extent to which increased RNA concentration or increased efficiency of utilization of the transcribed RNA accounts for the dramatic increases in Tat-directed HIV-1 LTR protein synthesis is controversial and appears to depend upon the experimental system used to measure the effect. All investigators concur that the concentration of HIV-1 LTR-directed RNA rises in the presence of Tat. However, some investigators report that the increase in RNA is much too small to account for the total increase in protein synthesis, whereas others find that the rise in RNA and protein levels is similar. It is possible that Tat has both transcriptional and posttranscriptional activities.

E. Tat as a transcription factor

It has been proposed that Tat is a very special sort of transcriptional factor, one that interacts with the nascent end of the RNA transcript itself. According to one view, the basal activity of the HIV-1 LTR results in low-level initiation of viral RNA and synthesis of a small amount of Tat protein. The newly made Tat protein binds to the TAR sequence at the 5′ end of the RNA and interacts with the transcription machinery to promote increased RNA initiation and/or efficiency of elongation of the initiated transcript. The Tat protein bound to this structure is proposed to interact with the transcription machinery to promote increased RNA initiation and/or efficiency of elongation of the initiated transcript.

The experimental basis for this hypothesis rests on the observation that the Tat protein binds to TAR RNA and not to DNA (see above) and that HIV-1 LTR-directed RNA initiation and elongation increase in the presence of Tat. One series of experiments in which the HIV-1 LTR directs synthesis of the chloramphenicol acetyltransferase (CAT) gene carried on an adenovirus vector argues that Tat primarily increases the rate of initiation, and that it secondarily decreases the probability that the polymerase, once initiated, will terminate RNA synthesis prematurely (58).

One specific proposal is that TAR serves as an "RNA enhancer", directing Tat binding to an initiation site where it interacts with proximal transcription initiation factors that bind to specific DNA sequences 5' to the site of initiation (Figure 7.1). Interaction with 5' sequences may increase transcription initiation frequency and increase the progressive nature of the subsequent elongation reactions. The viral DNA enhancer 5' to the site of RNA initiation has also been reported to be necessary for maximal Tat activity, but is not absolutely required because the sequences present within the HTLV-1 promoter as well as other enhancer sequences can substitute for those of HIV-1. A report that a fusion protein consisting of Tat and Ap-1 stimulates RNA transcription when the Ap-1 site is used to replace DNA sequences that specify TAR has also been used to support the hypothesis that Tat acts to increase RNA initiation by interaction with more traditional transcription initiation factors (59).

Tat has also been proposed to act primarily as an antiterminator of RNA elongation (60). When the HIV-1 LTR was placed on a replicating SV40 vector, the primary effect of Tat was reported to permit RNA polymerase II to continue to elongate past a strong termination site located approximately 60 nucleotides from the site of RNA initiation. The effect of Tat on the rate of RNA initiation in these experiments is not pronounced. Tat protein interactions with factors 5' to the RNA initiation site are proposed to induce the antitermination effect of Tat in this experimental system.

F. Tat as a posttranscriptional regulator

One series of experiments argues that Tat does act after the RNA has been made. Coinjection of purified Tat protein and purified TAR-initiated CAT-encoding RNA into the nuclei of frog oocytes is reported to result in substantial increases in CAT protein synthesis (61). In this experiment, injection of the purified Tat protein and the purified RNA into the cytoplasm had no effect on RNA transcription. These experiments led to the hypothesis that Tat binds to TAR RNA in the nucleus and facilitates its transport from the nucleus and subsequent translation. However, the relevance of this system to mammalian cells is not known. It is possible that *Xenopus* oocytes only support the postranscriptional effect of Tat, which is only a minor component of Tat transactivation in mammalian cells.

The observation that mutants that prevent nucleolar localization abrogate Tat activity raises the possibility that the nucleolus may be involved in Tat regulation of gene expression. It should be recalled that 5 S RNA, made in the nucleoplasm, is transported into the nucleolus, from which it is rapidly exported into the cytoplasm. The nucleolus also serves as the site of assembly and rapid transport of ribosomes, including ribosomal RNA from the nucleus to the cytoplasm. It is conceivable that Tat protein makes use of this cellular RNA transport process to achieve efficient export of TAR-initiated RNA from the nucleus.

Despite the remaining uncertainties regarding mode of action, it is clear that the Tat regulatory pathway is a novel one and that further study is likely to reveal important general features of the regulation of eukaryotic genes.

VI. EXPANDED REPERTOIRE OF *Tat* ACTIVITIES

A number of recent studies suggest that Tat function is not restricted to activation of virus gene expression in the infected cell, but may also affect uninfected cells through release and uptake, and activate genes from heterologous promoters. Additionally, Tat may modulate cell proliferation and contribute to the progression of one malignancy, Kaposi's sarcoma.

A. Uptake of Tat

Purified Tat protein added to the extracellular culture medium is taken up by cells and is able to trans-activate LTR-directed gene expression (62, 63). Tat protein tagged by radioactivity or fluorescein conjugation binds to the cell surface in discrete regions and migrates to the nucleus and the nucleolus of treated cells (Repke, Helland and Haseltine, unpublished observations, Frankel, personal communication). Binding of labeled Tat to the cell does not undergo competition by excess unlabeled Tat (Repke, Helland and Haseltine, unpublished observations), suggesting that Tat enters the cell via endocytosis in clathrin-coated pits rather than via a specific cell receptor.

B. Extracellular Tat

Tat protein is present in the medium of HIV-1-infected cells and cells that have been transfected with *tat*-encoded DNA (64). The amount of extracellular Tat observed under these conditions does not correlate directly with the amount of cell death. However, it cannot be entirely ruled out that the major source of extracellular Tat is derived from dying cells. Alternatively, Tat protein may be actively secreted. A number of cytokines, including IL-1α, IL-1β, and the acidic as well as basic fibroblast growth factors and platelet-derived endothelial growth factors, can be exported from cells in the absence of a known secretory consensus signal peptide. Tat may be an additional protein excreted from cells by a mechanism as yet unknown.

C. Transcellular activation

Cocultivation of a T cell line constitutively expressing HIV-1 Tat with cells that contain an integrated copy of the HIV-1 LTR reporter gene construct results in a significant increase in the activity of the reporter gene, indicating that Tat protein produced by one cell can activate the HIV-1 LTR in adjacent cells (Helland, Haseltine, unpublished observations).

D. Tat binding to cellular adhesion molecules

The carboxy terminus of Tat contains a highly conserved tripeptide sequence, Arg–Gly–Glu (RGD), which is characteristic of many extracellular matrix proteins that bind to cell adhesion molecules (65). Scanning of overlapping peptides derived from the Tat sequence for their ability to bind cells revealed that a variety of cell types adhere to peptides containing the RGD sequence (Lee, Saxinger and Wong-Staal, unpublished observations). Experiments using intact Tat protein and competition by RGD-containing peptides confirmed that Tat may bind to a cell adhesion molecule (66). However, this specific interaction is not required for internalization because one-exon *tat*-encoded proteins and two-exon *tat*-encoded proteins are taken up by cells with equal efficiency (62). In any event, the second exon of *tat*, previously thought to be devoid of function, may have a role in viral pathogenesis.

E. Tat trans-activates heterologous promoters

Although the HTLV trans-activator, Tax, is known to activate a number of cellular promoters besides the HTLV LTR, until recently, Tat was thought to be highly specific for the HIV LTR. Recently, one example of Tat trans-activation of a heterologous promoter, the JC virus late promoter, has been reported (67). Trans-activation of the JC virus promoter is observed only in glial cells, but not in T cells or fibroblasts. Perhaps specific cellular factors present in microglial cells are required for such activity. It is possible that this activity of Tat contributes to neurological disease by reactivation of latent JC virus. Replicating JC virus causes progressive multifocal leukoencephalopathy.

F. Tat as an inhibitor of the immune system

Purified Tat protein added to the culture medium is reported to inhibit antigen-induced proliferation of lymphocytes (68). The effect is specific for functional Tat protein, as oxidized and mutant proteins are inactive. The inhibitory effect of Tat protein on proliferation is itself inhibited by anti-Tat antibodies. The physiological significance of this observation remains unclear, as it is unlikely that circulating levels of Tat protein are sufficiently high to exert a general regulatory effect. If Tat does mediate such effect, it probably does so in the context of generation of new immune cells.

G. Tat as a growth factor for Kaposi's sarcoma cells

The incidence of Kaposi's sarcoma is increased 1000-fold in certain populations infected with HIV-1. The role of the HIV-1 virus in the disease must be indirect, as HIV-1 sequences are not found in the tumor cells. To study the relationship between infection and Kaposi's sarcoma, cell lines were established from the Kaposi lesions of AIDS patients. These cell lines have several characteristics similar to the original tumor cell. The cells are spindle shaped and induce neoangiogenesis as well as tumors in nude mice. The cell lines were established by culturing tumor explants in media conditioned by either activated T cells (mitogen-treated or HTLV-1-infected cells) or in the supernatant of HIV-1-infected cells (69, 70). The culture medium of HIV-infected cells also stimulates growth of the cultured Kaposi's sarcoma-derived cells, but has no effect on growth of smooth muscle cells or endothelial cells, the putative progenitor of the Kaposi's sarcoma tumor cells. Recently, it was shown that extracellular Tat protein present in the culture supernatant is the substance that provides growth stimulation, because this activity is blocked by anti-Tat antibodies (64). Moreover, purified Tat protein also stimulates growth of the Kaposi cell line in the depleted medium. Because the optimal threshold for this growth activity is much lower than that required for Tat protein-mediated LTR activation, the two phenomena may occur by different mechanisms. In addition, this low concentration of Tat may be attainable under physiological conditions. The inability of Tat to induce growth of the normal Kaposi progenitor cells indicates that Tat protein is by itself unable to induce formation of Kaposi's sarcoma. Tat protein may facilitate progression of this disease. The potential role of Tat for induction of Kaposi's sarcoma is also supported by studies indicating that mice carrying *tat* as a transgene developed lesions that some investigators think have a Kaposi tumor phenotype (71).

VII. THE *Rev* TRANS-ACTIVATION PATHWAY

The human pathogenic retroviruses, both HIV and HTLV display a novel type of genetic regulation whereby a trans-acting product controls differential expression of the spliced and unspliced primary RNA transcripts. It is this process that accounts for the early-to-late switch in the production of virus proteins during a single round of infection. These trans-activators are called regulators of virion protein expression, Rev for the HIV-like viruses and Rex for the HTLV family of viruses. In the presence of Rev or Rex, the full-length and singly spliced RNA transcripts of HIV, HTLV, and related viruses accumulate and can be translated. The capsid proteins are made from the full-length viral RNA and the envelope proteins are made from the singly spliced messenger RNA. In the absence of Rev or Rex, the only viral RNA species that accumulate are multiply spliced transcripts that specify the regulatory proteins of both HIV- and HTLV-like viruses.

A. The Rev protein

The Rev protein of HIV-1 is a 19-kDa phosphoprotein expressed by two coding exons. The Rev protein is made from several mRNAs (72, 73) (see Figure 7.2). Like Tat, Rev is located in the nucleus and predominantly in the nucleolus (74). A basic stretch of amino acids is located near the amino terminus (Figure 7.3). The motif NRRRRW confers nuclear localization (75–77), is essential for Rev function, and can substitute for the nuclear localization domain of the Tat protein (78). The basic sequence is also responsible for binding to the *rev* RNA target sequence RRE (C. Rosen; G. Pavlakis, personal communications). Mutations in the basic sequence that permit concentration of Rev in the nucleus but which eliminate concentration of Rev in the nucleolus are inactive (76–78).

A second essential region of Rev is a leucine-rich sequence: LQLP PLERLTLD. Substitutions of the underlined leucine residues yield mutant Rev proteins with a trans-dominant negative phenotype (79). It is suggested that the leucine-rich region functions as the trans-activating domain distinct from the RNA-binding domain.

B. Rev response element

The Rev response element (RRE) sequence was originally designated "cis-acting antirepression" (CAR) sequence (80). This sequence is present within the *env* gene and is removed by splicing of the small regulatory mRNAs (80–82). The virus structural proteins, including the capsid, replication enzymes, and envelope protein, cannot be made by viruses deleted for RRE, even in the presence of active Rev. Deletion of RRE does not prevent expression of the regulatory proteins Tat, Rev, and Nef.

The 250-nucleotide RRE sequence forms a complex folded structure (81) (Figure 7.4). A stable stem structure is formed by complementarity of the 5' and 3' termini of RRE. This is designated stem I. A series of stem–loop structures intervene and are designated in a clockwise fashion stem–loops II, III, IV, and V (Figure 7.4). Stem–loop II resembles a hammerhead, and can be subdivided into IIA and IIB. Activity of the RRE is completely destroyed with deletion of stem–loop II or IIA, but not of stem–loop III, IV, or V (83, 85); deletion of the lower part of stem I significantly reduced but did not abolish activity.

Purified Rev protein binds to RRE with high affinity (83–88). The first

90 nucleotides of RRE are sufficient for Rev binding (88). Interestingly, the same subfragment also binds to a cellular factor, which is the only detectable cellular factor that binds to the whole RRE (Y. Vaishnav and F. Wong-Staal, unpublished). However, the 90-nucleotide sequence is insufficient to confer activity.

C. Cis-acting repressive sequences

Expression of unspliced RNA to yield protein is prevented by sequences in the *gag, pol,* and *env* genes of the HIV genome. These sequences, called cis-acting repressive sequences (CRSs), account for the inability of the full-length transcript, and the *env* mRNA, to be translated in the absence of Rev.

Rosen *et al.* (80) have provided a formal genetic definition of CRS elements, which states that they are the cis-acting sequences that repress protein synthesis from messenger RNA. To be defined as a CRS sequence, the repressive effect must be overcome by Rev binding to RRE located on the same messenger RNA.

CRS elements repress expression when recombined into the mRNA of heterologous genes, such as the *CAT* gene, but the repression can be overcome if the heterologous mRNA also contains an HIV-1 RRE sequence and HIV-1 Rev is supplied in trans.

D. Mode of Rev action

Rev specifies a trans-acting regulatory protein that affects the fate of a completed RNA transcript, the classic definition of a posttranscriptional genetic regulator. Interpretations of existing experiments lead to different hypotheses for the mode of Rev action.

In the absence of Rev, small, highly spliced mRNAs accumulate in the cytoplasm. The primary transcripts that specify the capsid, replicative enzymes, and envelope proteins are found only in the nucleus. As a result, regulatory proteins but not virion structural proteins are made.

The role of CRS elements could be that of binding to repressive cellular factors, which would be counteracted by Rev/RRE interaction. A specific proposal has been made stating that CRS elements are inefficient splicing signals and that spliceosomes assembled around such signals prevent RNA transport from the nucleus. According to this view, Rev binding to RRE dissociates the incomplete spliceosomes from the messenger RNA. Alternatively, the Rev binding to RRE may establish an alternative nuclear transport pathway whereby the spliceosomes never assemble. It has been shown, using globin pre-mRNA, that artificially created inefficient splice sites can block nuclear-to-cytoplasmic transport of nascent messenger RNA and that Rev binding to RRE sequences on such RNA will permit unspliced messenger RNA to exit the nucleus (89).

There is evidence that some CRS elements do not act only as inefficient splice donor and acceptor signals. In some experiments, HIV-1 mRNA made from recombinant plasmids accumulates in both the nucleus and the cytoplasm of the transfected cells in the absence of Rev, yet no envelope protein is made from these messenger RNAs even though they are polysome associated (82, 90, 91). Evidently, under some conditions, the CRS elements can specify a block to the translation of cytoplasmic RNA, a block that can be overcome in the presence of Rev.

This observation raises the puzzle of how a protein present in the nuclei and nucleoli of cells can affect translation of cytoplasmic mRNAs. It is conceivable that the route of export of the mRNA from the nucleus effects subsequent translation. One intriguing possibility is that Rev binding to RRE directs mRNA to the nucleolus via the nucleolar localization signal on the Rev protein, wherein the messenger RNA exits the cytoplasm in a form in which it can be translated. Rev-independent export of similar mRNAs may occur by an independent route that precludes translation.

Although the details of the mode of Rev action remain to be clarified, it is already evident that Rev provides yet another novel paradigm of eukaryotic regulatory gene action. Rev activity permits the early-to-late switching in production of HIV-1 protein. Elucidation of Rev action may help to understand how cells differentially use information encoded in primary transcripts.

VIII. VIRAL PROTEINS

A. Viral protein R

Viral protein R (Vpr) is encoded by an open reading frame that is 96 amino acids long in most strains of HIV-1 (92), but is often truncated in viral strains grown extensively in tissue culture. An open reading frame corresponding to Vpr is present in HIV-2 isolates and in most but not all isolates of SIV. There is no protein similar to Vpr in HTLV-like viruses. Vpr is found in the cytoplasm of infected cells as well as in mature virus particles (93). In contrast to the other viral structural proteins that are incorporated into the virus as part of a precursor protein, Vpr can be incorporated in trans, as shown by cotransfection with a Vpr-expressing plasmid DNA and Vpr-negative provirus (93). Vpr is the first regulatory protein of any retrovirus shown to be associated with the virus particle. The Tat, Rev, Nef, Vif, and Vpu proteins are not associated with the mature virus particle.

Vpr increases the kinetics of replication of HIV-1 (94, 95). The effects of Vpr is most pronounced early in infection. Vpr functions to increase the initial rate of virus replication in cultured T cell lines as well as in primary cultures of T cells and monocytes and macrophages. Vpr is also able to stimulate expression of reporter genes directed by the HIV-1 LTR by approximately three-fold (96), accompanied by a proportionate increase in the steady-state level of HIV LTR-directed RNA. The effects of Vpr and Tat on HIV LTR gene expression are multiplicative. Cis-acting sequences responsive to Vpr have not been located.

Unlike Tat, Vpr is capable of stimulating expression of all reporter gene constructs used, regardless of whether the promoters are derived from viral or cellular genes. The level of enhancement from the HTLV-1 LTR, the Rous sarcoma virus LTR, the SV40 early promoter, and the IL-2 promoter is about threefold, whereas increases of expression from the murine retrovirus (SL3-3) LTR are almost 10-fold.

The mode of action of Vpr is unknown and may involve increases in RNA initiation or stabilization of transcribed RNA. The presence of the Vpr protein in mature virus particles raises the possibility that this gene may act upon the earliest events in the virus replication cycle, possibly to increase the efficiency of provirus formation, the efficiency of integration, or the initial rate of RNA transcription from the integrated provirus. Vpr may account for the efficiency of cell-free virus infection.

B. Vpu: A virus export protein

The *vpu* gene is located downstream from the fist coding exons of *tat* and *rev* (97–99). The gene encodes a 15- to 20-kDa protein. The protein is expressed from polycistronic mRNA that also encodes the envelope protein. A number of HIV-1 strains that have been extensively passaged in culture lack the *vpu* initiation codon and therefore do not produce the Vpu protein (Cohen and Haseltine, unpublished observations; Pavlakis, personal communication). The sequences corresponding to *vpu* are absent in HIV-2 and in most SIV isolates.

The Vpu protein is 81 amino acids long. The amino terminus is strongly hydrophobic and the carboxy terminus is strongly hydrophilic. Vpu is phosphorylated at one or more serine residues (98). Although the open reading frames encoding Vpu are relatively constant for different isolates, there is large variation in the apparent molecular weights of the Vpu proteins. For example, the ELI (an HIV-1 strain) Vpu protein migrates in denaturing SDS gels as bands with an approximate molecular weight of 15,000, whereas the HIV-1 IIIB strain Vpu has an apparent molecular weight of 20,000 (100). This observation suggests that the protein is highly ordered, or small changes in charge distribution dramatically alter the electrophoretic mobility of the protein. Vpu is a cytoplasmic protein and is not associated with the mature virus particle.

The phenotype conveyed by Vpu is subtle. Although the total amount of virus protein made in infected cultures is the same for Vpu-positive and Vpu-negative viruses, the latter show a decrease in the amount of extracellular virus that correlates with accumulation of intracellular proteins, and more rapid formation of syncytia and cytopathic effects (98, 100, 101). There is also an increase of virus particles present within intracytoplasmic vesicles of T cells infected by Vpu-negative virus (101). The phenotype of *vpu* mutant suggests that the *vpu* gene functions to facilitate assembly and/or release of virus particles, but the precise step at which it acts is not known. The Vpu protein may help to account for rapid spread of the epidemic by increasing the production of cell-free virus.

C. Vif: A protein that determines virion infectivity

The *vif* gene encodes a 23-kDa cytoplasmic protein (102, 103). The *vif* mRNA may also contain the coding sequences for Vpr and Tat (Figure 7.2) and may be expressed as a polycistronic mRNA. Comparison of *vif*-defective mutant viruses with the wild type showed that this gene does not contribute to the level of intracellular virus proteins and extracellular virus (104, 105). However, the mutant viruses, though morphologically indistinguishable from the wild type by biochemical and electron microscopy techniques, are greatly reduced in their efficiency to infect many $CD4^+$ cell lines (104, 105). This reduction in infectivity varies according to target cell and is particularly pronounced with cell-free virus infection. Transmission by cocultivation is less affected. There is little clue to the mode of action of Vif. The protein is not found associated with virus particles and is therefore unlikely to affect early infection events in the first round of replication. Like Vpu, the Vif product may facilitate transmission of the infection by increasing the infectivity of virus particles that are released from the infected cell.

D. Nef: A cytoplasmic regulatory protein

The Nef protein is made from a single open reading frame at the 3′ end of the virus genome overlapping the *env* gene and the 3′ LTR. A number of mRNAs encode the Nef protein, including a multiply spliced RNA that encodes only Nef, and several polycistronic mRNAs that also encode Env/Vpu, Vif/Vpr, and Tat or Rev.

    The Nef open reading frame is present in all HIV-2 and all SIV isolates. However, the Nef open reading frame frequently contains premature termination codons in strains of HIV-1, HIV-2, and SIV that have been extensively passaged in tissue culture. The ungulate lentiviruses, often compared to the HIV family of viruses, all lack the capacity to encode a Nef-like protein. Specifically, no sequences similar to those encoding Nef are present in the genomes of the visna virus, caprine arthritis and encephalitis virus, and equine infectious anemia virus.

The Nef protein is a 25- to 27-kDa protein. The protein is myristilated at the penultimate glycine residue of the amino terminus. The Nef protein is found to be associated with the inner plasma membrane (106), presumably via the amino-terminal myristylic acid. Free, nonmyrislyated Nef protein has also been detected in the cytoplasm. Extracellular Nef is found in the supernatant of hamster kidney cells infected with recombinant vaccinia virus expressing Nef (107). The protein is also phosphorylated at several sites, including a threonine residue at position 15 and a few unmapped serine residues.

Nef has been reported to be a GTP-binding protein, a GTPase, and an autokinase (108). However, not all groups report such activities for purified Nef protein. Nef is reported to share amino acid similarities with cellular G proteins, including Ras. G proteins bind GTP at two sites, the P site with a consensus sequence of GXXXXGK (the KGGLEG of Nef), and a G site comprising two domains with the consensus sequences NKXD and WRFD (the NKGE and RFDS of Nef). Mutations that alter the putative P site sequence in Nef increase the rate of cellular export and decrease the extent of phosphorylation of the protein. Deletions of the RFDS sequence result in dramatic reduction in the half-life of Nef (107).

Biological activities of Nef

Isogenic strains of HIV-1 were made, differing only in their ability to produce a Nef protein. The original studies demonstrated that viruses defective for Nef activity replicate slightly faster in CD4$^+$ T cell tumor lines (109, 110). These experiments were confirmed by other investigators (111). It was also reported that Nef down-regulates HIV-1 LTR-directed expression of heterologous genes (112, 113). Sequences within the HIV LTR required for Nef activity were reported to be located either within the NRE or between the NRE and the site of RNA initiation.

The *nef* gene is also reported to down-regulate surface expression of CD4 (108). Down-modulation of CD4 was not found to be associated with the decrease in CD4 mRNA concentration. Therefore, it was thought likely that Nef affects CD4 expression at a posttranscriptional or posttranslational level.

More recently, others have reported that isogenic strains of HIV-1 do not differ substantially in their ability to replicate on CD4$^+$ tumor cell lines (114). These studies also reported a slight replication advantage of Nef-expressing viruses as compared to *nef*-defective viruses on primary mixed lymphocyte cultures.

The role of *nef* in virus replication was recently reinvestigated using an allele of *nef* derived from an HIV-1 strain of African origin, ELI (Terwilliger, Langhoff, Gabuzda, Sodroski, Haseltine, unpublished observations). The ability of Nef-positive as compared to *nef*-defective viruses to replicate on CD4$^+$ T cell lines as well as in primary cultures of mixed lymphocytes, purified primary T cell populations, and purified populations of primary monocytes and macrophages was studied. This investigation revealed that in the genetic background of HXBc2, a provirus derived from the IIIB strain of HIV-1, the ELI *nef* allele provided an advantage for growth of the virus in primary T cells and was absolutely required for virus growth in primary monocyte and macrophage cultures. The ELI *nef* was also found to provide an advantage for growth of the recombinant virus in a CD4$^+$ T cell tumor line as well.

These experiments indicate that *nef* may be essential for growth of HIV-1 in natural infections in certain cell populations. According to this view, the results of the earlier experiments that suggest that *nef* may negatively regulate HIV-1 growth in CD4$^+$ T cell lines can be attributed to use of HIV-1 strains that are aberrant for *nef* function and extragenic *nef* regulatory sequences as a consequence of extensive tissue culture passage. An essential role for *nef* in virus replication has also been suggested for SIV. The *nef*-defective strains of SIV isolated from a macaque virus rapidly revert to Nef-positive viruses upon replication in monkeys (R. Desrosiers, personal communication).

The observation that the HIV-1 *nef* gene may be required for growth of wild-type HIV strains in primary cells justifies further studies of this unusual regulatory gene.

E. Vpt: An elusive viral protein

All HIV-1 genomes sequenced to date contain an open reading frame, designated T, that partially overlaps the first coding exons of *tat* and *rev* as well as *vpu* (115). Similar sequences are present in the chimpanzee isolates that are closely related to HIV-1 (116). The T open reading frame is not present in HIV-2 and SIV isolates.

The T open reading frame contains no AUG initiation codon. However, a consensus -1 frameshift sequence exists near its 5' end, which should permit expression of this open reading frame by ribosomes initiated within *tat*. Indeed, a 17-kDa Tat–T fusion protein (Vpt) is made upon translation *in vitro* of RNA transcripts derived from this region (117). Vpt is recognized by antisera raised against the amino terminus of Tat and peptides derived from the predicted sequence at the carboxy terminus of T. Elimination of the consensus frameshift sequence or the *tat* AUG precludes synthesis of Vpt. Vpt has neither Tat nor Rev activity, and does not interfere with these activities in cotransfection experiments.

The role of Vpt in natural infection is not known. The protein has not been detected in HIV-1-infected cells and antisera to T-specific peptides are not found in HIV-1-infected people (117). Nonetheless, the remarkable conservation of the T open reading frame and the consensus frameshift sequences among diverse HIV-1 isolates suggest that Vpt may play an important role in HIV infection.

IX. CONCLUSIONS

The complexity of the life cycle of human pathogenic retroviruses in natural infections is reflected in the genetic complexity of the regulatory processes that govern reproduction of these viruses. One of the most unusual processes described for both HIV- and HTLV-like viruses is the ability of these viruses to differentially control the expression of proteins encoded by a single primary RNA transcript. Such virtuosity in the control of RNA expression of genes already expressed as RNA is novel. Elucidation of this process may help to understand regulation of alternative splicing, a process that is assuming increasing importance in our understanding of gene expression during normal cell development and maturation.

The regulatory genes of HIV-1 can roughly be divided into two groups, those that regulate virus protein production (the Tat, Rev, and Nef proteins) and those that affect later processes in virus maturation (the Vpu protein, which affects virus assembly and budding, the Vif protein, which affects virus particle infectivity, and the Vpr protein, which increases the efficiency of early steps in replication.

The importance of these regulatory genes in virus replication has fueled an intensive search for specific inhibitors. Inhibitors of the *tat* and *rev* genes should be effective antiviral drugs and serve to block critical viral functions necessary for replication. Indeed, an intense search for inhibitors of these regulatory genes is in progress, with some prospects for early success. Inhibitors of functions that contribute to virus maturation and infectivity are also likely to play an important role in containment of the AIDS epidemic. Such drugs should be effective in reducing the probability of transmission of the infection. Ultimately, the complex regulation of the pathogenic human retroviruses may contribute to our ability to control these infections.

References

1. Zack, J., Arrigo, S., Weltsman, S., Go, A., Haislip, A., and Chen, I. (1990). HIV-1 entry into quiescent primary lymphocytes: Molecular analysis reveals a labile, latent viral structure. *Cell (Cambridge, Mass.)* **61**:213–222.
2. Garcia, J. Wu, F., Mitsuyasu, R., and Gaynor, R. (1987). Interaction of cellular proteins involved in the transcriptional regulation of the human immunodeficiency virus. *EMBO J.* **6**:3761–3770.
3. Jones, K., Kadonaga, J., Luciw, P., and Tjian, R. (1986). Activation of the AIDS retrovirus promoter by cellular transcription factor, SP1. *Science* **231**:755–759.

4. Rosen, C., Sodroski, J., and Haseltine, W. (1985). The location of cis-acting regulatory sequences in human T lymphotropic virus type III (HTLV-III/LAV) long-terminal repeat. *Cell (Cambridge, Mass.)* **41:**813–823.

5. Nabel, G., and Baltimore, D. (1987). An inducible transcription factor activates expression of human immunodeficiency virus in T cells. *Nature (London)* **326:**711–713.

6. Kawakami, K., Scheidereit, C., and Roeder, R. (1988). Identification and purification of a human immunoglobulin-enhancer-binding protein (NF-kappa B) that activates transcription from a human immunodeficiency virus type 1 promoter *in vitro*. *Proc. Natl. Acad. Sci. U.S.A.* **85:**4700–4704.

7. Verdin, E., Becker, N., Bex, F., Droogmans, L., and Burny A. (1990). Identification and characterization of an enhancer in the coding region of the genome of human immunodeficiency virus type 1. *Proc. Natl. Acad. Sci. U.S.A.* **87:**4874–4878.

8. Siekevitz, M., Josephs, S., Dukovich, M., Peffer, N., Wong-Staal, F., and Green, W. (1987). Activation of the HIV-1 LTR by T-cell mitogens and the trans-activator protein of HTLV-1. *Science* **238:**1575–1578.

9. Horvat, R., and Wood, C. (1989). HIV promoter activity in primary antigen-specific human T lymphocytes. *J. Immunol.* **143:**2745–2751.

10. Bohan, C., Robinson, R., Luciw, P., and Srinivasan, A. (1989). Mutational analysis of sodium butyrate inducible elements in the human immunodeficiency virus type I long terminal repeat. *Virology* **172:**573–583.

11. Lu, Y., Stenzel, M., Sodorski, J., and Haseltine, W. (1989). Effects of long terminal repeat mutations on human immunodeficiency virus type replication. *J. Virol.* **63:**4115–4119.

12. Okamoto, T., Benter, T., Josephs, S. F., Sadaie, M. R., and Wong-Staal, F. (1990). Transcriptional activation from the long-terminal repeat of human immunodeficiency virus *in vitro*. *Virology* **177:**606–614.

13. Sawadogo, M., and Roeder, R. (1985). Interaction of a gene-specific transcription factor with the Adeno virus major late promoter upstream of the TATA box region. *Cell (Cambridge, Mass.)* **43:**165–175.

14. Smith, M. R., and Greene, W. (1989). The same 50-kDa cellular protein binds to the negative regulatory elements of the interleukin 2 receptor alpha-chain gene and the human immunodeficiency virus type I long terminal repeat. *Proc. Natl. Acad. Sci. U.S.A.* **86:**8526–8529.

15. Shaw, J., Ultz, P., Durand, D., Toole, J., Emmel, E., and Crabtree, G. (1988). Identification of a putative regulator of early T-cell activation genes. *Science* **241:**202–205.

16. Franza, B., Rauscher, F., Josephs, S., and Curran, T. (1988). The fos-complex and fos-related antigens recognize sequence elements that contain AP-1 binding sites. *Science* **239:**1150–1153.

17. Lu, Y. C., Touzjian, N., Stenzel, M., Dorfman, T., Sodroski, J., and Haseltine, W. A. (1990). Identification of cis-acting repressive sequences within the negative regulatory element of human immunodeficiency virus type 1. *J. Virol.* **64:**5226–5229.

18. Wu, F., Garcia, J., Harrich, D., and Gaynor, R. (1988). Purification of the human immunodeficiency virus tupe 1 enhancer and TAR binding proteins EBP-1 and UBP-1. *EMBO J.* **7:**2117–2129.

19. Jones, K., Luciw, P., and Duchange, N. (1988). Structural arrangements of transcription control domains within the 5′-untranslated leader regions of the HIV-1 and HIV-2 promoters. *Gene Dev.* **2:**1101–1114.

20. Haseltine, W. A., and Wong-Staal, F. (1988). The molecular biology of the AIDS virus. *Sci. Am.* **256:**52–62.

21. Aldovini, A., DeBouck, C., Feinberg, M. B., Rosenberg, M., Arya, S. K., and Wong-Staal, F. (1986). Synthesis of the complete *trans*-activation gene product of human T-lymphotropic

virus type III in *Escherichia coli:* Demonstration of immunogenicity *in vivo* and expression *in vitro. Proc. Natl. Acad. Sci. U.S.A.* **83;**6672–6676.

22. Goh, W. C., Rosen, C. A., Sodroski, J. G., Ho, D. D., and Haseltine, W. A. (1986). Identification of a protein encoded by the transactivator gene, TAT, of a human T-cell lymphotropic retrovirus type III. *J. Virol.* **59:**181–184.

23. Muesing, M. A., Smith, D. H., Cabradilla, C. D., Benton, C. V., Lasky, L. A., and Capon, D. J. (1985). Nucleic acid structure and expression of the human AIDS/lymphadenopathy retrovirus. *Nature (London)* **313:**450–458.

24. Salfeld, J., Gottinger, H. G., Sia, R., Park, R., Sodroski, J. G., and Haseltine, W. A. (1990). A tripartitie HIV-1 Tat-Env-Rev fusion protein. *EMBO J.* **9:**965–970.

25. Benko, D., Schwartz, S., Pavlakis, G., and Felber, B. (1990). A novel human immunodeficiency virus type 1 protein, Tev, shares sequences with Tat, Env, and Rev proteins. *J. Virol.* **64:**2505–2518.

26. Sodroski, J., Patarca, R., Rosen, C. Wong-Staal, F., and Haseltine, W. A. (1986). Location of the trans-activating region of the genome of the human T-cell lymphotropic virus type III. *Science* **229:**74–77.

27. Arya, S. K., Guo, C., Josephs, S., and Wong-Staal, F. (1985). Transactivator gene of human T-lymphotrophic virus type III (HTLV-III). *Science* **229:**69–73.

28. Dayton, A., Sodroski, J., Rosen, C., Goh, W., and Haseltine, W. (1986). The trans-activator gene of the human T-cell lymphotrophic virus type III is required for replication. *Cell (Cambridge, Mass.)* **44:**941–947.

29. Fisher, A., Feinberg, M., Josephs, S., Harper, M. E., Marsella, L. M., Reyes, G., Gonda, M. A., Aldovini, A., Debouk, C., Gallo, R. C., and Wong-Staal, F. (1986). The trans-activator gene of HTLV-III is essential for virus replication. *Nature (London)* **320:**367–371.

30. Siegel, L., Ratner, L., Josephs, S., O'Brien, S., and Wong-Staal, F. (1986). Trans-activation induced by human T-lymphotrophic virus type III (HTLV-III) maps to viral sequence encoding 58 amino acids and lacks tissue specificity. *Virology* **148:**226–231.

31. Ptashne, M. (1988). How eukaryotic transcriptional activators work. *Nature (London)* **335:**683–686.

32. Rappaport, J., Lee, S.-J., Khalili, K., and Wong-Staal, F. (1989). The acidic amino-terminal region of the HIV-1 Tat protein constitutes an essential activating domain. *New Biol.* **1:**101–110.

33. Sadaie, M., Rappaport, J., Benter, T., Josephs, S., Willis, R., and Wong-Staal, F. (1988). Missense mutations in an infectious human immunodeficiency viral genome: Functional mapping of Tat and identification of the Rev splice acceptor. *Proc. Natl. Acad. Sci. U.S.A.* **85:**9224–9228.

34. Garcia, J. A., Harrich, D., Soultanakis, E., Wu, F., Mitsuyasu, R., and Gaynor, R. B. (1989). Human immunodeficiency virus type I LTR TATA and TAR region sequences required for transcriptional regulation. *EMBO J* **8:**765–778.

35. Ruben, S., Perkins, A., Purcell, R., Joung, K., Sia, R., Burghoff, R., Haseltine, W. A., and Rosen, C. A. (1989). Structural and functional characterization of human immunodefiency virus Tat protein. *J. Virol.* **63:**1–8.

36. Frankel, A., Bredt, D., and Pabo, C. (1988). Tat protein from immunodeficiency virus forms a metal-linked dimer. *Science* **240:**70–73.

37. Felber, B. K., and Pavlakis, G. N. (1988). A quantitative bioassay for HIV-1 based on trans-activation. *Science* **239:**184–187.

38. Hauber, J., Malim, M., and Cullen, B. (1989). Mutational analysis of the conserved basic domain of human immunodeficiency virus Tat protein. *J. Virol.* **63:**1181–1187.

39. Hauber, J., and Cullen, B. (1988). Mutational analysis of the trans-activation-response region of the human immunodeficiency virus type 1 long-terminal repeat. *J. Virol.* **62:**673–679.

40. Jakobovitz, A., Smith, D., Jakobovitz, E., and Capon, D. (1988). A discrete element 3' of human immunodeficiency virus (HIV-1) and HIV-2 initiation sites mediates transcriptional activation by an HIV trans-activator. *Mol. Cell. Biol.* **8:**2555–2561.
41. Selby, M., Bain, E., Luciw, P., and Peterlin, B. (1989). Structure, sequence, and position of the stem-loop in TAR determine transcriptional elongation by TAT through the HIV-1 long terminal repeat. *Genes Dev.* **3:**547–558.
42. Muesing, M., Smith, D., and Capon, D. (1987). Regulation of mRNA accumulation by a human immunodeficiency virus trans-activator protein. *Cell (Cambridge, Mass.)* **48:**691–701.
43. Okamoto, T., and Wong-Staal, F. (1986). Demonstration of virus-specific transcriptional activator(s) in cells infected with human T-cell lymphotropic virus type III by *in vitro* cell-free system. *Cell (Cambridge, Mass.)* **47:**29–35.
44. Parkin, N. T., Cohen, E., Darveau, A., Rosen, C., Haseltine, W., and Sonenberg, N. (1988). Mutational analysis of the 5' non-coding region of human immunodeficiency virus type 1: Effects of secondary structure on translation. *EMBO J.* **7:**2831–2837.
45. Feng, S., and Holland, E. (1988). HIV-1 tat trans-activation requires the loop sequence with tar. *Nature (London)* **334:**165–167.
46. Berhout, B., and Jeang, K.-T. (1989). Trans-activation of human immunodeficiency virus type 1 is sequence specific for both the single-stranded bulge and loop of the trans-acting-responsive hairpin: A quantitative analysis. *J. Virol.* **63:**5501–5504.
47. Roy, S., Parkin, N., Rosen, C., Itovich, J., and Sonenberg, N. (1990). Structural requirements for trans-activation of human immunodeficiency virus type 1 long terminal repeat-directed gene expression by TAT: Importance of base pairing, loop sequence, and bulges in the tat-responsive sequence. *J. Virol.* **64:**1402–1406.
48. Dingwall, C., Ernberg, J., Gait, M. J., Green, S. M., Heaphy, S., Karn, J., Lowe, A. D., Singh, M., Skinner, M. A., and Valerio, R. (1989). Human immunodeficiency virus 1 Tat protein binds trans-activation-response region (TAR) RNA *in vitro. Proc. Natl. Acad. Sci. U.S.A.* **86:**6925–6929.
49. Rappaport, J. F., Josephs, S. F., Klotman, M. E., Kang, C. Y., Daefler, S., Rusche, J., and Wong-Staal, F. (1989). HIV-1 tat binds to the 5' region of mRNA. Cold Spring Harbor Symposium on RNA Tumor Viruses.
50. Roy, S., Delling, U., Chen, C.-H., Rosen, C., and Sonenberg, N. (1990). A bulge structure in HIV-1 TAR RNA is required for tat binding and tat-mediated trans-activation. *Genes Dev.* **4:**1365–1373.
51. Selby, M., and Peterlin, B. (1990). Trans-activation by HIV-1 tat via a heterologous RNA binding protein. *Cell (Cambridge, Mass.)* **62:**769–776.
52. Southgate, C., Zapp, M., and Green, M. (1990). Activation of transcription by HIV-1 Tat protein tethered to nascent RNA through another protein. *Nature (London)* **345:**640–642.
53. Hart, C., Ou, C.-Y., Galphin, J., Morre, J., Bacheler, L. T., Wasmuth, J. J., Petteway, S., and Schochetman, G. (1989). Human chromosome 12 is required for HIV-1 expression in human–hamster hybrid cells. *Science* **246:**488–491.
54. Marciniak, R., Garcia-Blanco, M., and Sharp, P. (1990). Identification and characterization of a HeLa nuclear protein that specifically binds to the trans-activation-response (TAR) element of human immunodeficiency virus. *Proc. Natl. Acad. Sci. U.S.A.* **87:**3624–3628.
55. Gatignol, A., Kumar, A., Rabson, A., and Jeang, K.-T. (1989). Identification of cellular proteins that bind to the human immunodeficiency virus type 1 transactivation-response TAR element RNA. *Proc. Natl. Acad. Sci. U.S.A.* **86:**7828–7832.
56. Gaynor, R., Soultanakis, E., Kuwabara, M., Garcia, J., and Sigmon, D. (1989). Specific binding of a HeLa cell nuclear protein to RNA sequences in the human immunodeficiency virus transactivation region. *Proc. Natl. Acad. Sci. U.S.A.* **86:**4858–4862.

57. Nelbock, P., Dillion, P., Perkins, A., and Rosen, C. (1990). A cDNA for a protein that interacts with the human immunodeficiency virus Tat transactivator. *Science* 248:1650–1653.

58. Laspia, M., Rice, A., and Mathews, M. (1989). HIV-1 Tat protein increases transcriptional initiation and stabilizes elongation. *Cell (Cambridge, Mass.)* 59:283–292.

59. Berhout, B., Silverman, R., and Jeang, K.-T. (1989). Tat trans-activates the human immunodeficiency virus through a nascent RNA target. *Cell (Cambridge, Mass.)* 59:273–282.

60. Kao, S., Calman, A., Luciw, P., and Peterin, M. (1987). Anti-termination of transcription within the long terminal repeat of HIV by TAT gene product. *Nature (London)* 330:489–493.

61. Braddock, M., Chambers, A., Wilson, W., Esnout, M. P., Adams, S., Kingsman, A., and Kingsman, S. M. (1989). HIV-1 tat "activates" presynthesized RNA in the nucleus. *Cell (Cambridge, Mass.)* 58:269–279.

62. Frankel, A., and Pabo, C. (1988). Cellular uptake of the Tat protein from human immunodeficiency virus. *Cell (Cambridge, Mass.)* 55:1189–1193.

63. Gentz, R., Chen, C.-H., and Rosen, C. (1989). Bioassay for trans-activation using purified human immunodeficiency virus Tat-encoded protein: Trans-activation requires mRNA synthesis. *Proc. Natl. Acad. Sci. U.S.A.* 86:821–824.

64. Ensoli, B., Barillari, G., Salahuddin, S., Gallo, R., and Wong-Staal, F. (1990). Tat protein of HIV-1 stimulates growth of cells derived from Kaposi's sarcoma lesions of AIDS patients. *Nature (London)* 345:84–86.

65. Hynes, R. O. (1989). Integrins: A family of cell surface receptors. *Cell (Cambridge, Mass.)* 48:549–554.

66. Brake, D., Debouck, C., and Biesecker, D. (1990). Identification of an Arg-Gly-Asp (RDG) cell adhesion site in human Immonodeficiency virus type 1 transactivation protein, Tat. *Cell Biol.* 111:1275–1281.

67. Tada, H., Rappaport, J., Lashgari, M., Amini, S., Wong-Staal, F., and Khalili, K. (1990). Transactivation of the JC virus late promoter by the Tat protein of type1 human immunodeficiency virus in glial cells. *Proc. Natl. Acad. Sci. U.S.A.* 87:3479–3483.

68. Viscidi, R., Mayur, K., Lederman, H., and Frankel, A. (1989). Inhibition of antigen-induced lymphocyte proliferation by Tat protein from HIV-1. *Science* 246:1606–1608.

69. Salahuddin, S., Nakamura, S., Biberfeld, P., Kaplan, M. H., Markham, P. D., Larsson, L., and Gallo, R. C. (1988). Angiogenic properties of Kaposi's sarcoma-derived cells after long-term culture *in vitro*. *Science* 242:430–433.

70. Nakamura, S., Salahuddin, S., Biberfeld, P., Ensoli, B., Markham, P. D., Wong-Staal, F., and Gallo, R. C. (1988). Kaposi's sarcoma cells: Long-term culture with growth factor from retrovirus-infected CD4+ T cells. *Science* 242:426–429.

71. Vogel, J., Hinrichs, S., Reynolds, R., Luciw, P., and Jay, G. (1988). The HIV TAT gene induces dermal lesions resembling Kaposi's sarcoma in transgenic mice. *Nature (London)* 335:606–611.

72. Sodroski, J., Goh, W., Rosen, C., Dayton, A., Terwilliger, E., and Haseltine, W. (1986). A second post-transcriptional trans-activator gene required for the HTLV-III replication. *Nature (London)* 321:412–417.

73. Feinberg, M., Jarrett, R., Aldovini, A., Gallo, R., and Wong-Staal, F. (1986). HTLV-III expression and production involve complex regulation at the levels of splicing and translation of viral RNA. *Cell (Cambridge, Mass.)* 46:807–817.

74. Cullen, B., Hauber, J., Campbell, K., Sodroski, J., Haseltine, W., and Rosen, C. (1988). Subcellular localization of the human immunodeficiency virus trans-acting art gene product. *J. Virol.* 62:2498–2501.

75. Malim, M., Bohnlein, S., Fenrick, R., Le, S.-Y., Maizel, J. V., and Cullen, B. R. (1989). Functional comparison of the Rev trans-activators encoded by different primate immunodeficiency virus species. *Proc. Natl. Acad. Sci. U.S.A.* 86:8222–8226.

76. Cochrane, A., Perkins, A., and Rosen, C. (1990). Identification of sequences important in the nucleolar localization of human immunodeficiency virus rev: Relevance of nucleolar localization to function. *J. Virol.* **64:**881–885.

77. Kubota, S., Siomi, H., Satoh, H., Endo, S., Maki, M., and Hatanaka, M. (1989). Functional similarity of HIV-1 Rev and HTLV-1 Rex proteins: Identifications of a new nucleolar-targeting signal in Rev protein. *Biochem. Biophys. Res. Comm.* **162:**963–970.

78. Venkatesh, L. K., Mohammed, S., and Chinnadurai, G. (1990). Functional domains of the HIV-1 REV gene required for trans-regulation and subcellular localization. *Virology* **176:**39–44.

79. Malim, M., Bohnlein, S., Hauber, J., and Cullen, B. (1989). Functional dissection of the HIV-1 rev trans-activator-derivation of a trans-dominant repressor of rev function. *Cell (Cambridge, Mass.)* **58:**205–214.

80. Rosen, C., Terwilliger, E., Dayton, A., Sodroski, J., and Haseltine, W. (1988). Intragenic cis-acting art gene-responsive sequences of the human immunodeficiency virus. *Proc. Natl. Acad. Sci. U.S.A.* **85:**2071–2075.

81. Malim, M., Hauber, J., Le, S.-Y., Maizel, J., and Cullen, B. (1989). The HIV-1 rev trans-activator acts through a structured target sequence to activate nuclear export of unspliced viral mRNA. *Nature (London)* **338:**254–257.

82. Felber, B., Derse, D., Athanassopoulos, A., Campbell, M., and Pavlakis, G. N. (1989). Cross-activation of the res proteins of HTLV-1 and BLV and of the Rev protein of HIV-1 and non-reciprocal interactions with their RNA responsive elements. *New Biol.* **1:**318–330.

83. Malim, M., Tiley, L., McCarn, D., Rusche, J., Hauber, J., and Cullen, B. (1990). HIV-1 structural gene expression requires binding of the Rev trans-activator to its RNA target sequence. *Cell (Cambridge, Mass.)* **60:**675–683.

84. Olsen, H., Nelbock, P., Cochrane, A., and Rosen, C. (1990). Secondary structure is the major determinant for interaction of HIV Rev protein with RNA. *Science* **247:**845–848.

85. Zapp, M., and Green, M. (1989). Sequence-specific RNA binding by the HIV-1 Rev protein. *Nature (London)* **342:**714–716.

86. Daly, T., Cook, K., Gray, G., Maione, T., and Rusche, J. (1989). Specific binding of HIV-1 recombinant Rev protein to the rev-responsive element *in vitro*. *Nature (London)* **342:**816–819.

87. Heaphy, S., Dingwall, C., Ernberg, I., Gait, M. J., Green, S. M., Karn, J., Lower, A. D., Singh, M., and Skinner, M. A. (1990). HIV-1 regulator of virion expression (Rev) protein binds to an RNA stem-loop structure located within the rev response element region. *Cell (Cambridge, Mass.)* **60:**685–693.

88. Daefler, S., Klotman, M., and Wong-Staal, F. (1990). Trans-activating Rev protein of the human immunodeficiency virus 1 interacts directly and specifically with its target RNA. *Proc. Natl. Acad. Sci. U.S.A.* **87:**4571–4575.

89. Chang, D., and Sharp, P. (1989). Regulation by HIV rev depends upon recognition of splice sites. *Cell (Cambridge, Mass.)* **59:**789–795.

90. Knight, D. M., Flomerfelt, F. A., and Ghrayeb, J. (1987). Expression of Art/Trs protein of HIV and study of its role in viral envelope synthesis. *Science* **236:**837–840.

91. Hammarskjold, M., Heimer, J., Hammarsjkold, B., Sangwan, I., Albert, L., and Rekosh, D. (1989). Regulation of human immunodeficiency virus env expression by the Rev gene product. *J. Virol.* **63:**1959–1966.

92. Wong-Staal, F., Chanda, P. K., and Ghrayeb, J. (1987). Human Immunodeficiency Virus Type III: The eighth gene. *AIDS Res. Hum. Retroviruses* **3:**33–39.

93. Cohen, E., Dehni, G., Sodroski, J., and Haseltine, W. (1990). Human immunodeficiency virus vpr product is a virion-associated regulatory protein. *J. Virol.* **64:**3097–3099.

94. Ogawa, K., Shibata, R., Kiyomase, T., Higuchi, I., Kishida, Y., Ishimoto, A., and Adachi, A.

(1989). Mutation analysis of the human immunodeficiency virus vpr opening reading frame. *J. Viriol.* **63**:4110–4114.

95. Cohen, E., Terwilliger, E., Jalinoos, Y., Proulx, J., Sodroski, J., and Haseltine, W. (1990). Identification of HIV-1 vpr product and function. *J. Acquir. Immune Defic. Syndrome* **3**:11–18.

96. Cohen, E., Lu, Y., Gottlinger, H., Dehni, G., Jalinods, Y., Sodroski, J., and Haseline, W. (1990). The T open reading frame of human immunodeficiency virus type 1. *J. Acquir. Immune Defic. Syndrome* **3**:601–608.

97. Cohen, E. A., Terwilliger, E. F., Sodroski, J. G., and Haseltine, W. A. (1988). Identification of a protein encoded by the Vpu gene of HIV-1. *Nature (London)* **344**:532–534.

98. Strebel, K. T., Klimkait, T., and Martin, M. A. (1988). A novel gene of HIV-1, vpu, and its 16-kilodalton product. *Science* **241**:1220–1223.

99. Matsuda, Z., Chou, M. J., Matsuda, M., Huang, J. H., Chen, Y. M., Redfield, R., Mayer, K., Essex, M., and Lee, T. H. (1988). Human immunodeficiency virus type 1 has an additional coding sequence in the central region of the genome. *Proc. Natl. Acad. Sci. U.S.A.* **85**:6968–6972.

100. Terwilliger, E. F., Cohen, E. A., Lu, Y. C., Sodroski, J. G., and Haseltine, W. A. (1989). Functional role of human immunodeficiency virus type 1 vpu. *Proc. Natl. Acad. Sci. U.S.A.* **86**:5163–5167.

101. Klimkait, T., Strebel, K., Hoggan, M. D., Martin, M. A., and Orenstein, J. M. (1990). The human immunodeficiency virus type 1-specific protein vpu is required for efficient virus maturation and release. *J. Virol.* **64**:621–629.

102. Kan, N. C., Franchini, G., Wong-Staal, F., DuBois, G. C., Robey, W. G., Lautenberger, J. A., and Papas, T. S. (1986). Identification of HTLV-III/LAV SOR gene product and detection of antibodies in human sera. *Science* **231**:1553–1555.

103. Lee, T. H., Coligan, J. E., Allan, J. S., Mclane, M. F., Groopman, J. E., and Essex, M. (1986). A New HIV-III/LAV protein encoded by a gene found in cytopathic retroviruses. *Science* **231**:1546–1548.

104. Fisher, A. G., Ensoli, B., Ivanoff, L., Chamberlain, M., Petteway, S., Ratner, L., Gallo, R. C., and Wong-Staal, F. (1987). The SOR gene of HIV-1 is required for efficient virus transmission *in vitro*. *Science* **237**:888–893.

105. Strebel, K., Daugherty, D., Clouse, K., Cohen, D., Folks, T., and Martin, M. A. (1987). The HIV 'A' (SOR) gene product is essential for virus infectivity. *Nature (London)* **328**:728–730.

106. Franchini, G., Robert-Guroff, M., Wong-Staal, F., Ghrayeb, J., Kato, N., and Chang, N. (1986). Expression of the 3′ open reading frame of the HTLV-III in bacteria: Demonstration of its immunoreactivity with human sera. *Proc. Natl. Acad. Sci. U.S.A.* **83**:5282–5285.

107. Guy, B., Acres, R. B., Kieny, M. P., and Lacocq, J. P. (1990). DNA binding factors that bind to the negative regulatory element of the human immunodeficiency virus type 1: Regulation by nef. *J. AIDS* **3**:797–809.

108. Guy, B., Kieny, M. P., Riviere, Y., Le Peuch, C., Dott, K., Girard, M., Montagnier, L., and Lecocq, J. P. (1987). HIV F/3′ orf encodes a phosphorylated GTP-binding protein resembling an oncogene product. *Nature (London)* **330**:266–269.

109. Terwilliger, E., Sodroski, J. G., Rosen, C. A., and Haseltine, W. A. (1986). Effects of mutations within 3′ orf open reading frame region of human T-cell lymphotropic virus type III (HTLV-III/LAV) on replication and cytopathogenicity. *J. Virol.* **60**:754–760.

110. Luciw, P. A., Cheng-Mayer, C., and Levy, J. A. (1987). Mutational analysis of the human immunodeficiency virus: The orf-B region down-regulates virus replication. *Proc. Natl. Acad. Sci. U.S.A.* **84**:1434–1438.

111. Cheng-Mayer, C., Iannello, P., Shaw, K., Luciw, P. A., and Levy, J. A. (1989). Differential effects of nef on HIV replication: Implications for viral pathogenesis in the host. *Science* **246**:1629–1632.

112. Ahmad, N., and Venkatesan, S. (1988). Nef protein of HIV-1 is a transcriptional repressor of HIV-1 LTR. *Science* **241**:1481–1485 (published erratum appears in *Science* **242**:4875).

113. Niederman, T. M., Thielan, B. J., and Ratner, L. (1989). Human immunodeficiency virus type 1 negative factor is a transcriptional silencer. *Proc. Natl. Acad. Sci. U.S.A.* **86**:1728–1732.

114. Kim, S., Ikenuchi, K., Byrn, R., Groopman, J., and Baltimore, D. (1989). Lack of a negative influence on viral growth by the NEF gene of human immunodeficiency virus type 1. *Proc. Natl. Acad. Sci. U.S.A.* **86**:9544–9548.

115. Sonigo, P., Alizon, M., Staskus, K., Klatzmann, D., Cole, S., Danos, O., Retzel, E., Tiollais, P., Haase, A., and Hobson, S. (1985). Nucleotide sequence of the visna lentivirus-relationship to the AIDS virus. *Cell (Cambridge, Mass.)* **42**:369–382.

116. Huet, T., Cheynier, R., Meyerhans, A., Roelants, G., and Wain-Hobson, S. (1990). Genetic organization of a chimpanzee lentivirus related to HIV-1. *Nature (London)* **345**:356–359.

117. Cohen, E., Terwilliger, E., Sodroski, J., and Haseltine, W. (1989). A novel HIV-1 Transactivator that specifies viral rapid growth —rap/Vpr. *AIDS Res. Hum. Retroviruses* **6**:56–57.

Index